AQUARIUM
Sharks & Rays

WARNING

MISHANDLING OR LACK OF PROPER PRECAUTION when working with aquarium sharks and rays can result in physical injury to the aquarist. Shark bites can cause puncture wounds, lacerations, and even, in the case of larger species, amputation. The venomous tail spine of the stingrays can inflict serious wounds, excruciating pain, and possibly death if the spine should penetrate a major blood vessel. The toxicity of the venom associated with the tail spine is not known for all species. In short, there are inherent risks associated with keeping certain elasmobranchs. Some of the medications prescribed in this book could also be dangerous to the aquarist if improperly handled. Follow manufacturer's and/or a veterinarian's instructions when using, storing, and disposing of any medication.

Front Cover
Juvenile Horn Shark (*Heterodontus francisci*) (Scott W. Michael)
Back Cover
Top: Brownbanded Bamboo Shark (*Chiloscyllium punctatum*) (Scott W. Michael)
Center: Bluespotted Ribbontail Ray (*Taeniura lymma*) (Scott W. Michael)
Bottom: Tasseled Wobbegong (*Eucrossorhinus dasypogon*) (Fred Bavendam)

Produced and distributed by
T.F.H. Publications, Inc.
One T.F.H. Plaza
Third and Union Avenues
Neptune City, NJ 07753
www.tfh.com

AQUARIUM
Sharks & Rays

An Essential Guide to Their Selection,
Keeping, and Natural History

SCOTT W. MICHAEL

WITH A FOREWORD BY MARTIN A. MOE, JR.
PRINCIPAL PHOTOGRAPHY BY SCOTT W. MICHAEL AND KELVIN AITKEN
ILLUSTRATIONS BY LAURA WILLIAMS

MICROCOSM

t.f.h.

PROFESSIONAL
SERIES™

T.F.H. Publications
One T.F.H. Plaza
Third and Union Avenues
Neptune City, NJ 07753
www.tfh.com

This book has been published with the intent to provide accurate and authoritative information in regard to the subject matter within. While every precaution has been taken in preparation of this book, the publisher and author assume no responsibility for errors or omissions. Neither is any liability assumed for damages resulting from the use of the information herein.

ISBN 1-890087-57-2

Printed and bound in the United States of America

Library of Congress Cataloging-in-Publication Data
Michael, Scott W.
  Aquarium sharks & rays : an essential guide to their selection, keeping, and
natural history / Scott W. Michael ; with a foreword by Martin A. Moe, Jr. ;
principal photography by Scott W. Michael and Kelvin Aitken; illustrations
by Laura Williams.
      p. cm.
  Includes bibliographical references (p.).
  ISBN 1-890087-57-2 (hc)
  1. Sharks. 2. Rays (Fishes). 3. Marine aquarium animals.
  I. Title: Aquarium sharks and rays. II. Title.
  SF458.S53 M53 2001
  639.3'73—dc21   2001030587

Color separations by T.F.H. Publications, Inc.
Designed by Eugenie Seidenberg Delaney

Co-published by
Microcosm Ltd.
P.O. Box 550
Charlotte, VT 05445
www.microcosm-books.com

To Margaret Cairns, my New Zealand Mum,
and the late William Cairns—
thank you for putting up with your
shark-obsessed son-in-law and
for raising such a wonderful daughter.

We miss you, Willy.

Chiloscyllium punctatum (Brownbanded Bamboo Shark): one of a growing group of smaller elasmobranchs available to home aquarists, this species acclimates well and is reported to reproduce readily in captive conditions. Species account, page 102.

Contents

Introduction, page 13

Catalog of Species, page 69

Captive Reproduction, page 209

Foreword

SHARK! NO OTHER ANIMAL, TERRESTRIAL OR aquatic, creates the same degree of fear and horror in the human mind as the shark. Whenever and wherever humans encounter the sea, the fear of sharks is a lurking presence. They come from the deep, seemingly out of nowhere, to rend and rip their helpless victims with razor-sharp teeth and bodies powerful enough to tear small boats to shreds. They strike when we are most vulnerable and helpless, our keen sense of sight reduced, our movements hindered by water, trapped in an alien and dangerous environment by an efficient and relentless predator. No wonder sharks have been the focus of fear and fascination, myth and legend, since ancient times.

We have found it easy to attribute human characteristics to sharks. Even the pioneering oceanographer, William Beebe, wrote in 1926 that he first saw sharks as "sinuous, crafty, sinister, cruel-mouthed, and sneering." When he got to know them better, he revised his opinion, calling them "indolent, awkward, chinless cowards."

We now know, of course, that shark behavior is guided by instincts developed through eons of evolution and that equating human behavioral characteristics to sharks or other animals has no real meaning. A shark may be hungry or reproductively active, but it cannot be cruel or lustful. It is simply filling its role as a top-level aquatic predator struggling to survive and reproduce. This realization does not reduce the great fascination we have for sharks, rays, and their kin; if anything, it increases our interest in the behavior and biology of these ancient aquatic animals.

The subclass of animals that we call elasmobranchs contains fishes as diverse as the powerful Great White Shark and the delicate Butterfly Ray. Elasmobranchs do not reproduce quickly or in great numbers, and it is important to learn all that we can about these fishes in order to help them survive in a rapidly changing world. It is often the public perception that sharks and rays are dangerous and should be killed whenever they are encountered. This mentality is gradually changing, but there is still a great need to educate the public on the true nature of sharks and rays. Aquarists, who are uniquely concerned about the sea and its great reservoir of life, are focal points for the dissemination of this knowledge. It is a great experience for an aquarist to keep these "primitive" fishes in aquariums and learn firsthand about their behavior and living requirements.

There are those who say that sharks should not be kept in aquariums, especially home aquariums, because aquarists cannot successfully care for them, and the attempt to keep them ends badly for both shark and aquarist. In many instances, this is quite true, for it requires both commitment and knowledge to keep large predatory fishes, such as sharks, in a captive environment. Often, this knowledge has been obtained through trial and error, costly to both the aquarist and his or her charges. However, marine aquarium technology has advanced by leaps and bounds in the last decade, and the equipment and techniques that allow certain species to be kept in aquariums are now well within reach of advanced aquarists. Thus, there is now even more interest in captive husbandry of sharks and rays. Books about sharks, however, generally fall into one of two categories: scientific works on taxonomy, anatomy, fisheries, and/or natural history; or popular compilations of horror stories. It has been very difficult for an aquarist to find authoritative information on maintaining elasmobranchs in captivity.

This book, by Scott Michael, has changed all that. Scott is an accomplished author, reef naturalist, and dedicated aquarist with a special interest in elasmobranchs. He has compiled his considerable knowledge of marine aquarium systems, natural history of elasmobranchs, and captive maintenance of these fishes into a very readable book packed with practical information. The state of the art of maintaining sharks and rays in captivity rests within these pages.

—*Martin A. Moe, Jr.*
Islamorada, Florida

Acknowledgments

Writing a book of this type is not possible without the assistance of many, and I would like to express my gratitude to the following people for their contribution. First, I must thank Tony Wagner for his early encouragement and suggestions for the content of this book. Kathleen Wood, Dr. Joe Hancock, James Dankert, and Lee Finley, deserve recognition for reading and helping me improve the manuscript. Laura Williams created the fine line drawings, Dr. David Jones provided valuable guidance on the length/weight relationship tables, and Alan Henningsen at the National Aquarium in Baltimore provided invaluable information on elasmobranch feeding and husbandry.

My good friend and expert fish finder, Dennis Reynolds of Aqua Marines, helped obtain sharks and rays for photography and observation purposes, while Nigel Marsh exposed me to some great diving and a myriad of Australian sharks and rays. Michael Cufer allowed me to use some of his wonderful photographs and also showed me some magnificent underwater sites "down under," while fellow Aussie Cameron Snow helped in my quest to find and photograph "wobbies," as did Dennis Kemp and Ron Hunter. Roger Steene has been a great dive buddy and also let me pilfer some much-needed transparencies from his incredible photographic library. I am very thankful to some of the greatest shark photographers in the world: Kelvin Aitken, for providing his amazing images, as well as Dr. Gerald Allen, Fred Bavendam, Mark Conlin, Debra Fugitt, Bob Halstead, Keisuke Imai, Innerspace Visions, Rudie Kuiter, Doug Perrine, Dr. John Randall, and Gregory Schiemer. Without their marvelous shots this book would be incomplete.

Dr. Daniel Leger, Dr. John Lynch, and Dr. Timothy Tricas provided academic support, while the late Dr. Thomas B. Thorson was responsible for fanning the flames of my elasmobranch interest and was always willing to sit down and talk sharks and rays, even when I was a young lad. There are a number of professional aquarists who freely provided information for use in this book, including Dr. Bruce Carlson, Gerald Crow, and J. Charles Delbeek (Waikiki Aquarium), Charles Cumber Que, Bob Fenner, Ian Gordan, Jay Hemdal (Columbus Zoo and Aquarium), John Hewitt (Aquarium of the Americas), John Kerivan and Tom Schmid

(Sea World of Florida), Ray Keyes, Joseph Keyon (Sea World of Texas), Peter Mohan (Sea World of Ohio), Christian Schreiber (Florida Aquarium), Mike Shaw (Sea World of San Diego), John West (Taronga Zoo-Aquarium), and Reid Winthrow. A huge thanks goes out to the crew of the Omaha Henry Doorly Zoo Aquarium, especially the always helpful Mitch Carl, Kay Kunze ("Ms. Stegostoma"), and Kathy Vires—thanks for sharing your ideas and information, and for letting me dive in your shark tanks. Steven Freed (Apet Inc.), Richard Harker, Morgan Lidster (Inland Aquatics), Alf Jacob Nilsen, Mike Schied (Reef Tectonics), Matt Schuler, Dr. Hiroyuki Tanaka, Jeff Turner (Oceans, Reefs & Aquariums), Jeff Voet (Tropical Fish World, Raleigh, NC), Jim Walters (Old Town Aquarium, Chicago), Forrest Young and Angus Barnhart (Dynasty Marine Associates, Marathon, FL) also shared some of their expert knowledge about these animals and large aquarium design. Kelly Jedlicki (the "Puffer Queen"), one of the most enthusiastic aquarists I've ever met, was unstintingly generous about sharing her insights into shark husbandry.

My traveling buddies, including Joe and Melisa Hancock, Larry Jackson, David Salmanowitz, and Larry and Denise Nielsen Tackett have been there to share observations, photography tips, and film. Woody Mayhew of Nexus America has kept me supplied with needed strobe arms, o-rings, lens ports, and great advice on how to take better photographs. I also extend a big thank you to my Coral Realm business partners and good friends, Terry Majewski and Terri Parson, for their support.

All amateur marine aquarists are in the debt of Martin and Barbara Moe (Green Turtle Publications) for all they've done to provide information and encouragement to saltwater hobbyists.

James Lawrence, Alice Lawrence, Alesia Depot, and Eugenie Seidenberg Delaney of Microcosm Ltd. deserve many thanks from me and all other aquarists for enthusiastically supporting serious book projects that help improve our hobby. I am also indebted to the folks at T.F.H. Publications, who have chosen to include this volume in their new MICROCOSM/TFH PROFESSIONAL SERIES list of aquatic titles. Special thanks to Glen S. Axelrod for his support of this project and to Mary Sweeney, editor of *Tropical Fish Hobbyist*, who came to the rescue and helped track down images of several seldom-photographed shark species.

I want to extend heartfelt gratitude to my parents for encouraging an 11-year-old Nebraska boy who developed an interest in elasmobranchs and for their ongoing moral support in all my research endeavors and aquarium projects. Thanks also to my sister Suzie and my brother-in-law Tommy McDaniel for providing logistical support during the summer months when I was shark collecting on piers in the Gulf of Mexico, and to my sister Sandy Michael for taking me 40 miles each way to scuba lessons before I was able to drive.

I thank God for creating the magnificent natural world that brings me so much joy, and to which he has called us to be responsible stewards.

But, most of all, I want to thank my "life buddy," Janine Cairns-Michael, whose love and incredible support make life worth living.

—*Scott W. Michael*
Lincoln, Nebraska

Introduction

*"I have known the shark in many seas,
but I do not know the shark. No one does . . ."*

—WILLIAM E. YOUNG,
Shark! Shark!, 1934

FOR CENTURIES, THE SIMPLE WORD "SHARK" HAS BEEN synonymous with gut-wrenching fear because of the nature of the potential threat that some species pose to human beings. Of all the creatures that inhabit the oceans, none evokes a more emotional reflex. For example, in 1558, Guillaume Rondelet, a prominent French biologist, wrote of the School Shark (*Galeorhinus galeus*), "This fish so longs to wound men in the thighs, the groin, the heels, or any exposed part, that it sometimes leaps onto dry land when it sees men with bare legs near the water . . ." This aggressive behavior, no doubt a product of Rondelet's imagination, is amazing when one considers that this particular fish attains a length of only 1.8 m (5.9 ft.) and generally eats small fishes and squids. Over 300 years later, Henry David Thoreau penned, "I have no doubt that one shark in a dozen years is enough to keep up the reputation of a beach a hundred miles long."

One long-standing misconception about sharks and rays is that

"Of all the creatures that inhabit the oceans, none evokes a more emotional reflex."

Perception: the classic shark-as-evil image in John Singleton Copley's dramatic recording of an event in Havana Harbour, 1749. The man survived to tell the tale.

they are primitive and dim-witted or lacking brain-power (except for overgrown olfactory lobes, which are in part responsible for their extremely keen sense of smell). In fact, studies on the central nervous systems of sharks and rays have shown that not only do many of the more "advanced" species have large brains relative to their body size (many fall within the range of birds and mammals), but that the development of the divisions of the elasmobranch brain is similar to that of mammals.

Behavioral studies bear this out. Many sharks and rays often surprise researchers with their intelligence, displaying complex behavioral repertoires and learning simple tasks at rates comparable to rats. As scientists continue to piece together the puzzle of shark behavior, human emotion has begun to shift from fear to fascination. Today, many appreciate even such feared species as the Tiger Shark (*Galeocerdo cuvier*), mako sharks (*Isurus* spp.), and Great White Shark (*Carcharodon car-*

Reality: once proclaimed a ruthless man-biter, the mild-mannered School Shark (*Galeorhinus galeus*) actually feeds on small fishes and squids.

charias) for what they are: efficient, finely adapted super-predators.

Among the noteworthy characteristics shared by some sharks are:

• **An exquisitely developed sense of smell**. Some are able to detect substances dissolved in water in concentrations as low as 1 part per million.

• **Phenomenal sensitivity to electromagnetic charges**, unmatched by any other animal. They can pick up charges of one-millionth of a volt—enabling them to detect even the faint bioelectrical impulses produced by the nervous systems of their prey.

• **Acoustic monitoring abilities** that astonish scientists. A low-frequency disturbance, such as the thrashing of a wounded fish underwater, can attract sharks hundreds of yards away.

• **A remarkably tough skin** armored with minuscule toothlike scales called denticles. In one British report, pellets from a 12-gauge shotgun blast fired at a range of 61 cm (23.8 in.) bounced off the hide of a live Whale Shark (*Rhincodon typus*).

• **Tremendous speed** in some species. The Shortfin Mako, (*Isurus oxyrinchus*) has been clocked at 56 km/h (35 mph), and may even be able to attain bursts of speed in excess of 96 km/h (60 mph).

• **Exceptionally strong jaw muscles**. A powerful shark can exert some 3,069 kg of bite pressure per sq. cm (44,000 lbs. per sq. in.), compared to a bite pressure of about 10 kg per sq. cm (150 lbs. per sq. in.) in humans.

• **A huge range of sizes**, from the 15 m (49 ft.) Whale Shark (*Rhincodon typus*) to the Spined Pygmy Shark (*Squaliolus laticaudus*), a widespread deep-water dwarf species that reaches full adulthood at a length of only 15 cm (5.9 in.).

• **Live birth in some species**; in some noteworthy others, young survive as intrauterine cannibals, feeding on eggs produced by their mothers to spur their own growth before birth.

• **A fascinating family tree**—biologist John E. McCosker of the California Academy of Sciences' Steinhart Aquarium calls it an "evolutionary bramble bush." It includes the largest-known fish ever to swim Earth's seas, *Carcharodon megalodon*, a 15 m (49 ft.) apex predator known by its 15 cm (5.9 in.) fossilized teeth, as well as the bizarre chimeras or "ghost sharks" that have been discovered at depths down to 2,432 m (7,977 ft.). The Order Myliobatiformes includes some of the most elegant and awesome creatures in the ocean, including the giant manta rays, which can have wingspans of 6 m (19.7 ft.) and weigh up to 1.36 metric tons (1.5 U.S. short tons).

An Aquarist's Challenge

IT IS NOT SURPRISING, therefore, that many marine aquarists—professionals and amateurs alike—are drawn to these animals. While the fierce reputation of sharks in the popular mind causes some people to recoil in fear, many others of us find them irresistibly interesting and worth knowing better. For anyone fascinated by aquariums, it doesn't take much to spark a keen interest in keeping sharks and rays in captive systems where they can be observed close at hand and over long periods of time. Indeed, most marine aquarists, at one time or another, entertain the idea of purchasing a shark for their home saltwater systems.

When I was preparing to acquire my own first

shark, there was a real paucity of information available on elasmobranchs suitable for larger home aquariums. The sharks were available, but the information was not. The purpose of this book is to give some insights into the biology and husbandry of these special animals and

Sphyrna tiburo (Bonnethead Shark): a sleek beauty and ancient mystique surrounds the elasmobranchs—even scaled-down species kept by home aquarists.

to help the aquarist in selecting a species that can be adequately cared for in a home system. Unfortunately, some readers will come away discouraged by the realities of potential shark ownership. Most sharks, including species that appear in the pet trade with some frequency, are very poor candidates for captivity. Some adapt poorly, while others simply grow too large to be contained in a home aquarium. However, a number of the inshore and coral reef sharks will thrive in good aquarium habitats, living—and even reproducing—for many years, providing the dedicated aquarist with an unforgettable experience.

In addition, we will also investigate the sharks' spectacular relatives, the rays, which also offer a few species that are good candidates for the determined aquarist. (Again, a number of available rays ought to be avoided by the average aquarist, and the species catalog in Chapter 4 will steer the reader through all of the likely choices.)

The Ethics of Keeping Sharks and Rays

HAVING A LIVE SHARK OR RAY is a great responsibility, and ownership brings with it the obligation to provide an adequate facility to house your specimen comfortably. If you do not have the resources available to keep an adult specimen, do not purchase a juvenile. While some species can be kept as adults in aquariums of 285 to 684 L (75 to 180 gal.), others we will discuss require systems in the 912 to 1520 L range (240 to 400 gal.). A rambunctious shark that has outgrown the usual

Urobatis jamaicensis (Yellow Stingray): collected in the Caribbean and U.S. waters, this small, handsome ray does well in captive systems.

hobbyist-size tanks can be very, very difficult to sell or even give away.

I once received a rather desperate telephone call from a young woman who was trying to maintain a "shark aquarium" in an Omaha sports bar. At the time, I was the owner of a tropical fish store in Omaha, Nebraska, and she had been told of my interest in sharks and wondered if I might be able to help her with a problem. Expecting the usual questions about parasitic infections, feeding problems, or troublesome tankmates, I was surprised to learn that she was trying to find a home for a 1.2 m (3.9 ft.) Nurse Shark (*Ginglymostoma cirratum*) living in a 1.8 m (5.9 ft.) tank.

She had called a number of public aquariums to see if they would take her oversized specimen, but none had room for a large and growing shark. It is a widely held misconception that public aquariums are eager to take these animals from aquarists when they become too large. In fact, the biologists and keepers who manage these institutions routinely turn down offers of overgrown animals due to lack of space. She had even called *Aquarium Fish Magazine* in California to see if they had any suggestions. The editor gave her my name.

I wish that I could report that I was able to save the day, but in the end I had tell her that the only real option seemed to be for her to euthanize the animal. This may seem harsh, but consider what else you might do with a 1.2 m (3.9 ft.) shark that could easily reach more than 3 m (9.8 ft.) in length. She suggested that she could drive it to Florida and set it free. I warned her strongly that this was an idea she should put out of her mind. Releasing a captive shark into the wild after it outgrows its tank is always ill advised—a specimen exposed to species from other regions (for example, an Atlantic species kept in captivity with a Pacific species) may carry parasites or pathogens that are not native to the area where it originated, and freeing such an animal in the wild may introduce pests or diseases not indigenous to the area, with potentially catastrophic consequences. Also, you should never release a species into an area where it does not naturally occur, for it can disrupt the ecological balance of the region (witness the devastation of North America's Great Lakes fisheries by the accidental introduction of sea lampreys). A Puerto Rican aquarist once admitted to me that he had released a Blacktip Reef Shark (*Carcharhinus melanopterus*)—an Indo-Pacific species—into the waters off his Caribbean island. This is the sort of irresponsible act that biologists dread and that conscientious shark keepers ought to discourage as strongly as possible.

Hemiscyllium ocellatum (Epaulette Shark): this popular species was the first kept by the author. Aquarium specimen shown is newly hatched from an imported egg case.

Because it is not easy to dispose of an overgrown shark or ray, it is critical for the aquarist considering ownership of one to investigate its needs thoroughly (especially its space requirements) *before* making the purchase and commitment. Under good conditions, most of the shark species we keep in our aquariums can live for more than 25 years. If you have any doubts about taking on this sort of responsibility, be sure to select one of the smaller species that is much more likely to find a new home if the aquarist's circumstances happen to change.

One final caution: an interest in sharks and rays can be infectious and incurable. There is seemingly no end to the books, videos, research papers, and ongoing discoveries about living and prehistoric elasmobranchs—easily enough to feed an aquarist's interests for a lifetime. I acquired my first shark while a teenager, a bouncing baby Epaulette Shark (*Hemiscyllium ocellatum*) that proved to be a magnificent aquarium specimen. It

would clamber about the tank on its four paired fins, grub in the sand for food, and probe the nooks and crannies of a little coral head I had constructed looking for live grass shrimp. It learned to take food from my fingers and became a real "pet." More importantly, the little Epaulette Shark gave me some valuable insights into shark husbandry and stimulated my desire to learn more about its natural history. Several years later, I found myself photographing and studying its wild relatives on the Great Barrier Reef and in Papua New Guinea.

Over the years, as a hobbyist, aquarium store owner, marine biology student, and underwater photographer, I have kept and observed many, many different species of sharks and rays. They are as appealing to me today as they were decades ago. These are truly fascinating animals, and I am pleased to share the information and advice presented here in hopes that others may better understand, select, and care for captive sharks and rays.

CHAPTER I

Basic Anatomy

Strength, Speed, Aerodynamics—and Not a Bone in Its Body

WHAT IS IT ABOUT THE SHARKS AND RAYS THAT MAKES them so powerfully attractive and fascinating to us? There is no debating the mystique that surrounds these animals, but it is their uncommon physical presence that seems to magnetize the attention of human observers. Survey a group of casual viewers glued to the front of an elasmobranch display aquarium, and you are likely to hear: "They're so sleek . . . so beautiful . . . so different."

In fact, the elasmobranchs *are* very different from the more commonly known and kept saltwater reef fishes. Anyone planning to provide proper care for a captive shark or ray needs a basic appreciation of these differences and at least an elementary understanding of their distinctive biology and anatomy.

Sharks and rays belong to the Class Chondrichthyes, which includes all of the cartilaginous (nonbony) fishes with jaws, among them the chimeras—strange creatures with an erectable, large first dorsal spine sometimes called "ghost sharks," "ratfishes," "spookfishes," or "elephant-

> "As aquarium inhabitants, sharks and rays can provide years of watching pleasure for all observers."

Awesome anatomy: the world's largest elasmobranch, *Rhincodon typus* (Whale Shark), shadowed by a Golden Jack.

Carcharhinus perezi (Caribbean Reef Shark): a semi-rigid, lightweight skeleton of cartilage distinguishes the sharks and rays from most teleosts (bony fishes) such as these Yellowtail Snappers.

The differences between these two groupings are relatively slight. In essence, rays are simply flattened sharks, with the gill slits under the body and the pectoral fins joined to the side of the head. In the rays, the upper eyelid is also fused to the eyeball, while both the upper and lower eyelids are free in the squalomorphs. (There are other small morphological [body form] differences between the groups as well.) The complete classification scheme of the sharks and rays is detailed in Table 1-1, page 22.

How, then, do the elasmobranchs differ from the bony fishes (Class Actinopterygii) that we normally encounter in aquariums? To begin with, the shark's skeleton is composed of cartilage, while most other fishes have skeletons made of less-elastic bone. Another more obvious difference is that male sharks have a pair of claspers, modifications of the pelvic fins used to inseminate the female. These structures are not found in bony fishes. During mating, the male shark rotates its claspers forward and inserts one (in most cases) or both into the cloaca of the female. Sperm is then transferred from the male sex organs, through channels in the claspers, and into the female reproductive tract. These conspicuous organs make it easy to differentiate males from females, even in newborn sharks.

Body Plans

IN COMPARISON TO THE BONY FISHES, sharks and rays display body plans that are much less diverse. The most common shark shape is a slightly compressed, cylindrical body, that is round to slightly oval in cross section, with a long tail. This is referred to as a **sagittiform** body plan. These sharks typically swim by undulating the posterior portion of the body, with the upper lobe of the caudal fin providing most of the forward propulsion. Certain sharks exhibit slight modifications to the gen-

fishes." The chimeras are grouped in the Subclass Holocephali, characterized by an upper jaw fused to the skull and a single flap of skin covering the gill slits.

The sharks and rays fall into the Subclass Elasmobranchii, which includes the jawed fishes with cartilaginous skeletons, multiple gill slits, a skin covered with denticles (tiny, toothlike scales), and rows of constantly regenerating teeth.

Many classification schemes next divide the elasmobranchs into two superorders: the Squalomorphii (sharks) and the Rajomorphii (stingrays, electric rays, skates, sawfishes, and guitarfishes). The Squalomorphii are sometimes referred to as the selachians, while the term batoids is sometimes used for the Rajomorphii.

eral sagittiform plan. For example, in some of the bottom dwellers, such as the nurse sharks and—to an even greater extent—the wobbegongs, the head and anterior portion of the body is more flattened. This modification helps these animals to blend with their surroundings and/or to insert their heads into crevices when hunting concealed prey. The trade off is that they're less hydrodynamically suited to open-water swimming.

Some of the sharks that are more "fleet-of-fin" exhibit a **fusiform** body plan. This shape creates less turbulence (i.e., drag) as it moves through the water. These sharks are often more stiff-bodied, and propel themselves forward with relatively short strokes of their tail fins. They also have conical snouts. Sharks that exhibit this type of body plan include the makos (*Isurus* spp.), which are known as some of the fastest fishes in the sea. To reduce drag even further, the makos (along with the other members of the mackerel shark family [Lamnidae]) possess keels running along the caudal peduncle that reduce turbulence as the tail is beat from side to side. These speedsters are capable of reaching speeds of more than 36 km/h (22 m.p.h.).

A handful of sharks have more of an **anguilliform** (eel-like) body plan. For example, the Frill Shark (*Chlamydoselachus anguineus*), the collared carpetsharks (Family Parascylliidae), and the epaulette sharks (*Hemiscyllium* spp.) have eel-like bodies. In the latter two groups, the head and trunk are elongate and cylindrical, while the tail is extremely long. Like eels, these sharks spend much of their time slipping into crevices or between coral branches. Some of these sharks have muscular paired fins, an adaptation to this specialized way of life. Because of its deep-dwelling habits, the behavior of the Frill Shark is not well known, but it has been said that it spends much of its time resting on the seafloor and may strike at its prey like a snake.

Carcharhinus obscurus (Dusky Shark): typical sagittiform body plan.

Isurus oxyrinchus (Shortfin Mako Shark): built-for-speed fusiform shape.

Chlamydoselachus anguineus (Frill Shark): elongate anguilliform body.

TABLE 1-1.

Taxonomy of Subclass Elasmobranchii (Sharklike Fishes)
(after Compagno, 1999)

Subclass Elasmobranchii: Sharklike Fishes

Subcohort Neoselachii: Modern Sharks and Rays

Superorder Squalomorphii

Order Hexanchiformes: Cow and Frill Sharks

Family Chlamydoselachidae: Frill Sharks

Family Hexanchidae: Cow Sharks

Order Squaliformes: Dogfishes

Family Echinorhinidae: Bramble Sharks

Family Squalidae: Dogfish Sharks

Family Centrophoridae: Gulper Sharks

Family Etmopteridae: Lantern Sharks

Family Somniosidae: Sleeper Sharks

Family Oxynotidae: Rough Sharks

Family Dalatiidae: Kitefin Sharks

Order Pristiophoriformes: Sawsharks

Family Pristiophoridae: Sawsharks

Superorder Squatinomorphii

Order Squatiniformes: Angel Sharks

Family Squatinidae: Angel Sharks

Superorder Galeomorphii: Galeomorph Sharks

Order Heterodontiformes: Bullhead Sharks

Family Heterodontidae: Bullhead Sharks

Order Orectolobiformes: Carpet Sharks

Family Parascylliidae: Collared Carpet Sharks

Family Brachaeluridae: Blind Sharks

Family Orectolobidae: Wobbegongs

Family Hemiscylliidae: Bamboo and Epaulette Sharks

Family Ginglymostomatidae: Nurse Sharks

Family Stegostomatidae: Zebra Sharks

Family Rhincodontidae: Whale Sharks

Order Lamniformes: Mackerel Sharks

Family Mitsukurinidae: Goblin Sharks

Family Odontaspididae: Sandtiger Sharks

Family Pseudocarchariidae: Crocodile Sharks

Family Megachasmidae: Megamouth Sharks

Family Alopiidae: Thresher Sharks

Family Cetorhinidae: Basking Sharks

Family Lamnidae: Mackerel Sharks

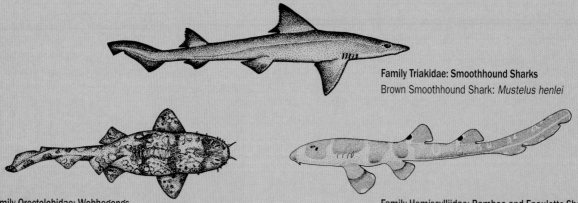

Family Triakidae: Smoothhound Sharks
Brown Smoothhound Shark: *Mustelus henlei*

Family Orectolobidae: Wobbegongs
Cobbler's Wobbegong: *Sutorectus tentaculatus*

Family Hemiscylliidae: Bamboo and Epaulette Sharks
Gray Bamboo Shark: *Chiloscyllium griseum*

Order Carcharhiniformes: Ground Sharks

Family Scyliorhinidae: Catsharks

Family Proscylliidae: Finback Catsharks

Family Pseudotriakidae: False Catsharks

Family Leptochariidae: Barbeled Hound Sharks

Family Triakidae: Smoothhound Sharks

Family Hemigaleidae: Weasel Sharks

Family Carcharhinidae: Requiem Sharks

Family Sphyrnidae: Hammerhead Sharks

Superorder Rajomorphii (Batoidea): Rays

Order Pristiformes: Sawfishes

Family Pristidae: Sawfishes

Order Rhiniformes: Wedgefishes

Family Rhinidae: Wedgefishes

Order Rhinobatiformes: Guitarfishes

Family Rhinobatidae: Guitarfishes

Family Platyrhinidae: Thornback Rays

Family Zanobatidae: Panrays

Order Torpediniformes: Electric Rays

Family Narcinidae: Electric Rays

Family Narkidae: Sleeper Rays

Family Hypnidae: Coffin Rays

Family Torpedinidae: Torpedo Rays

Order Rajiformes: Skates

Family Arhynchobatidae: Softnose Skates

Family Rajidae: Skates

Family Anacanthobatidae: Legskates

Order Myliobatiformes: Stingrays

Family Plesiobatidae: Giant Stingarees

Family Hexatrygonidae: Sixgill Stingrays

Family Urolophidae: Stingarees

Family Potamotrygonidae: River Stingrays

Family Dasyatidae: Whiptail Stingrays

Family Gymnuridae: Butterfly Rays

Family Myliobatidae: Eagle Rays

Family Rhinopteridae: Cownose Rays

Family Mobulidae: Devil Rays

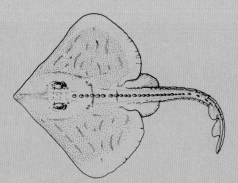

Family Rajidae: Skates
Clearnose Skate: *Raja eglanteria*

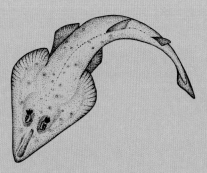

Family Rhinobatidae: Guitarfishes
Southern Guitarfish: *Rhinobatos percellens*

Taeniura meyeni (Marbled Ribbontail Ray) with four small Jenkins Whiprays (*Himantura jenkinsii*): typical depressiform body plans.

Most of the rays, and fewer sharks, have a **depressiform** (dorsally flattened) body plan. This body type enables benthic (bottom-dwelling) rays and skates to blend better with, or hide under, the substrate and to avoid easy detection by predators. The depressiform body shape may provide a hydrodynamic advantage for the rays that live a more pelagic (ocean-going) lifestyle. Many of these, like the Pelagic Stingray (*Pteroplatytrygon violacea*), eagle rays, and manta rays, do not have to exert as much energy to stay afloat as their shark cousins, because the large, flattened body surface provides more lift. Depressiform elasmobranchs with whip-like tails swim by undulating the edges of their enlarged pectoral fins or by flapping them like wings. The flattened sharks and rays with a well-developed caudal fin (e.g., angelsharks, guitarfishes, electric rays) swim in a typical shark-like manner.

Fins

ONE DIFFERENCE BETWEEN BONY FISHES and elasmobranchs that has practical considerations for the aquarist is the fact that most members of the bony fish tribe are better at subtle maneuvering. This is mainly due to the greater fin mobility of bony fishes (i.e., they can rotate their pectoral fins), which enables them to perform more precise swimming movements. For example, a Yellow Longnose Butterflyfish (*Forcipiger flavissimus*) can hover over a piece of coral, nimbly move forward to pluck a tiny crustacean from between the coral branches, then move backward to its original position in the water column. Although several of the more agile reef-dwelling sharks can "crawl" backward, none can execute such exact maneuvers. The different types of elasmobranch fins provide clues to their functions and the swimming characteristics of the species that have them.

Carcharhinus perezi (Caribbean Reef Shark): swimming strength.

Forcipiger flavissimus (Yellow Longnose Butterflyfish): swimming agility.

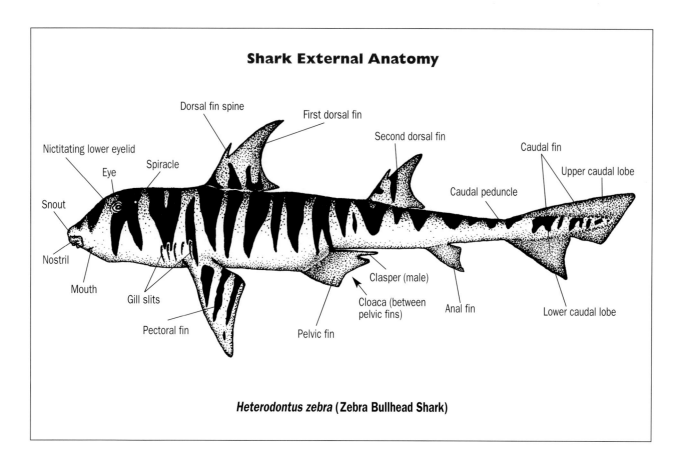

Shark External Anatomy

Heterodontus zebra (Zebra Bullhead Shark)

Pectoral Fins

The pectoral fins of the sharks are stiff and don't rotate around their axis to the same degree seen in most bony fishes. Sharks cannot use their pectoral fins to propel themselves either forward or backward like many of the teleosts we keep in our aquariums. This is one reason they are less adept at maneuvering in tight spaces. The pectoral fins do have some range of movement. For example, when a shark wants to brake or bite a mouthful of flesh from a larger prey item it will depress the rear margin of the pectoral fins so that it creates a water foil or a fulcrum.

The primary function of the shark's pectoral fins is lift. The ventral surface of these fins opposes the down- ward force created by the upper caudal fin—the shark's primary source of propulsion. The pectoral fins also prevent the shark from yawing from one side to the other, providing it with lateral stability. If it were to lose its pectoral fins, a shark would swim in downward spirals until it collided with the seafloor.

While lift maybe the primary function of the pectoral fins in many sharks, they also serve a locomotory function in some smaller, reef-dwelling sharks and in some rays. Certain bottom-dwelling sharks (e.g., the bullhead and epaulette sharks) use their pectoral fins to clamber over the seafloor. These species have very muscular paired fins that they employ to get in and out of tight spaces. With these fins, they can even crawl back-

Hemiscyllium freycineti (Freycinet's Epaulette Shark): benthic or bottom-dwelling sharks may use their pectoral fins to "walk" across substrate.

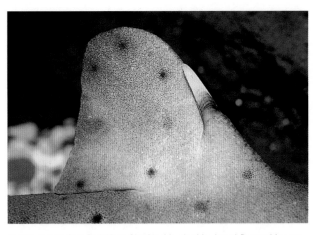

Heterodontus francisci (Horn Shark): this shark's dorsal fin provides motion stability and the formidable spine gives protection from predators.

ward out of a reef crevice. These sharks are better suited to life in the more limited confines of the home aquarium as well, because of their modified fins. For those rays that lack the well-developed upper and lower caudal lobes, the pectoral fins are important in locomotion. Some species, such as the whiptail and round stingrays, swim by undulating the disc margin (i.e., the margins of the pectoral fins). Other species, like the devil, eagle, and bat rays, swim by flapping their pectoral fins, as a bird flies by flapping its wings.

Pelvic Fins

The pelvic fins provide some degree of lift, but are more important in their role in reproduction. The male shark or ray's intromittent organs, the claspers, are extensions of the inner edge of the pelvic fins. These fins also surround the cloaca, the remarkable orifice that serves the urinary, digestive, and reproductive tracts. Some skates and rays, like the electric rays and stingarees, use their pelvic fins to "hop" over the seafloor. The fins are brought fully forward and then pushed back against the substrate, enabling the ray to move slowly along the bottom.

Anal Fin

Most sharks have one anal fin situated behind the cloaca. However, there are a few shark orders (Squaliformes, Squatiniformes, and Pristiophoriformes) and many ray groups, that lack this fin. Even in those species that have one, the anal fin is usually quite small. Like the other median fins, it functions to provide stabilization, helping to prevent the body from rolling to either side as the fish swims forward.

Dorsal Fins

These are the fins that have made sharks so famous—or infamous. The mental image that many conjure up when thinking of these predators is the ominous first dorsal fin breaking the water's surface and tracing the path of the shark as it homes in on its target. The function of this fin is not to terrorize moviegoers. It, along with its less-prominent and typically smaller counterpart, the second dorsal fin, provide the shark with stabilization as it swims. The dorsal fins function in the same way that the upper fin on the tail of a fighter aircraft stabilizes the plane—it prevents the fish from yawing to one side or the other. While all sharks have dorsal fins, a few families have only one. There are also some rays that lack them all together.

Some sharks have stout spines in front of the dorsal fins, and these can have mildly venomous tissue in a groove on the rear edge of the spine. The dorsal spines are effective protection from some piscivores that attack these sharks; they can also cause a painful wound to the careless aquarist.

Caudal Fin

The tail of the shark consists of an upper and lower lobe. In most species, the upper lobe is much longer then the lower. This type of tail shape is referred to as **heterocercal**. When a heterocercal tail is thrown from side to side, a forward and downward force is created by the upper lobe. The much smaller lower caudal fin produces some forward and a slight upward force. Although the pectoral fins and flattened snout provide lift to counteract this downward force, if a typical shark doesn't swim at a certain rate of speed it will begin to sink.

The most active, faster sharks have a **homocercal** (lunate), tail. With this type of tail, the upper and lower lobes are almost equal in size. When one of these sharks

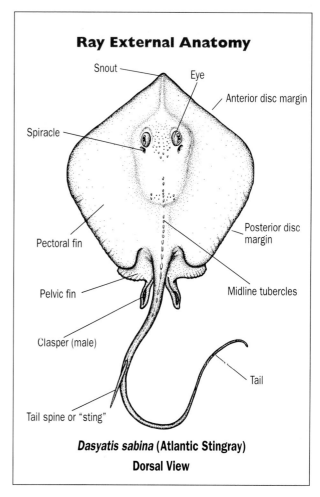

Ray External Anatomy

Snout • Eye • Anterior disc margin • Spiracle • Pectoral fin • Posterior disc margin • Pelvic fin • Midline tubercles • Clasper (male) • Tail • Tail spine or "sting"

Dasyatis sabina (Atlantic Stingray)
Dorsal View

Rhincodon typus (Whale Shark): powerful heterocercal caudal fin.

Carcharodon carcharias (Great White Shark): balanced homocercal tail.

stroke its tail from side to side, the downward and upward forces produced by each lobe negate those of its opposite, resulting in a balanced, forward force. In these species, the area of lift provided by the snout and pectoral fins is usually reduced. For example, the Shortfin Mako (*Isurus oxyrinchus*) has a conical, rather then a dorsally flattened snout and relatively small pectoral fins. By reducing the surface areas of these structures, this shark also experiences less drag as it propels itself through the water.

Several shark species use their tails to capture their prey. The thresher sharks (*Alopias* spp.), for example, use their exaggerated upper caudal lobes (the caudal fin is as long as the body of the shark) as a whip to stun their prey. These sharks have been observed to slap fishes and even sea birds with this lethal weapon. (Many thresher sharks captured on hook-and-line are actually snagged in the tail when they lash and attempt to stun the bait.) There is also a cunning, sedentary shark species that employs its caudal fin to lure its prey. The lower lobe of the Tasseled Wobbegong (*Eucrossorhinus dasypogon*) tail looks like a small fish (complete with an eyespot) as it is drawn back and forth through the water.

When a piscivore approaches the fishlike fin of the wobbie, the tables are suddenly turned with the potential predator becoming the prey (see pages 90-91).

The stingrays, stingarees, eagle rays, bat rays and cownose rays have a stinging apparatus on or at the base of the tail. These long, sharp spines often have recurved barbs along the edges and a venomous sheath. They are used as defensive weapons against predators or (in at least one species) overzealous suitors (see page 232). However, the stings don't seem to deter certain specialized predators. For example, Great Hammerhead Sharks (*Sphyrna mokarran*) have been found with up to 96 stingray spines broken off in their head and jaws. The sting is easy to entangle in a fishnet and may inflict a painful wound to an aquarist trying to capture one of these fish. As a result, these rays should be handled with great care.

Fins and Communication

Another function fins may serve is communication. For example, in some closely related species of requiem sharks, the black markings on the fins can help individuals recognize members of their own kind. This is

Taeniura lymma (Ribbontail Ray): closeup of venomous spines ("stings").

Carcharhinus longimanus (Oceanic Whitetip): white patches attract prey.

Carcharias taurus (Sandtiger Shark): this species is known to gulp and retain air in its stomach to provide bouyancy control and hovering ability.

of course important when a fish is trying to find a mate or trying to recognize a potential conspecific competitor. In at least one species of shark, the Oceanic Whitetip (*Carcharhinus longimanus*), the large white patches on its fins are thought to attract potential prey. The conspicuous markings stand out in the open ocean environment and resemble a cluster of schooling fish from a distance. This rather lethargic shark is known to feed on piscine speedsters, and it has been suggested that it does so by luring its prey into striking range. When a swift-moving tuna or dolphinfish races in to at-tack the pseudo-school, it may get close enough for the shark to launch a successful strike.

Buoyancy Control

SHARKS AND RAYS LACK AN AIR BLADDER, an organ most bony fishes use to adjust their buoyancy. This means that most elasmobranchs are negatively buoyant and will sink if they stop swimming. To help overcome the problems associated with negative buoyancy, some sharks have relatively large livers that are permeated with oil and other fats. The liver can range from 1 to

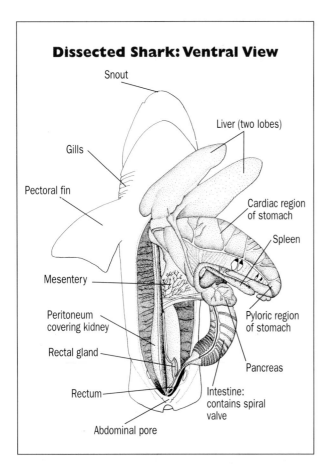

Dissected Shark: Ventral View

- Snout
- Gills
- Pectoral fin
- Mesentery
- Peritoneum covering kidney
- Rectal gland
- Rectum
- Abdominal pore
- Liver (two lobes)
- Cardiac region of stomach
- Spleen
- Pyloric region of stomach
- Pancreas
- Intestine: contains spiral valve

28% of a shark's weight. In those elasmobranchs that spend their time resting on the seafloor, the liver usually weighs from 1 to 6% of the total body weight, while in more active species it can range from 6.5 to 28%. The liver not only serves a hydrostatic function, the fats it contains provide an important energy reserve. When sharks fast (as females do during breeding season), the weight of the liver decreases appreciably as these fat reserves are exhausted. (Fat cells can constitute as much as 80% of the liver's volume.)

Not only the liver serves to make a shark or ray more buoyant; these animals have other anatomical features that effectively reduce their weight. For example, sharks and rays have a light, cartilaginous skeleton that has a specific gravity half that of bone. In some deep-sea species, like Megamouth (*Megachasma pelagios*) and the Sharpnosed Sevengill Shark (*Heptranchias perlo*), the skeleton is even more poorly calcified, making it even lighter. An elasmobranch's body fluids also contribute to its relative buoyancy. These fluids are comprised of compounds such as urea and trimethylamine oxide (TMAO), which are less dense than seawater.

Not all sharks sink when motionless. Some small deep-water sharks have such large, oil-laden livers that they are neutrally buoyant; the Sandtiger Shark (*Carcharias taurus*) will take gulps of air at the water's surface and hold them in its stomach enabling it to hover in midwater. The fact remains, however, that most sharks are negatively buoyant and function as extremely efficient cruisers.

The Brain

ALTHOUGH ELASMOBRANCH BRAINS CAN VARY somewhat in overall morphology and cellular organization from one species to the next, many sharks and rays have a relatively large brain when compared to their body sizes. In fact, it compares favorably to the brain:body ratio found in some birds and mammals. The species that are known to have the largest brains relative to their body weight are certain requiem sharks, at least one species of hammerhead, whiptail stingrays, and river stingrays. The hammerheads, stingrays, and devil rays are all known to display complex behavior patterns. Take for example, the mating system of the Round Stingrays (*Urobatis halleri*)—see page 232—and the complex social behavior of the Scalloped Hammerhead Shark (*Sphyrna lewini*). Some elasmobranchs have relatively small brains compared to their body weight. This includes the spiny dogfishes, angel sharks, bullhead sharks, nurse sharks, basking sharks, thornbacks, electric rays, and certain skates.

At least one group of elasmobranchs has "warm" brains. The devil rays have an intricate network of arteries (known scientifically as the arterial rete mirabile cranica) that enable them to retain heat in the chondrocranium. Warming the brain allows chemical reactions to occur more rapidly. This structure might also help to support and protect the brain and possibly to enhance blood monitoring by the brain.

Shark Senses

SHARKS ARE WELL KNOWN for their acute sensory capabilities. Their sense of smell has long been legendary. In fact, the term "swimming nose" was once a common moniker applied to the shark. This is an apt label, as in most species the olfactory lobes of the brain are very large. Sharks also have visual systems that are well adapted to their varied lifestyles, and they can detect minute changes in water pressure and can sense weak electrical fields. Sharks and rays use their sensory systems and their relatively large brains to analyze their environment and respond accordingly.

Vision

The eyes of sharks and rays are found on the sides or top of the head. They vary in size from quite small (less than 1% of the body length) in some sharks that live in turbid water or that are nocturnal, to quite large in

some of the mesopelagic and deep-sea forms (up to 10% of the total body length in the Bigeye Thresher Shark, *Alopias superciliosus*). The eye of the elasmobranch is similar in overall form to that of other vertebrates. It has a nearly transparent cornea, a pupil, an iris (which regulates the amount of light entering the eye),

Furgaleus macki (Whiskery Shark): hunts octopuses with its nasal barbels and short holding teeth.

a spherical lens (for focusing the image on the back of the eye), and a retina. The retina is duplex—that is, it has both rod cells and cone cells. (Skates have one type of photoreceptor that acts like both a rod and a cone.) Rods are important for seeing in low-light conditions and can be used to discriminate between light and dark objects. The cones, on the other hand, are involved in color discrimination and in increasing visual acuity, es-

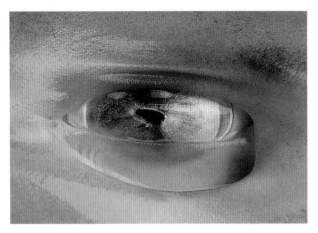

Mustelus antarcticus (Gummy Shark): note protective nictitating eyelid.

Specialized operculum pupillare is seen in some dark-adapted stingrays.

pecially in brighter conditions. The ratio of these photoreceptors differs (to some degree) from one species to the next, with rod:cone ratios of 1:6 to 100:1 having been reported in the literature. The number of cones is small when compared to most bony fishes and other vertebrates.

Moss (1984) suggested that vision plays a part in keeping some of the larger, more pelagic sharks in captivity. He suggested that these sharks may be hyperopic (farsighted) and unable to focus on close objects. This is why they often bump into and abrade their pectoral fins on the sides of the tank. He suggests that nearshore, shallow-water sharks may be myopic (nearsighted) and thus better able to navigate in a confined area. This is all speculative at this time.

Most sharks have two eyelids (in rays the upper eyelid is fused to the eyeball), but they are not capable of totally covering the eye. In others (the requiem sharks) there is a third eyelid, called the **nictitating membrane**, that can entirely cover the eye and protect it from mechanical damage. For example, when a requiem shark feeds it will close its nictitating membranes to protect its eyes.

Smell and Taste

Sharks and rays have a keen sense of smell. They use this sensory modality to locate their prey and to find mates (and possibly to determine their reproductive state). The nostrils are located on the underside of the snout. There is a flap over the nostril, which creates an anterior (incurrent) and posterior (excurrent) opening into the nostril chamber. This chamber is equipped with platelike lamellae along its length that are covered with sensory cells. As the shark swims, the water is forced through the incurrent opening, over the lamellae, and then out of the excurrent aperture.

In many elasmobranchs, there is a **nasoral groove**—a channel that extends from the nostril to the mouth. This structure enables a benthic species to irrigate the nostrils with seawater when it pulls water through the mouth and out the gills. I have seen many bottom-dwelling sharks increase their rate of respiration when food was nearby. By pulling more fresh seawater and more scent molecules into the nostrils, they can sample the surrounding environment more rapidly. In some sharks, the anterior nasal flap may be elongated into a **nasal barbel**. This structure is used to sense prey buried in the substrate or hiding in reef crevices.

When water enters the nostril chamber, any amino acids present will bind to the lamellae and cause the chemoreceptor cells to fire. Some sharks will swim toward the source of the smell, turning in the direction of the nostril that is being stimulated the most. As a result, their hunting pattern usually follows an S-shaped trajectory. Other sharks (e.g., the Lemon Shark, *Negaprion brevirostris*) swim straight upstream when they detect a food source, apparently relying on other senses (e.g., vision, electroreception) to find the source of the scent. No one really knows the maximum range of a shark's sense of smell, although it has been suggested that they can follow a scent trail from at least a mile away. It has been shown experimentally that sharks will respond to fish extracts at a concentration of 1 part per 10 billion parts water.

The tastebuds of sharks and rays are found on papillae located on the floor and roof of the mouth, on the tongue (many rays lack a tongue), and in the pharynx. An elasmobranch's sense of taste is used to distinguish between potential prey and inedible objects. It does this by mouthing the potential food item. Studies have also shown that sharks prefer the taste of some food items over others. For example, when requiem sharks were presented with fish and mollusk flesh, they consistently rejected the mollusk flesh. Likewise, a captive Tasseled Wobbegong (*Eucrossorhinus dasypogon*) ate several different types of fish presented to it, but rejected scallops. It has also been suggested that sharks can use their tastebuds to detect changes in salinity.

Touch

Sharks and rays, like most other fishes, have a sense of distant touch. The organs responsible for this sense are the lateral line and pit organs. Water is a noncompress-ible medium. As a result, whenever something moves in the water it produces pressure waves. Any aquarist knows that it is impossible to sneak up on a fish with a net. Even if you approach the fish from behind, it can feel the net coming with its sense of distant touch. With their lateral line and pit organs, sharks and rays can feel changes in water pressure produced by moving objects, prey animals, or potential predators. They can also determine changes in current direction and in pressure associated with depth changes.

The **lateral line** consists of a series of small pores that occur on the head and flank of the shark. The pores lead to a water-filled channel system that contains neuromasts (clusters of sensory hair cells). These hair cells consist of hairlike (cilia) projections extending from an innervated cell. When there is a change of pressure at the opening of the lateral line, hairs are bent in one direction or the other, and an electrical impulse is sent to the nervous system. The **pit organs**, which are "naked" neuromasts on the skin, are found on various parts of

Cephaloscyllium isabellum (Draughtsboard Shark): nerve organs provide sharks a sense of "distant touch" to detect pressure waves in the water.

the head, body, and tail. In rays, there are numerous pit organs at the base of the tail. These may function to detect approaching predators.

Hearing

Sharks and rays have a pair of inner ears located near the top of the skull, but the size and shape of these organs varies widely. Each of the inner ears is connected to the outside world by a pair of cartilaginous tubes (**endolymphatic ducts**) that end in small pores (**endolymphatic pores**) on the top of the head. When a fish is injured and swimming erratically, the sound pressure waves produced pass through these ducts and stimulate the inner ear. Studies have shown that sharks are capable of sensing such sounds at a distance greater than 250 m (820 ft.). (It has been suggested that they may even be able to detect sound waves from miles away.) However, there are differences between the auditory abilities of the different elasmobranch species. For example, skates and rays apparently do not hear as well as requiem sharks. The inner ear not only serves a hearing function, it also enables the fish to maintain its balance.

Electroreception

Sharks and rays can detect weak electric fields with the **ampullae of Lorenzini**. These organs are visible to the observer as pores on the head of the shark or ray. These pores are connected, via a jelly-filled canal, to a cluster of saclike structures. The ampullae are connected to the brain by sensory nerves.

An elasmobranch's electroreceptive capabilities are important in locating living prey. For example, Kalmijn (1978) demonstrated that the Smallspotted Catshark (*Scyliorhinus canicula*) can detect the electric field produced by a buried flounder from a distance of 25 cm (9.8 in.). It has been determined that elasmobranchs are sen-

sitive to electrical gradients of less than 0.01 microvolt per centimeter!

Sharks and rays do not merely use their electroreceptive sense to find prey. It has been suggested that they use this super sense to navigate by using the Earth's magnetic field. The ampullae of Lorenzini are also employed to locate mates. Research conducted by Dr. Timothy Tricas and this author demonstrated that male Round Stingrays (*Urobatis halleri*) use their electroreceptors to find buried females.

The elasmobranch's acute sensory system can cause problems for the aquarist. For example, anomalies in an aquarium's electric field may cause active sharks to bump into the sides of a tank and never adapt to captive life. Copper medications are also reported to interfere with the capabilities of, or irritate, the ampullae in at least some species. For this reason, copper medications should be used sparingly or, more prudently, not at all. Aquarists can also use the shark's acute electrical sense to their advantage. Public aquarists will sometimes put metal at the end of a feeding pole. The sharks are not only attracted to the scent produced by the food fish, they also cue in on the weak electric field produced by the metal.

Respiration

SHARKS PUSH WATER OVER THEIR GILLS in order to respire. The water goes through the mouth, or through **spiracles** located on the head, into the branchial cavity, and out of the **gill slits**. (Most sharks and rays have five gill slits, but there are some with six or seven.) Before the water is expelled from the gill cavity, it moves over the gill filaments, which are supported by the gill arches. Gas exchange occurs on the surface of the capillary-rich, gill filaments. Oxygen binds to the hemoglobin, while carbon dioxide is extracted from the elasmobranch's blood stream. Spiracles vary in size from nonexistent in the carcharhinids and lamnids, to quite large in certain rays. There is also variation in gill size between species. Some less-active, bottom-dwelling forms have small gill slits, while there are more-active species that have very long gill slits.

Most sharks use **ram-jet ventilation**—forcing water through the mouth and over the gills—to irrigate the gill chamber with fresh seawater. The benthic sharks and rays respire by actively pumping water over the gills. This action is achieved by reducing and then increasing the size of the oral and buccal cavities, pulling water through the mouth and/or the spiracles. (When skates and rays are lying on the substrate, water enters through the spiracles only.) Even the more active sharks can engage in buccal pumping when at rest, but most are not able to pump enough water over their gills to rid the body effectively of waste products and provide enough oxygen to the blood. Gruber (1981) demonstrated that the Lemon Shark, a species that occasionally does rest on the seafloor, uses 9% more energy when at rest than when swimming.

Carcharhinus amblyrhynchos (Gray Reef Shark): note gill slits that are involved in ram-jet ventilation.

Jaws, Teeth, and Diet

THE FEEDING BEHAVIOR OF THE SHARK has fascinated elasmophiles and lay people alike. It was once thought that most sharks had to turn on their sides or back to feed, because most have jaws that are greatly under slung. Aristotle was one naturalist who thought the shark had to turn its body to feed and stated that:

"Nature has thus arranged it, not only in order to preserve other animals, since thanks to the slowness of this obligatory movement other fishes have time to save themselves [from the sharks] which are all carnivores, but it is also to blunt their excessive voracity, since they perish quickly if allowed to gorge themselves with food."

Shark biologists have since shown that the jaw suspension of most sharks enables them to rotate their jaws forward (especially the upper jaw) to capture or gouge mouthfuls of flesh from their prey without turning over. In more primitive sharks, such as the Frill Shark (*Chlamydoselachus anguineus*), the upper jaws are tightly affixed to the cranium (skull). This is known as an **amphistylic jaw suspension**. In these species the upper jaw cannot be moved independently and the jaws are usually long. These sharks are most effective at grasping and ingesting prey that can be swallowed whole.

Most sharks have a **hyostylic jaw suspension** system. In these sharks the upper jaw is loosely attached to the cranium by ligaments, while the rear portion is tightly braced against a structure known as the hyoid arch. The jaws are shorter than in more "ancient" sharks, and thus capable of a more powerful bite. The Great White

Carcharodon carcharias (Great White Shark) approaching bait: hyostylic jaw allows attack gape.

Shark (*Carcharodon carcharias*) is a good example of a species with a hyostylic jaw morphology. This shark will lift its snout and depress its lower jaw to achieve maximum jaw gape when biting. It will first contact the prey item with the lower jaw, which is rotated upward and forward. This enables the narrower lower jaw teeth to gain purchase and hold the prey. Simultaneously, the upper jaw is thrown forward and down as the mouth begins to close (the jaws are fully protruded when the mouth of the Great White Shark is about halfway closed). The upper teeth, as well as the pink connective tissue, become fully exposed and slice into the flesh of the victim. After the sawlike upper teeth have penetrated the flesh, the head and anterior portion of the body are usually thrown from side-to-side, resulting in the shark excising a mouthful of food. The Great White Shark is capable of biting large chunks of flesh from something too large to swallow whole, like a bloated whale carcass or a basking elephant seal. This behavior is not possible in sharks with an amphistylic jaw suspension system.

Tooth shape and mouth size also have some bearing on the types of prey a particular elasmobranch consumes. For example, members of the smoothhound shark family (Triakidae) have teeth that are well-suited to clutching and crushing the carapaces of the crabs on which they feed, while the needlelike teeth of the Sandtiger Shark (*Carcharias taurus*) are adapted to grasping small, slippery fishes. The specialized cephalopod-feeder, the Atlantic Weasel Shark (*Paragaleus pectoralis*), has a very small mouth and small teeth. The teeth of the Tiger Shark (*Galeocerdo cuvier*) or Great White Shark have large, serrated teeth that are adapted to cutting larger prey items into pieces (even sea turtles, in the case of the Tiger Shark), or gouging mouthfuls of flesh from their prey. In the case of the Great White, a single mouthful of flesh may weigh well over 10 kg (22 lbs.).

Although most sharks are thought of as oceanic

scavengers, feeding on whatever they can sink their teeth into, the diets of elasmobranchs are very diverse and vary greatly from one species to the next. Some feed on relatively large prey, while others feed on minute food items. For example, the swell sharks (*Cephaloscyllium* spp.) and torpedo rays (Torpedinidae) have been known to consume prey items that are up to their own body length. Curiously, the small Cookiecutter Shark (*Isistius brasiliensis*) will consume squid almost as long as itself, while some of the largest fishes in the sea, such as the Whale Shark (*Rhincodon typus*), Basking Shark (*Cetorhinus maximus*), manta, and devil rays (Mobulidae), eat very small food items like planktonic crustaceans.

Aristotle did have one thing right: all elasmobranchs are carnivorous—that is, they feed on animal flesh. Some sharks and rays incidentally ingest plant material, like algae or seagrass, and at least one species may do so intentionally. It has been suggested that the Bonnethead Shark (*Sphyrna tiburo*) may eat seagrass to protect its stomach from the sharp spines on the carapace of its favorite prey, blue crabs.

Although there are sharks that eat a wide range of prey items (e.g., Tiger Shark, *Galeocerdo cuvier,* Bull Shark, *Carcharhinus leucas*), the majority of species exhibit more narrow dietary preferences. Blue Sharks (*Prionace glauca*) feed most heavily on relatively small prey items, showing a particular taste for small, schooling bony fishes (e.g., anchovies) and squids. This shark has an adaptation that may facilitate its feeding on smaller prey items. They have longer gill-rakers that prevent small fishes and invertebrates from escaping through their gill slits. Although the Blue Shark usually exhibits defined dietary predilections, like many sharks it can also be opportunistic.

Other examples of elasmobranchs that show some degree of prey preference include the Crested Port Jackson Shark (*Heterodontus galeatus*)—adults feed heavily on sea urchins; the Great Hammerhead (*Sphyrna mokarran*)—adults often target stingrays; and the Cownose Rays (*Rhinoptera bonasus*)—bivalve mollusks are their preferred food.

Some sharks and rays have very specialized diets. For example, the Sicklefin Weasel Shark (*Hypogaleus microstoma*) is known to feed almost exclusively on cephalopods (both squids and octopuses). The Whiskery Shark (*Furgaleus macki*) lives almost entirely on octopuses. This Australian native has a sinuous, supple body and will ferret into rocky reef crevices to extract its cephalopod prey. The Bonnethead Shark feeds primarily on swimming crabs, while the Bentfin Manta Ray (*Mobula thurstoni*) feeds exclusively on mysid shrimp and krill.

Sharks and rays are well known for having multiple rows of functional teeth, as well as an ability to replace teeth as they are lost. Instead of being firmly affixed to the jaw cartilage, the teeth are connected to the tissue that covers the jaw. The teeth continually move forward and are lost when they reach the outer edge of the jaw. Known tooth row replacement rates in sharks range from 8 days to 5 weeks. They also lose their teeth more rapidly during the warmer months of the year (when growth rates are highest) than during the winter. Likewise, juveniles lose their teeth more rapidly than adults. This makes sense considering that younger sharks are growing at a more rapid rate.

The dentition of sharks and rays is not only important for feeding, but is also employed in courtship and copulation in many of these fishes. Male elasmobranchs regularly bite females, possibly to elicit cooperation, and many use their teeth to hold the female during the mating act (see Chapter 8, page 209, for more on elasmobranch mating behavior). In fact, in some elasmobranchs, the shape and size of the teeth differ between the sexes. In many cases, this sexual dimorphism is related to biting behavior during courtship.

Digestive System

ONCE THE FOOD IS INGESTED, it enters the alimentary tract. The digestive tract of elasmobranchs, like those of other vertebrates, is comprised of the mouth, pharynx, esophagus, stomach, intestine, rectum, and cloaca. Elasmobranchs may cut/crush their prey into smaller pieces or ingest them whole. Those items that are not digested and/or that cannot pass through the alimentary tract will be regurgitated.

The most unique attribute of the alimentary sys-

Fish Scale Types

Cycloid Scale (bony fishes)   Placoid Scale (elasmobranchs)

tem is found in the intestine. The elasmobranch intestine is short compared to that of other animals. However, the surface area of the intestine is increased by a structure called the **spiral valve**. This consists of a spiraling fold of mucosa and submucosa. The morphology of the spiral valve can be classified into one of four categories. Holmgreen & Nilsson (1999) describe these categories as:

- a spiral winding around a central column and attached to the outer wall;
- a series of interconnecting cones directed posteriorly;
- a series of interconnecting cones directed anteriorly;
- a scroll valve with the central border free and the outer border attached along the length of the intestinal wall.

The number of turns in the spiral valve is species-dependent, ranging from several (in chimaeras) to up to 50 (in the Basking Shark, *Cetorhinus maximus*). Instead of moving straight down a tubular intestine, the food moves around this spiraling or scroll-like structure. This ensures that more nutrients can be absorbed before the remaining food material is evacuated into the rectum. The cloaca is the site at the end of the alimen-

Carcharhinus amblyrhynchos (Gray Reef Shark): typical countershading color pattern, with dark upper body and white belly, provides camouflage.

tary tract that serves as a common exit point for products of the digestive tract, the urinary tract, and the reproductive system and is the entry point in females for sperm during mating.

Skin and Coloration

ELASMOBRANCH INTEGUMENT IS VERY DIFFERENT from that seen in bony fishes. The scales of elasmobranchs look more like teeth than the round, thin plates found in teleosts. This unique body covering consists of **placoid scales** (dermal denticles). The form of the scales is somewhat variable, but in most sharks they are mushroom-shaped, with a flat crown, resting on a pedicel that is imbedded in the skin. The crown often has ridges and spines that point toward the tail of the shark (this is why a shark's skin feels rougher when stroked from tail to head). The placoid scales are often closely spaced, but they do not overlap like the scales of most bony fishes. Instead, channels run between the scales. The shape and arrangement of the scales may serve to reduce turbulence as the shark moves through the water. It may also serve to reduce hydrodynamic "noise," making the shark less detectable to the mechanosensory organs (e.g., lateral line, inner ear) of their prey. The scales and skin also protect sharks from abrasions and parasites and act as a barrier to prevent the loss of body fluids to the external environment.

Skates and rays have far fewer scales than their cousins. In some species, the scales are enlarged, forming protective thorns on the body and/or tail. In fact, the sting on the tail of certain rays is simply an enlarged placoid scale. Some batoids have patches of placoid scales, while others are completely naked (scaleless). These fishes rely on a heavy slime coat (known as the cuticle) to protect them from their external environment, parasites, and disease.

Chiloscyllium punctatum (Brownbanded Bamboo Shark): juvenile banding.

Chiloscyllium punctatum (Brownbanded Bamboo Shark): drab adult color.

Hemiscyllium ocellatum (Epaulette Shark): note dark false eye or ocellus.

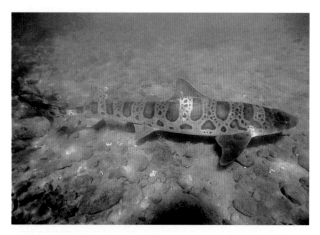

Triakis semifasciata (Leopard Shark): note distinctive dark saddles.

Orectolobus ornatus (Ornate Wobbegong): handsome yellowish phase.

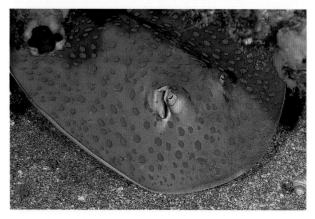

Taeniura lymma (Bluespotted Ribbontail Ray): fluorescing blue spots.

Most sharks and rays are gray or brown on the back and sides, with lighter ventral surfaces. This color scheme, known as countershading, makes them more difficult to see as they move through the water. Most deep-water sharks are black or brown overall, reflecting very little of the luminescent light produced by potential prey and predators and making them more difficult to detect.

While many sharks are rather monochromatic, others exhibit ornate color patterns and attractive hues. For example, juvenile Zebra Sharks (*Stegostoma varium*) have bold black and white bands on the head, body, and tail. The Leopard Shark (*Triakis semifasciata*) is bronze overall with dark brown saddles and black spots. The Atlantic Weasel Shark (*Paragaleus pectoralis*) has yellow lines on the body. And the Bluespotted Ribbontail Ray (*Taeniura lymma*) is golden brown or greenish with fluorescent blue spots on the disc. Some of the benthic elasmobranchs, such as the wobbegongs, certain catsharks, torpedo rays, electric rays, stingrays, and stingarees rely on complex color patterns to help them blend in with the substrate. In this way, they can avoid detection by predators and prey. Other sharks incorporate the chromatic pigments present in their prey into their own integument. For example, the Smalleye or Golden Hammerhead (*Sphyrna tudes*) has a bright yellow or orange body, head, and fins, while the dorsal fin and dorsum are gray to grayish yellow. The coloration results from its diet of carotenoid-laden shrimp and bright yellow sea catfish eggs.

Some sharks have **ocelli** (eyespots), which are dark spots on the body that may or may not be trimmed with white. Certain epaulette sharks, the Ornate Angel Shark (*Squatina tergocellata*), some skates, a few electric rays, and several torpedo rays are known to have conspicuous ocelli. These are thought to serve an antipredation function. For example, in some bony fishes, the ocelli serve to dupe would-be predators into attacking less-vulnerable parts of the body. This does not appear to be the case with elasmobranchs. The spots on sharks, skates, and rays are usually present on more vulnerable parts of the body, often on or over the pectoral fins. It is more likely that the spots serve to mimic the head-on perspective of a piscivore. A diurnal predator that approached an ocelli-bearing elasmobranch from above would possibly be discouraged from attacking upon catching sight of two large false eyes "staring" up at them.

The color patterns of some sharks change as they grow. For example, some juvenile bamboo and Zebra Sharks have distinct bands that disappear as they age. Similar banding patterns are seen in a variety of reef-associated fishes. It is thought that they act to disrupt recognition of their actual body shape or to help them blend with seagrass or coral branches. In the case of the bony fishes and these juvenile sharks, the color pattern appears to make them less susceptible to predation. As the shark gets larger, and becomes a less-attractive target of piscivorous predators, the bands fade away.

Some of the deepest-dwelling sharks have **photophores** (light-producing organs). For example, many of the lanternsharks (*Etmopterus* spp.), which get their name from their light-producing capabilities, and the cookiecutter sharks (*Isistius* spp.) possess photophores. The light is produced when the simple organic compound luciferin is oxidized by the enzyme luciferase. The chemical reaction produces almost no heat (less than 1% of the energy produced), but does create light. The chemical reaction occurs in specific cells, or in spaces between cells, in the light-producing organs. In sharks, the color of the light produced may be greenish, greenish blue, blue, or white. (In other deep-sea

Etmopterus spinax (Velvetbelly Lanternshark): one of the unusual deep-water species that is able to emit cool light with chemical photophores.

fishes, colors like lemon yellow, ruby red, violet, and purple-orange have been reported.) Shark photophores may aid in catching prey, as well as communicating with members of their own species. In mesopelagic sharks, these light-producing organs may also serve to obliterate their silhouettes so that predators are less likely to see them against any down-welling light that may be present.

In conclusion, although sharks and bony fishes have many attributes in common, they are also very different—different enough to make them truly irresistible for many who take up elasmobranch husbandry. As aquarium inhabitants, they can provide years of watching pleasure and an educational show for all observers. Their unique anatomies also create special husbandry challenges, as amplified in the next chapter.

References

Bleckmann & Hofmann (1999), Compagno (1999a, 1999b), Compagno et al. (1989), Gruber (1977, 1981), Hamlett (1999), Holmgren & Nilsson (1999), Kalmijn (1978), Kemp (1999), Moss (1984), Springer & Gold (1989), Taylor (1997), Tricas et al. (1995).

CHAPTER 2

The Elasmobranch Aquarium System

Planning and Setting Up a Home Tank for Sharks or Rays

AMONG THE TRULY WELL-FUNDED PUBLIC AQUARISTS AND theme-park biologists, the Holy Grail of shark husbandry is being able to display a healthy Great White Shark. But *Carcharodon carcharias* has thus far stubbornly thwarted all efforts at keeping it alive in captivity, despite the spending of huge sums of money, the building of shark tanks in the 1.1 to 1.9 million-liter range (300,000 to 500,000 gal.) costing millions of dollars, and the creation of special transportation and maintenance systems. Home aquarists will have a much easier time putting together hospitable settings for their specimens. In many respects, caring for a small elasmobranch is similar to keeping a lionfish or a marine angelfish, but there are several factors to consider in order to ensure success.

> *"When it comes to choosing a tank for these fishes, bigger is not only better, it is imperative."*

The Tank

ONE DIFFERENCE BETWEEN THE SHARKS available to the aquarist and most bony fishes is size. The majority of sharks at aquarium stores

Parascyllium ferrugineum (Rusty Carpet Shark): home aquarists may be able to mimic the natural surroundings of some species, using live rock and macroalgae.

An impressive 13,300-liter (3,500-gallon) office shark tank by House of Fins in Greenwich, CT, supports three Blacktip Reef Sharks, a Whitetip Reef Shark, a Bluespotted Ribbontail Ray, two Southern Stingrays, as well as moray eels, various bony fishes, and a spiny lobster. Measuring 8.5x1.2x1.2 m (28x4x4 ft.), the tank has a live rock reef and is run on two quad skimmers, six trickle filters, and water circulation of 66,500 L/hr (17,500 gph).

reach over 1 m (3.3 ft.) in total length, while many of the bony fish species mature at a length of less than 20 cm (7.8 in.). This is a very important difference to consider when selecting a tank in which to house your shark or ray. Most elasmobranchs need plenty of space to carry out their normal activities, such as feeding and locomotion. When it comes to choosing a tank for these fishes, bigger is not only better, it is *imperative*. If you cannot afford or don't have room for a tank of at least 684 L (180 gal.) measuring 183 cm (6 ft.) in length by 61 cm (24 in.) in width, you will not be able to keep most aquarium-suitable sharks and rays for their entire lives. The residency time of potentially large specimens in your aquarium will be directly proportional to the size of your tank (i.e., a large tank will allow you to keep

them for a longer time).

When purchasing a tank, keep in mind that the surface area of the aquarium is more important than its volume. Not only does increased surface area mean better gas exchange and more area for biological filtration, but it also translates into more usable living space for your elasmobranch. Good rules of thumb for planning a system involve taking into account the ultimate size and activity level of your intended specimens, giving them room to swim, glide, and turn without serious constraint. In planning the ultimate tank size needed to house a particular species of shark or ray, the following rough guidelines can be used: **For a less-active species**, the aquarium should be 0.75 times as wide as the full adult length of the fish in question and 2 to 2.5

times as long as the full adult length. **For an active species**, the aquarium should be 1.5 times as wide as the fish's adult length and 4 to 5 times as long. Similarly, a ray should be given a tank that is 1.5 times as wide and 4 times as long as the adult disc length.

Common sense should come into play in selecting an appropriate aquarium. For example, a Brownbanded Bamboo Shark (*Chiloscyllium punctatum*), an inactive species, grows to a maximum total length of about 100 cm (39 in.) and thus—using the rules above—warrants a theoretical tank measuring 201-249 x 76 cm (79-98 x 30 in.). However, juvenile specimens can comfortably be kept in less-capacious tanks, and a standard 684 L (180 gal.) aquarium measuring 183 x 61 cm (72 x 24 in.) should suffice for most adults. (See Chapter 4 for maximum species lengths and suggested aquarium sizes for all commonly available aquarium sharks and rays.)

Table 2-1 gives the dimensions of some larger tanks in standard sizes produced by several well-known aquarium manufacturers. Many companies will also custom-build a tank that better suits your specimen (see Table 2-2 for some examples). Specifically, acrylic tank makers can produce the round tanks favored for some species of active sharks, albeit at a substantial cost. Generally speaking, acrylic tanks are more expensive than comparably sized glass models and are prone to being scratched. Benefits of acrylic include lighter weight, better thermal insulation (important for cold-water or chilled systems) and, in the eyes of some aquarists, superior aesthetics. Glass tanks are easier to clean when razor-sharp maintenance is required and can be cheaper, gallon for gallon, than acrylic.

It is important to remember that "tall" configurations of standard tanks may not be as appropriate as longer or broader designs of equal volume. Some companies offer "low" versions of popular sizes, giving them

TABLE 2-1.

Standard Larger Rectangular Aquarium Sizes

Volume liters (gallons)	Dimensions (l x w x h) centimeters (inches)
122 cm (4 ft.) Long Tanks	
285 (75)	122 x 46 x 53 (48 x 18 x 21)
342 (90)	122 x 46 x 61 (48 x 18 x 24)
456 (120)	122 x 61 x 61 (48 x 24 x 24)
152 cm (5 ft.) Long Tanks	
285 (75)	152 x 46 x 41 (60 x 18 x 16)
380 (100)	152 x 46 x 51 (60 x 18 x 20)
475 (125)	152 x 61 x 51 (60 x 24 x 20)
570 (150)	183 x 61 x 61 (72 x 24 x 24)
183 cm (6 ft.) Long Tanks	
418 (110)	183 x 46 x 46 (72 x 18 x 18)
475 (125)	183 x 46 x 56 (72 x 18 x 22)
513 (135)	183 x 46 x 61 (72 x 18 x 24)
570 (150)	183 x 61 x 51 (72 x 24 x 20)
684 (180)	183 x 61 x 61 (72 x 24 x 24)
836 (220)	183 x 61 x 76 (72 x 24 x 30)
213 cm (7 ft.) Long Tanks	
608 (160)	213 x 46 x 61 (84 x 18 x 24)
760 (200)	213 x 61 x 61 (84 x 24 x 24)
1,007 (265)	213 x 61 x 76 (84 x 24 x 30)
243 cm (8 ft.) Long Tanks	
912 (240)	244 x 46 x 76 (96 x 18 x 30)
912 (240)	244 x 61 x 61 (96 x 24 x 24)
1,140 (300)	244 x 61 x 76 (96 x 24 x 30)

Note: These are approximate volumes and dimensions. Always obtain exact external dimensions of a tank for actual installation planning.

TABLE 2-2.

Large Custom Shark & Ray Tanks

Volume liters (gallons)	Dimensions (l x w x h) centimeters (feet)	Volume liters (gallons)	Dimensions (diam. x depth) centimeters (feet)
Rectangular Aquariums		**Circular Tanks or Ponds**	
2,850 (750)	305 × 122 × 76 (10 × 4 × 2.5)	3,610 (950)	244 × 76 (8 × 2.5)
4,560 (1,200)	366 ×137 × 91 (12 × 4.5 × 3)	4,940 (1,300)	244 × 107 (8 × 3.5)
6,365 (1,675)	457 ×183 × 76 (15 × 6 × 2.5)	7,790 (2,050)	305 × 107 (10 × 3.5)
9,880 (2,600)	610 × 213 × 76 (20 × 7 × 2.5)	17,480 (4,600)	457 × 107 (15 × 3.5)
17,100 (4,500)	610 × 229 × 122 (20 × 7.5 × 4)	25,270 (6,650)	549 × 107 (18 × 3.5)
37,525 (9,875)	914 × 335 × 122 (30 × 11 × 4)	34,390 (9,050)	640 × 107 (21 × 3.5)
		45,030 (11,850)	732 × 107 (24 × 3.5)

a better configuration for smaller sharks and rays.

Custom-built shark tanks can be constructed of glass, acrylic, fiberglass, or plywood coated with two-

The typical elasmobranch system demands plenty of swimming space with one or more rocky hiding places. (Brownbanded Bamboo Shark)

part waterproof epoxy—or a combination of materials. However, for more active species, which are prone to rubbing their bodies or fins against the sides as they swim, the smoother and less abrasive the material, the better. Concrete, for example, has been found to irritate the skin of electric rays and stingrays, resulting in lethal bacterial infections. When plastic is placed over the concrete sides, the mortality rate greatly decreases. Active sharks will often swim around the perimeter of an aquarium with a pectoral fin contacting the side. In concrete tanks, sharks have been known to abrade their fins as a result of this behavior.

Although somewhat unconventional, some hobbyists and retail stores construct "shark ponds" to house larger sharks or rays. You can put together such a pond with just two plastic pond liners (each 20 mils, or 1/50 in., thick) and a heavy wooden frame to support the liners. Using two liners reduces the possibility of leakage, and the backup liner also helps prevent a disaster in case a shark should bite through the inner layer. Biological filtration in such a facility can be provided by a large external canister filter or a trickle filter. Aquaculture supply houses can provide all the materials needed to construct and plumb pond-type shark systems. (See Contacts, page 240.)

The Filter

AS WITH BONY FISHES, it is important to maintain good water quality to sustain the health of your shark or ray. This includes converting toxic nitrogenous waste products into their less-harmful by-products. Elasmobranchs, like bony fishes, excrete ammonia and urea from their gills and in their urine. Ammonia is toxic to these fishes at relatively low concentrations, so in order to deal with this potential problem, it is imperative that we encourage the growth of certain bacteria (specifically those in the genus *Nitrosomonas*) to convert ammonia into nitrite. Because nitrites are also toxic, interfering with the oxygen-carrying capability of the blood, you need to "farm" another form of bacteria (*Nitrobacter*) to convert nitrite to nitrate. Nitrate is the least problematic of the three forms of nitrogen, becoming a danger to elasmobranchs only at much higher concentrations and

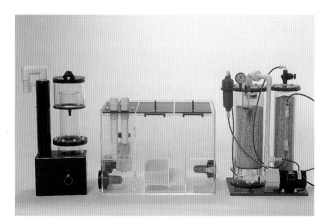

System components may include a skimmer, sump, and calcium reactor.

TABLE 2-3.

System Volume Calculations

Determining the volume of a rectangular tank:

length (ft.) × width (ft.) × depth (ft.) × 7.48 = gallons

or

[length (in.) × width (in.) × depth (in.)] ÷ 231 = gallons

Determining the volume of a circular tank:

diam. (ft.) × diam. (ft.) × depth (ft.) × 5.86 = gallons

Converting gallons to liters:

volume in gallons × 3.7854 = volume in liters

---

usually only if the animals are exposed for long periods of time. Note that nitrates along with low iodine levels have been implicated in causing thyroid hyperplasia, or goiter (for more on this see page 186). The best way to prevent the buildup of nitrates is to change 20 to 25% of the tank water every month. (Some aquarists prefer to make smaller, weekly changes of about 5%.)

A number of different filtration methods can be employed to manage the accumulation of nitrogenous waste products. The popular wet-dry (trickle) filters, most often used for keeping sensitive invertebrates, can be used to maintain excellent water parameters. Many types of wet-dry filters on the market are well-suited for the elasmobranch aquarium. However, if you choose a model that has an overflow box that hangs over the side of the tank (rather than having a hole drilled in the corner of the tank and installing an overflow box, or purchasing a "reef ready" system), be sure it is securely fitted

TABLE 2-4.

Elasmobranch Aquarium System Components

SMALL SYSTEM

For small juvenile specimens and hatching egg cases.

Tank:	209 L (55 gal.)
Filtration:	• small wet/dry filter (380 L [100 gal.] tank capacity)
	• external protein skimmer
Temp. Control:	150-watt heater (optional)
Lighting:	minimum of one 40-watt fluorescent light (full spectrum)
Substrate:	• fine coral sand (5 cm [2 in.] deep)
	• several pieces of live rock, strapped securely with cable ties to form small caves or ledges

MEDIUM SYSTEM

For relatively inactive swimmers, such as epaulette or bamboo sharks.

Tank:	684 L (180 gal.)
Filtration:	• wet-dry or trickle filter, powered by 1,000 gph pump
	• external protein skimmer
Circulation:	additional circulation-only water pumps (capacity 900-1,500 gph)
Temp. Control:	two 200-watt heaters (placed in sump of wet-dry filter)
Lighting:	four 40-watt fluorescent lights (full spectrum or 3:1 full:blue actinic)
Substrate:	• fine coral sand (5 cm [2 in.] deep)
	• several pieces of live rock, strapped securely with cable ties to form small caves or ledges

LARGE SYSTEM

For aquarists with the room and resources to graduate to larger and more-active species.

Tank:	1,520-2,280 L (400-600 gal.) or larger
Filtration:	• high-capacity wet-dry or trickle filter (1,000 gph pump) OR large sump (380 L [100 gal.]) with biomedia or live rock and sand bed (typically in basement below system or in adjacent utility room), plumbed with minimum 1,000-gph pump OR pool or spa pump (1/2-3/4 HP) and heavy-duty cartridge filter system
	• external or in-sump heavy-duty foam fractionator (skimmer)
Circulation:	1/2-3/4 HP water pump plumbed to provide circulation through several return ports (hourly turnover of 6-8 times system volume)
Temp. Control:	two 200-watt heaters (placed in sump of wet-dry filter)
Lighting:	four to eight 40-watt fluorescent lights
Substrate:	• fine coral sand (5 cm [2 in.] deep)
	• faux coral, coral rock, or live rock,
Options:	• automatic freshwater top-off system
	• reverse osmosis unit to treat freshwater source
	• ultraviolet (UV) filter
	• chiller (for temperate-water species or seasonal overheating)
	• calcium reactor for pH control

to the aquarium frame. A rambunctious shark or ray might bump the overflow box and disrupt the siphon, which could lead to major flooding. An overflow box with readily accessible pre-filter material is also desirable because it is more likely you will rinse it out with greater regularity.

Canister filters, filled with materials that provide good substrate for nitrifying bacteria growth, will also furnish adequate biological filtration. I prefer canister filters that can be completely packed with filter media, as opposed to those that have a smaller central cartridge. The filter media should be cleaned every 2 weeks or so with water from the aquarium to remove accumulating detritus. Just fill a bucket with tank water and agitate the canister media in the bucket. Some canister filters have a foam prefilter that will allow you to clean the media less frequently.

One of the most effective ways to control nitrogenous waste is with a fluidized bed filter. This type of filter usually consists of a chamber or cylinder filled with granular filter media (usually quartz sand), through which the aquarium water rapidly flows. The water flow causes the sand to be constantly buffeted about and oxygenated. There are no "dead" spots in the filter media, providing a maximal surface area for bacteria to colonize. Because the media is always in motion, it should never clog, like the media in a wet-dry or trickle filter.

(Earlier models were reported to have clogging problems, but this has been remedied in newer designs.) The fluidized bed filters are ideal for a tank with large preda-

Massive display of sharks and other fishes is an attraction at the Aquarium of the Americas, New Orleans, LA.

tors, such as sharks and rays, that produce excessive amounts of nitrogenous waste. One advantage to using an external filter, like wet-dry, canister, or fluidized bed models, is that there is less clutter in the tank to impede your elasmobranch's movement. It also makes it easier to use a finer substrate that is more suitable for rays to bury in and less irritating to a shark or ray's ventral surface.

An undergravel filter, either set up in the conventional fashion or "reverse flow" (pumping water down rather than up the lift tubes), can be used to filter the tank of a very small shark or ray, **although it is less desirable than the aforementioned filter types.** If you use

TABLE 2-5.

7 Common Setup Mistakes

1. The aquarium has too little surface area. (Deep "show" tanks are not well-suited to keeping elasmobranchs.)

2. The tank doesn't have adequate biological filtration and/or circulation.

3. Aquascaping does not allow adequate swimming space. (The aquarium is cluttered with too much decor.)

4. The rockwork, caves, and ledges created in the tank are unstable. (Toppling rock can injure specimens.)

5. A substrate is used that will irritate the elasmobranch's ventrum.

6. A secure cover is not placed on the tank.

7. Internal equipment (heaters, filter intakes, and the like) are unprotected and a potential hazard to active specimens.

an undergravel filter, I suggest you use powerheads to irrigate the gravel with oxygenated seawater, but airstones and an air pump will also work. It is prudent to silicone the lift tubes to the undergravel plate, as some shark species are proficient at unseating these tubes, causing gravel to pour under the filter.

Approximately 5 to 8 cm (2.0 to 3.1 in.) of gravel should be placed on top of the undergravel filter plate. If you choose to use a finer substrate, such as coral sand, a plastic screen may be placed between the sand and the undergravel filter to prevent the substrate from getting under the plate. Sharks and rays will often displace the substrate, leaving part of the undergravel plate uncov-

ered. It is important to push the substrate back over the filter promptly to ensure that it functions properly. If the plate is left uncovered, most of the water will follow the path of least resistance, going through the exposed part of the plate, rather than through the areas covered with gravel. Because oxygen is no longer being carried to the bacteria living in these areas, the aerobic (oxygen-requiring) bacteria will be replaced by anaerobic (non-oxygen-requiring) types, which produce toxic metabolites and do not convert ammonia to nitrites. A harmful by-product of anaerobic bacteria metabolism is hydrogen sulfide, which is as poisonous as cyanide gas. One way to prevent sections of the filter plate from being totally exposed is to add an inch of substrate and place a piece of plastic screen or eggcrate on top of it, then bury this under the remaining crushed coral or sand.

It is also important to use a gravel vacuum to pull detritus out of the substrate when doing water changes. Allowing debris and detritus to accumulate in the gravel will cause areas of the filter bed to become plugged, encouraging the growth of anaerobic bacteria. The digging activities of some sharks and rays, as well as some of their tankmates, can assist in keeping the filter from becoming clogged.

Finally, many modern marine aquarists employ "live" substrate as a biological filter. They add a layer of live sand on the bottom of the aquarium and also introduce live rock. The numerous beneficial microorganisms that live on this substrate help keep toxic nitrogenous waste products in check. Live biomedia have the additional advantage of effectively preventing nitrate from accumulating, as it often does in older, traditionally filtered systems.

Although live substrate can provide adequate filtration for a tank housing a smaller shark or ray, this kind of setup is not as desirable for elasmobranchs as it

Flattish Panamanian live rock is ideal for creating safe reefscapes.

Branching rock or coral decor should have no sharp projections.

Exterior biological filtration may include the use of plastic media.

Smooth-surfaced coral rock is excellent for the elasmobranch aquarium.

is for most other aquarium inhabitants. This is due to the fact that the amount of live rock necessary to promote such filtration would too-severely limit the swimming space needed for most elasmobranchs. For example, it is usually recommended you fill at least one-third to one-half of the tank volume with live rock when setting up a reef aquarium. This would be too restrictive for active sharks or rays.

For less-active species in a larger tank, it may be possible to include enough live rock and live sand to provide adequate filtration. However, if a situation should arise in which there is suddenly an excessive amount of nitrogenous waste in the tank (e.g., the shark is overfed or it regurgitates) there may not be a large enough population of nitrifying bacteria in the rock and sand to keep ammonia and nitrite in check. Certainly, a few pieces of live rock and a layer of live sand can provide valuable supplemental biological filtration, but this typically ought to be an adjunct to an external filter, rather than the main workhorse.

Many reef aquarists prefer the lower maintenance of open sumps to pressurized canister systems, which

Dasyatis kuhlii (Bluespotted Stingray) buried under substrate: a 5-cm (2-inch) layer of fine coral sand offers aquascaping and natural refuge.

much be shut down, opened, and cleaned regularly. Some keepers of larger marine specimens now plumb a large sump to their display tank and fill this container with live rock and live sand for needed nitrification.

Foam Fractionator

CAPTIVE SHARKS AND RAYS have messy feeding habits and can produce copious amounts of waste. The ideal tool for dealing with the pollution created by large captive fishes is a foam fractionator, or protein skimmer. Protein skimming is a process by which charged particles of protein and fat are removed from the water by exposing them to a stream of air bubbles. The molecules stick to the bubbles and the resultant foam froths over into an overflow cup. The concentrated waste in the skimmer can then be discarded.

Skimmer design has continued to evolve over recent years, and excellent results can be had from a variety of different technologies. (See Harker [1999], for an ex-

haustive review on how foam fractionators work, how they should be set up, and the benefits of the various types of skimmers.) While reef enthusiasts wrangle over the effects of aggressive skimming on their corals and other invertebrates, it is difficult to imagine overskimming an elasmobranch system. In addition to extracting wastes, a good skimmer promotes constant gas exchange and oxygenation of the water. For a tank housing one or more sharks or rays, a well-designed, heavy-duty skimmer is a definite plus, if not an essential item. A reputable aquarium store or online aquarium newsgroups should be able to help you choose a skimmer that is right for your specific requirements.

One thing to keep in mind when selecting a skimmer for your shark or ray tank is that these animals may buffet and bump an internal skimmer (i.e., a skimmer that is placed directly in the aquarium), detaching it from the side of the tank. A shark might also lodge itself between the skimmer and the aquarium glass. Therefore, a sump with an external skimmer or a skimmer that hangs on the outside of the aquarium has clear advantages. If you choose an internal type for a small or temporary system, be sure it is securely attached to the aquarium and does not create a hazard in which a specimen could become trapped.

Cleaning the skimmer is relatively simple, but it is essential to do so regularly (one to two times a week, if possible). The buildup of fatty substances in the reaction chamber (where air is mixed with water) and foam concentrating components can inhibit foam production.

Substrate

ANOTHER IMPORTANT CONSIDERATION in the elasmobranch tank is the bottom substrate. The ideal substrate for all sharks and rays is a smaller grade of coral sand or fine aragonite sand used by many marine aquarists. In fact, for some species that bury or spend lots of time lying on the bottom, finer substrates are a prerequisite. The larger grades of crushed coral and dolomite can irritate the animal's ventral surface and cause bacterial infections. You may have observed specimens with red ventral areas, a result of irritation caused by such materials. This is especially a problem with guitarfishes, whiptail stingrays, stingarees, and electric rays, which, unlike sharks, lack placoid scales (dermal denticles) on their ventral surfaces. Another problem with some larger, sharp-edged substrates is that sharks might inadvertently ingest the material and damage their digestive tracts.

If an undergravel filter is not used, the depth of substrate material should be kept to a minimum (5 cm [about 2 in.] or less). This is especially true for very fine sand, which can readily become anaerobic. If you are using a finer grade of sand and see areas where the surface becomes black, immediately siphon these spots out using a large-diameter siphon tube, because anaerobic activity is occurring there. Remove the areas very carefully, disturbing them as little as possible, because hydrogen sulfide could be released into the aquarium, possibly killing the inhabitants. (Fine coral sand, which acts as a natural buffering agent, is always a better choice for marine aquariums than silica-type sands— often sold as "beach sand" or "playbox sand.")

Aquascaping

ONE OF THE BIGGEST DIFFERENCES between an aquarium that houses a bony fish and one that is home for a shark or ray is the decor. In most fish aquariums, the aquarist attempts to duplicate the highly structured reef environment in order to create hiding places and to make the tank look like a reef. In contrast, the shark tank places a premium on swimming and maneuvering space and decorative aquascaping should be used only sparingly. If you are keeping bullhead sharks, wobbegongs, nurse sharks, bamboo sharks, or epaulette sharks (i.e., species that spend most of the daytime hours concealed in reef crevices), a coral cave or a rock ledge will make them feel more secure and facilitate their settling-in period.

Port Jackson Shark in natural setting: reefkeeping techniques can make for more realistic habitats.

Triakis semifasciata (Leopard Shark): juvenile aquarium specimen.

In contrast, active species may collide with decorations and abrade or damage their skin, which can lead to lethal bacterial infections. Therefore, if you are keeping species like the Leopard Shark (*Triakis semifasciata*), the Gray Smoothhound (*Mustelus californicus*), and some rays, aquascaping should not be included.

I recently witnessed a case of improper aquascaping for a shark species in a public aquarium. Juvenile Sandbar Sharks (*Carcharhinus plumbeus*) kept in a medium-sized oceanarium with fiberglass coral decorations had abrasions on their noses from colliding with the aquascaping, while Blacktip Reef Sharks (*Carcharhinus melanopterus*) of a similar size had no such injuries. Why? The Blacktip, because it is a coral reef dweller, is accustomed to navigating around coral heads and through reef channels. The Sandbar Shark, on the other hand, is usually found on mud and sand flats in areas where there is little or no reef structure and has greater difficulty maneuvering in these conditions. Even in the case of inactive species, a more conservative approach to aquascaping will provide increased room for movement.

If you think some type of decor is necessary, I recommend using faux (synthetic) corals. These are usually less abrasive than bleached coral skeletons or lava rock. Also, the trade in dead coral skeletons has fallen into disfavor, and many marine biologists are urging the aquarium industry to discontinue the use of such materials. Synthetic corals, especially those without sharp projections or rough surfaces, are a more acceptable choice for most elasmobranch keepers.

You can also add a few smaller pieces of live rock to give the tank a more natural appearance and consider including some invertebrate fauna, such as shrimps, hermit crabs, and sea stars (see Chapter 5 for appropriate elasmobranch tankmates). These invertebrates are interesting to observe and also provide a natural food source for some smaller elasmobranchs, such as juvenile bamboo and epaulette sharks. If you use live rock that has good coralline algae growth and maintain the calcium level of the water, these attractive calcareous plants will sometimes spread and grow on the glass and the artificial coral.

Lighting

THE OPTICAL SYSTEMS OF SHARKS AND RAYS are well adapted to their environments and way of life. Their pupils are very responsive, constricting in bright light and dilating in darker conditions. Some of the rays have a structure in front of the cornea known as the **operculum pupillare**. This structure expands in bright conditions to block light from entering the pupil, which may increase the animal's depth of field and make the retina more responsive to movement. Sharks and rays also possess a **tapetum lucidum**, which increases the sensitivity of the eyes to light. In dim light, this structure reflects light back through the retina and is responsible for the mirrorlike "eyeshine" you can observe in elasmobranchs and in some other vertebrates, like cats.

Cold-Water Sharks

A number of smaller catsharks that live in cooler climes will do fantastically well in smaller aquariums. Some of these species, such as the Chain Catshark (*Scyliorhinus retifer*), the Cloudy Catshark (*S. torazame*), several members of the genus *Poroderma* and the Swell Shark (*Cephaloscyllium ventriosum*) are readily bred in smaller tanks at public aquariums, and some of these sharks may be more readily available to home aquarists in the future.

These sharks present the aquarist with one unique challenge. They need to be housed at cooler water temperatures. For example, the Chain Catshark should be kept at water temperatures no warmer than 12.7°C (55°F). The other species mentioned above do best at temperatures of less than 15.5 to 18.3°C (60 to 65°F). In order to keep these species, then, the aquarist will need to invest in a good chiller. There are many chillers available to marine aquarium keepers, but there is a great degree of variation in quality. This is a case where it is prudent to invest in a very reliable unit, as some cold-water sharks will die if the chiller malfunctions and the water temperature gets too high. Elasmobranch keepers with treasured specimens often have a backup chiller, or at least a contingency plan, if mechanical problems arise. The size of the chiller you purchase will be a function of the tank size and the difference

Scyliorhinus canicula (Smallspotted Catshark): typical of the many species that can thrive in cool-water aquariums.

between the ambient room temperature and the desired aquarium temperature.

One problem with cold-water tanks is that they have a tendency to "sweat" during hot, humid weather. This annoying problem will make it difficult to view the tank's inhabitants. This condensation is less likely to be a problem if the tank is kept in a cool, air-conditioned room. Also, Plexiglas or acrylic tanks have better insulating properties and are less likely to become a condensation site. The thicker the Plexiglas, the better insulator it will be and the fewer condensation problems you'll have. Other options for coping with condensation problems include directing a fan toward the front of the tank and/or locating the tank in the coolest part of the house—and never in direct sunlight.

The cold-water species can be kept on the same kind of substrate as their warm-water relatives (e.g., aragonite sand or crushed coral and shell). Cold-water live rock is more difficult to find, although some individuals who collect specimens for scientific study along the U.S. west coast may be able to supply cold-water live rock in small quantities. All other equipment needed, excluding the heater, is the same as for tropical species (see Elasmobranch Aquarium System Components, page 48).

Shallow-water sharks and rays have a light-absorbing curtain that is draped protectively in front of the tapetum during the day. These anatomical features make elasmobranch vision extremely effective in low-light conditions. In fact, the visual systems of some of these animals are capable of functioning by moonlight alone.

Aquarist's dreamland: sandtiger sharks at the Aquarium of the Americas.

In the case of nocturnal species, lighting in the aquarium should be kept to a minimum. These sharks spend the daylight hours in reef crevices and caves. If kept under dim light, they will often adapt to aquarium life more rapidly and spend more time in the open where the aquarist can view them. This is especially true during the first few weeks of acclimation. You can watch a nocturnal species at night by extinguishing all lights except for a red fluorescent or red incandescent bulb over the tank; sharks are not sensitive to this wavelength of light and will behave as if they are in total darkness.

Diurnal sharks and rays can be kept at a variety of light levels. These species seem to be less sensitive to more-intense lighting, although reduced illumination is recommended during the first few days of their captive lives. A simple 12-hour-light and 12-hour-dark cycle, similar to that in the tropics where our aquarium species are collected, works well in a diurnal elasmobranch tank. Some adjustments can be made if a longer display/daylight period is desired (e.g., 14 hours "on" and 10 hours "off"), but if lights are left on constantly, the continuous stimulation may damage the eyes' photoreceptors, and other deleterious effects on the animals' physiology or behavior may be seen.

Water Parameters

THE CONDITIONS in which a shark or ray is kept should be as similar to those in its natural environment as possible. The physiological machinery of an elasmobranch is tuned to operate most efficiently in the surroundings in which it typically lives. If we duplicate these conditions in the aquarium, we should have greater success maintaining these animals. The appropriate temperature, specific gravity (salinity), pH, and nitrogen levels are important environmental parameters to achieve.

Temperature

The proper water temperature for an elasmobranch tank will depend on the sharks or rays you are keeping. Most species commonly available in North America will do well between 22 and 27°C (72 to 81°F), with the lower part of this range being preferred in order to slow growth rates. Some species from cold or temperate water do better at water temperatures below 18°C (64°F), necessitating a chiller. Aquarists living in areas where tank temperatures rise considerably in the summer must avoid species from cold-temperate regions if they cannot afford a chiller. Although some of these temperate species may be able to tolerate higher temperatures, they have adapted over millions of years to perform optimally in the conditions where they live. Keeping them in warmer water may shorten their lives.

Some sharks and rays can withstand temperatures of 29°C (84°F) or more. Sharks that inhabit shallow waters in tropical regions may be exposed to temperatures higher than 32°C (90°F) for short periods of time. I once had an Ornate Wobbegong (*Orectolobus ornatus*), a known tidepool dweller, withstand a temperature of 35°C (95°F) when the aquarium heater malfunctioned. Several specimens of the Marbled Catshark (*Atelomycterus macleayi*), have been taken in shallow waters at temperatures of 32 to 35°C (90 to 95°F). At such high temperatures, the oxygen-carrying capacity of the water is very low, but the respiratory system of some tropical sharks is adapted to hypoxic conditions. For example, the blood of the Lemon Shark (*Negaprion brevirostris*) has a much greater affinity for oxygen than most other fishes. But it is best to keep water temperatures below 27°C (81°F), even for tropical species.

A word about submersible heaters (the most popular instrument employed to heat the home aquarium): if possible, it is best to place this type of heater in a sump, not directly into the shark or ray display aquarium. When sharks get rambunctious, as they often do at feeding time, they can bump into glass-encased heaters, causing cracks or breakage and setting up dangerous situations. Benthic sharks and rays might also rest against a submersible heater and burn themselves. For these reasons, its best to keep the heater in a sump or external filter compartment. If it must be in the display tank, be sure to form a protective structure around it, using plastic eggcrate material or acrylic with holes drilled in it. In effect, the heater should be in a boxlike structure that is inaccessible to the shark but with plenty of water movement to dissipate the heat it generates.

Salinity

Sharks and rays vary in their tolerance for different levels of salinity (concentration of total salts, measured as specific gravity) for the waters they inhabit. Some species, such as the Atlantic Stingray (*Dasyatis sabina*) and Gray Smoothhound Shark (*Mustelus californicus*), can be found over a wide range of salinity levels; these species are referred to as **euryhaline**. Others are apparently less tolerant of salinity levels much lower than that of normal seawater, and are referred to as **stenohaline**. I have kept such species as the Leopard Shark (*Triakis semifasciata*) and the Gray Smoothhound at a specific gravity (SG) of 1.016 for extended periods with no apparent ill effects. These sharks are sometimes found in estuarine environments where the water is hyposaline (i.e., less "salty"). I have also kept the Tasseled Wobbegong (*Eucrossorhinus dasypogon*) and the Coral Catshark at lower salinity levels (e.g., down to 1.018 SG) without incident. Some rays, like the Atlantic Stingray, can be kept at a specific gravity of 1.014 or even less. This ray has been reported from freshwater and is not uncommon in brackish-water estuaries. One advantage to

Active species, like this juvenile Zebra Shark, require large systems and expert care.

midity). A wise practice is to check the specific gravity at least every 3 days and adjust it accordingly. If salinity levels rise too high, sharks may cruise with their heads partially out of the water. This swimming behavior, however, is not always indicative of high salinity. For example, healthy smoothhound sharks and some rays will engage in this behavior, even under optimal conditions. Newly acquired Bonnethead Sharks (*Sphyrna tiburo*) will also swim with their snouts out of the water, but usually cease doing so after they have acclimated. There are also some sharks, such as the Broadnosed Sevengill (*Notorynchus cepedianus*), Spiny Dogfish (*Squalus acanthias*), and Great White Shark (*Carcharodon carcharias*), that lift their heads from the water in the wild.

A word about the hydrometers typically used by home aquarists: there are pros and cons to both the floating and box (dip-and-read) types. The box hydrometer is easier to read but is more likely to give erroneous readings if not used properly. For example, it is very important to tap it against a hard surface to loosen air bubbles from the pointer. Also, it should be rinsed thoroughly with freshwater after each use and soaked in vinegar if crusty deposits ever form on its interior.

keeping euryhaline species at lower salinity levels is that it can help rid them of certain parasites.

Elasmobranchs are very permeable to water—much more so than the majority of saltwater bony fishes. When they are placed in diluted seawater, freshwater enters their body, causing a reduction in plasma osmotic pressure and ionic concentration. In stenohaline species, the reduction in these parameters is greater than in euryhaline forms. These changes in body chemistry affect the functioning of various enzymes (like those in the cells of muscles and neurons), and blood hemoglobin. The latter affects respiratory gas transport. Placing a stenohaline species into highly diluted seawater may cause death from these physiological disturbances. (Most elasmobranchs fall into the stenohaline category.)

In order to avoid physiological stress to your charges, it is best not to let the specific gravity fluctuate. Evaporation, a common cause of specific gravity fluctuation, is dependent on many factors (aquarium setup, filter type and construction, and the ambient hu-

pH

As with other saltwater systems, it is best to maintain the pH between 7.8 and the natural seawater level of 8.3, although some species show no ill effects when kept at pH levels as low as 7.2. Some sharks and rays are very sensitive to sudden changes in pH, however, showing signs of distress at sudden drops of as little as 0.2 pH points. Keep the pH as stable as possible; if adjustments need to be made, they should be made slowly.

Normal biological filtration in an aquarium produces nitric acid that will lower the pH. This is especially true in the elasmobranch aquarium, because these fishes produce copious amounts of waste and are often kept in smaller volumes of water relative to their body size. Although fresh seawater (natural or synthetic) contains natural buffers, it will lose this capacity with time. The best and easiest way to maintain the appropriate pH level is to carry out monthly water changes. Sodium bicarbonate can also be used to raise pH, but remember that pH changes should always be done gradually to avoid stressing your elasmobranch with sudden changes or overdosing. Dissolve 1 level teaspoon of sodium bicarbonate in 1 gallon of tank water for every 20 gallons of water in your aquarium, and add this over a period of 1 hour (e.g., for a 200-gallon aquarium, dissolve 10 teaspoons in 10 gallons of tank water). Check the pH the next day and repeat this procedure if necessary. Calcium carbonate or aragonite substrates, such as coral sand and live rock, also act as effective buffers.

If you have persistent problems with low pH, it may be that the tank is overcrowded, has insufficient filtration, or does not have enough gas exchange at the water's surface or in the skimmer and filter components. Problems are often seen when the aquarium is equipped only with powerheads and has a tight-fitting glass top. To rectify this problem, add an airstone and/or make a weighted fiberglass screen or eggcrate top to allow adequate gas exchange. (Many sharks can knock off a top that is not heavy enough, so lightweight covers should be securely fastened in place or weighted down.)

High pH, although rare, can be a problem because ammonia is more toxic at higher pH levels. If your tank's pH rises above 8.3, it is often due to carbon dioxide uptake caused by algal photosynthesis. In this case, harvesting some of the algae can lower the pH.

Nitrogen Levels

Ammonia and nitrite levels should read zero. Ammonia levels as low as 0.01 parts per million are toxic to some sharks, so be very sure any newly setup tank has completed the nitrogen cycle before introducing an elasmobranch. It is also important not to be in a hurry to add specimens to your aquarium. Although sharks are not known to be particularly sensitive to the buildup of nitrates and dissolved organic compounds, good water quality can help prevent stress. Stoskopf (1993) suggests that deteriorating water quality may cause some species to stop feeding, lose color, scratch against the aquarium bottom, have periodic seizures, and be more susceptible to disease. Unfortunately, he does not specifically define what he means by deteriorating water quality.

To be safe, it is best to maintain the nitrate level below 100 mg/L NO_3^--N (nitrate-nitrogen), even though most sharks show no ill effects even when the nitrates rise to 250 mg/L NO_3^--N. Some have been observed to tolerate even higher levels for short periods of time. To keep nitrogenous waste products from accumulating, make sure you have a good biological filter, promptly remove uneaten food, and change 20 to 25% of the aquarium water every month, using high-grade seawater to replace the old.

As stated previously, a good protein skimmer is a valuable piece of equipment, and good-quality activated carbon filters are also useful for pulling out dissolved organic compounds.

References

Copper & Morris (1998), R. Davis (personal communication), Gruber (1977, 1981), Gruber & Keyes (1981), Harker (1999), Moe (1982), Moss (1984), Stoskopf (1993), R. Withrow (personal communication).

CHAPTER 3

Selecting the Right Specimen

Picking a Healthy Elasmobranch—
and One That Is Right for You

JUST AS SOME ANIMAL LOVERS ARE UNABLE TO RESIST BRINGING home a sick puppy or kitten, determined to nurse it back to health, some aquarists willingly purchase unfit fishes in hopes of making them well. With elasmobranchs, this is a highly risky approach and not one I would recommend—especially to anyone acquiring a first shark or ray. In fact, starting with a healthy specimen is one of the keys to the long-term maintenance of these animals in captivity.

As with bony fishes, there are physical and behav-ioral clues that can help the aquarist determine the con-dition of an elasmobranch, but in order to recognize an unhealthy shark or ray, you must first know how a healthy specimen looks and acts. There are species-spe-cific differences in appearance and behavior. For example, prolonged inactivity may be a sign of distress in some species (such as smooth-hounds) and not in others (such as wobbegongs). It may be necessary to observe a single individual for a long period of time—an hour or more—in order to obtain an accurate behavioral profile. The species

> *"A healthy shark will be alert, moving its eyes to watch things that move into its path."*

Negaprion brevirostris (Lemon Shark): a durable species sometimes sold as juveniles to hobbyists but growing far too large for most amateurs to maintain.

Hemiscyllium freycineti (Freycinet's Epaulette Shark): a handsome, healthy specimen and an ideal species for many marine aquarists.

Eyes

A HEALTHY SHARK WILL BE ALERT, moving its eyes to watch things that move into its path or even a person watching through the aquarium glass. Shining a flashlight into the shark's eye should cause the pupil to constrict, but the rate of constriction can vary from one species to another. If the pupil does not constrict or does so very slowly, it may indicate that the specimen is suffering from bacterial meningitis. Do not purchase it. Also abstain from choosing any shark or ray that exhibits continually dilated pupils while the animal is in the light.

Swimming Behavior

AVOID SPECIMENS that frequently chafe against the substrate, respire heavily, yawn frequently, swim erratically, appear disoriented, or have problems maintaining their position in the tank without floating toward the surface. Species that are known to be active should spend most of their time swimming about the tank. In an inactive species, on the other hand, continuous swimming during the day may indicate distress.

Cephaloscyllium isabellum (Draughtsboard Shark): unhealthy individual is emaciated, with wrinkled skin and a noticeable loss of musculature.

accounts in Chapter 4 (beginning on page 69) will help familiarize aquarists with the behavior of those species most often seen in the aquarium trade. When choosing a shark or ray for a home aquarium, carefully consider the following:

However, there may be a reason for the activity: if food has recently been introduced, it is not unusual for a diurnally inactive species to patrol the aquarium for 5 to 15 minutes. Be sure to ask when the animals were most recently fed.

Respiration

CHECK THE RESPIRATION RATE of the animal, as indicated by the opening and closing of its gill slits. If it appears to be respiring very heavily (two to three times the "normal" respiratory rate for that species) it may be suffering from a parasitic infestation of the gills or from oxygen deprivation. Table 3-2 (page 65) lists the "normal" respiration rates of several sharks commonly found in the aquarium trade. Be aware that the animal's respiration rate can be affected by factors unrelated to the animal's overall health, such as water temperature, the presence of food, or a threatening object (e.g., the aquarist's hand).

Appearance

AS FAR AS PHYSICAL APPEARANCE is concerned, the stomach should not be sunken and the dorsal musculature should not be atrophied. Remember, some sharks are naturally slimmer and more streamlined (e.g.,

Chiloscyllium punctatum (Brownbanded Bamboo Shark): starvation, parasitism, or disease may be responsible for the sunken sides seen here.

Heterodontus francisci (Horn Shark): when selecting a specimen for purchase, be sure it has recovered from shipping and has a healthy appetite.

smoothhound sharks) than others (e.g., nurse sharks). Shrunken muscles or a hollow-appearing abdomen may indicate that the animal has gone through a period of starvation or refusal to eat, or may be afflicted with disease or parasites, from which the shark may not recover. In an emaciated ray, the pelvic bones will be very conspicuous, poking up against the skin near the base of the pelvic fins. This condition results from an atrophied dorsal musculature. Avoid any specimens with patches of discoloration, excessive mucus production, blisters, open wounds or lesions, badly torn or frayed fins, reddish skin, or curvature of the back.

One sure sign of near death in rays is when the margins of the pectoral fins are continually curled up or inward toward the center of the disc. This condition is commonly known as the "death curl." The condition usually begins near the tail of the ray and will work its way to the front of the disc margin. It has been suggested that it results from a loss of brain function, due to the animals exposure to long periods of stress. It is an irreversible condition and a ray suffering from it will not live long. Always purchase rays that hold their disc mar-

TABLE 3-2.

"Normal" Respiration Rates in Some Common Elasmobranch Species

Species	Water Temperature	Respiration Rate (gill or spiracle movements per minute)
Tasseled Wobbegong (*Eucrossorhinus dasypogon*)	26°C (79°F)	9 gmm
Ornate Wobbegong (*Orectolobus ornatus*)	18°C (64°F)	10 gmm
Brownbanded Bamboo Shark (*Chiloscyllium punctatum*)	24°C (75°F)	22 gmm
Whitespotted Bamboo Shark (*Chiloscyllium plagiosum*)	26°C (79°F)	26 gmm
Epaulette Shark (*Hemiscyllium ocellatum*)	25°C (77°F)	30 gmm
Southern Stingray (*Dasyatis americana*)	26°C (79°F)	36-48 smm

gins flat against the aquarium bottom when at rest. (Note that that the disc margin of a ray resting in a direct current may lift off the substrate. This is not an indication of a health problem.)

History

ANY INFORMATION YOU CAN GET from the retailer on the history of the animal may also prove helpful. Ask the store owner how long they have had the specimen, if it has been eating, and what they have been feeding it. Then ask them to feed it while you watch, unless you plan on having it in the bag or transport container for a long period of time. Unless the animal has been recently fed, it should clearly display an interest in food. Any shark or ray that refuses to eat in such circumstances should be avoided until its behavior changes. Some stores will hold a specimen, perhaps requiring a deposit, until it is eating and obviously healthy.

Habitat Preferences

IS THIS SPECIES USUALLY ENCOUNTERED in the highly structured reef environment, or is it a species that spends most of its time swimming over a featureless ocean bottom? Species that fall into the latter category

Young sharks in live wells await shipment to North American importers.

Chiloscyllium plagiosum (Whitespotted Bamboo Shark): a newly hatched specimen and one of the author's recommended species for beginners.

Chiloscyllium plagiosum (Whitespotted Bamboo Shark): the same species as an adult, still attractive and suitable for the home aquarium.

TABLE 3-3.

Best Beginners' Sharks and Rays

Hardy species that generally acclimate well to aquarium conditions, ranked in order of increasing adult length.

Smaller Adult Sizes

Cortez Round Stingray	(*Urobatis maculatus*)
Round Stingray	(*Urobatis halleri*)
Bullseye Stingray	(*Urobatis concentricus*)
Yellow Stingray	(*Urobatis jamaicensis*)
*Bluespotted Stingray	(*Dasyatis kuhlii*)
Coral Catshark	(*Atelomycterus marmoratus*)
Gray Bamboo Shark	(*Chiloscyllium griseum*)
Arabian Bamboo Shark	(*Chiloscyllium arabicum*)
Bluntnose Stingray	(*Dasyatis sayi*)
Ward's Wobbegong	(*Orectolobus wardi*)
Whitespotted Bamboo Shark	(*Chiloscyllium plagiosum*)
Brownbanded Bamboo Shark	(*Chiloscyllium punctatum*)
Epaulette Shark	(*Hemiscyllium ocellatum*)

Medium-to-Large Adult Sizes

Horn Shark	(*Heterodontus francisci*)
Eastern Fiddler Ray	(*Trygonorrhina* sp.)
Tasseled Wobbegong	(*Eucrossorhinus dasypogon*)

* Not to be mistaken for the more common, and less hardy, Bluespotted Ribbontail Ray (*Taeniura lymma*).

TABLE 3-4.

Sharks and Rays for Experts & Very Large Systems

These species demand special care and/or oceanarium-scale quarters and are not recommended for beginning elasmobranch keepers.

*Zebra Shark	(*Stegostoma varium*)
*Nurse Shark	(*Ginglymostoma cirratum*)
Smoothhounds	(*Mustelus* spp.)
*Leopard Shark	(*Triakis semifasciata*)
*Blacktip Reef Shark	(*Carcharhinus melanopterus*)
*Lemon Shark	(*Negaprion brevirostris*)
*Whitetip Reef Shark	(*Triaenodon obesus*)
*Bonnethead Shark	(*Sphyrna tiburo*)
*Shovelnose Guitarfish	(*Rhinobatos productus*)
Leopard Torpedo Ray	(*Torpedo panthera*)
Lesser Electric Ray	(*Narcine brasiliensis*)
Bullseye Electric Ray	(*Diplobatis ommata*)
*Southern Stingray	(*Dasyatis americana*)
Atlantic Stingray	(*Dasyatis sabina*)
Bluespotted Ribbontail Ray	(*Taeniura lymma*)
*Bat Ray	(*Myliobatis californica*)

*These species readily acclimate to aquarium life, but they get too large for the vast majority of home aquariums.

habitat preferences of the sharks and rays you are likely to encounter.

Activity Level

ALTHOUGH LESS-ACTIVE SPECIES may not be as interesting to watch, they are better suited to confined quarters. Wobbegongs, for example, are the epitome of laziness (at least during daylight hours), and do well in smaller living spaces. In contrast, the Leopard Shark (*Triakis semifasciata*) is more active and needs a lot of room to behave normally. A more active shark will need a larger, longer aquarium so that it can swim and glide as it moves through the water. Oval tanks are also preferred for some of the more active species.

Maximum Length

UNFORTUNATELY, MOST OF THE "DWARF" shark and ray species are not available to the aquarist due to their geographical and bathymetric (depth) ranges, although the number of appropriate species being collected is growing. The sharks and rays most commonly available to the aquarist range in maximum length from around 1 to 4.2 m (3.3 to 14 ft.), with most exceeding 1 m (3.3 ft.). You will definitely want to consider the maximum length of the species at maturity and choose or plan accordingly. Many of the better aquarium species do well in captivity when they are small, but inevitably outgrow most home aquariums. Before purchasing a species that reaches a larger size, you should check with a local public aquarium to see if they would be willing to take an overgrown pet at a later date. (A word of warning: most of these facilities are *not* interested in adopting sharks or rays that outgrow home aquariums.)

References
Ross (1999), Stoskopf (1990).

usually need a larger aquarium devoid of decorations, while the former are better adapted for maneuvering in tight spaces and even prefer some coral pieces among which to hide. See Chapter 4 (starting on page 69) for

A Catalog of Sharks & Rays

Choosing Among the Elasmobranchs
Available to Home Aquarists

T HERE ARE JUST OVER 390 SHARK SPECIES AND APPROXIMATELY 507 species of rays roaming the oceans of the world, but only a small number of these enter the marine aquarium trade. Of the sharks and rays potentially obtainable by marine hobbyists, some make fascinating and commendable aquarium specimens while others, because of their size, temperaments, or dietary needs, are not well suited to the conditions provided by typical home aquariums. Most of the elasmobranchs available in the trade are collected from areas where reef-dwelling bony fishes are captured and exported. The exceptions to this are the temperate-water forms from the coast of California (i.e., the Horn Shark, Leopard Shark, Round Stingray) that are targeted by collectors.

Many other sharks and rays would make great aquarium residents, but they live in areas where little or no collecting occurs for the ornamental marine trade. In the future, some of these more suitable aquarium species may be available to hobbyists. The Family Hemiscylliidae,

> *"Choose carefully, for the lifespan of a captive shark can extend well beyond that of most other household pets."*

Heterodontus francisci (Horn Shark): cute as a juvenile and a good candidate for cool-water systems.

for example, contains a number of colorful or ornately marked species that reach modest adult sizes and would thrive in aquariums as small as 135 gallons. Currently, few of these species enter the aquarium trade (see Table 4-1, page 99). One ideally suited hemiscylliid that I have found to be quite common in northern New Guinea is the Hooded Epaulette Shark (*Hemiscyllium*

Brownbanded Bamboo or Gray Carpet Shark (*Chiloscyllium punctatum*): 6-week-old juvenile is an ideal candidate for the reef-like home shark tank with a choice of rocky nooks and caves.

strahani). The largest specimen examined to date measured only 80 cm (31.2 in.), and my observations suggest that it probably attains a maximum length of under 1 m (3.3 ft.). Freycinet's Epaulette Shark (*Hemiscyllium freycineti*) is another attractive species, resident to Papua New Guinea, that would be perfect for the home aquarium. The collared carpet shark family (Parascylliidae) contains four species, at least two of which inhabit shallow water in the cool waters off Australia. These sharks

are small (under 90 cm, 35.1 in.) and would be excellent for the chilled home aquarium.

A handful of eye-catching catsharks (Family Scyliorhinidae) from the coast of South Africa (with colorful names like Pyjama Catshark, Leopard Catshark, Puffadder Shyshark, and Tiger Catshark) would also make excellent display animals for the cold-water aquarium. Many of these sharks reach maximum lengths of less than 50 cm (19.5 in.). Because of their small adult sizes and readiness to acclimate to a captive environment, these sharks are also good candidates for captive-breeding programs (see Table 4-2, page 116). Other handsome and diminutive catsharks occur in warm-temperate Japan and Australia, and some of these have already been bred in public aquariums. The Australian catsharks in the genus *Asymbolus* would be perfect for the chilled home aquarium

Some smaller rays that are not yet imported in numbers also appear to be well suited to a captive existence. For example, the genera *Trygonoptera* and *Urolophus* contain a number of species from warm-temperate and temperate waters around east, west, and southern Australia that attain dinner-plate size and are attractively marked. One of these, known as the Oval Stingaree (*Trygonoptera ovalis*) appears to be covered with black velvet, while another, the Crossback Stingaree (*Urolophus cruciatus*) is yellowish brown with dark bars and stripes. When threatened, it holds its tail and spine over its body like a scorpion. Although these rays would need to be kept at cooler water temperatures (necessitating a chiller), they would make excellent aquarium inhabitants. As home aquarists become more adept at maintaining elasmobranchs, the number of appropriate species—both wild-caught and captive bred—available to us is likely to increase.

What follows in this chapter is a survey of the sharks and rays currently available to North American hobbyists. Remember, not all of these fishes are good candidates for long-term care in the home aquarium. Be sure to read the species accounts before making a purchase to determine if you have the resources to house a particular elasmobranch successfully as it grows toward adulthood. Choose carefully, for the lifespan of a captive shark—not to mention its full adult size—can extend well beyond that of most household pets. Some of these species may live for more than 25 years if given proper care.

ANGEL SHARKS
Family Squatinidae

THERE ARE CURRENTLY 13 SPECIES recognized in this family of raylike sharks. All of them have flattened bodies, with terminal mouths, no anal fin, pectoral fins that are not attached to the head (as they are in rays), and no spines in front of the dorsal fins. They are benthic, spending most of their day in repose on the seafloor. They often bury just under the sand or mud surface. If a prey item moves too close, the angel shark rapidly lifts its head from the substrate and throws its jaws forward to snatch its prey. This feeding mechanism is extremely fast, rivaling the speed of many bony fish predators that ambush their prey. After the strike, the angel shark settles back down into the sediment and waits for its next victim to swim past. They are found singly or in aggregations. Angel sharks move over the bottom at night and hunt sleeping and dead fish and nocturnal invertebrates (squid, octopuses, crustaceans). All these sharks are **ovoviviparous** (young are born live after hatching within the female, and bear a yolk sac when first emerging into the water), but nothing is known of their mating behavior. One species that has yet to be formally described from the Gulf of California has spines on the edges of the pectoral fins like the alar spines of male skates. In skates, these spines help anchor the male to the female during copulation.

Captive Care
The angel sharks are not common in the aquarium trade, but at least one Western Australian species is occasionally available to aquarists. (The North American species may also show up on rare occasions.) Little information exists on the husbandry of these sharks. They are considered to be somewhat difficult to keep, often refusing to feed in captivity. Reported captive longevity records for Japanese species (i.e., *Squatina japonica* and *S. nebulosa*) range from 4 weeks to 14 months. The European species, *Squatina squatina*, has been reported to

Squatina japonica (Japanese Angel Shark): a rarely seen raylike shark.

live as long as 2 years in aquarium confines. They will require a large aquarium, even though they spend their days buried under the substrate. The angel sharks should be provided with a sand bed, at least 5 cm (2.0 in.) deep, in which to bury. Try feeding live food or present pieces of fish flesh or large table shrimp on the end of a feeding stick. Do not attempt to hand feed. These sharks have large mouths and may ingest any fish or crustacean that is small enough to swallow whole. Concrete or fiberglass substrate can cause an inflamed ventrum and bacterial infections that are often lethal.

Species Accounts

Squatina australis Regan, 1906

Common Name: Australian Angel Shark.

Size, Growth, and Age: This shark is born at a length of 22 to 27 cm (8.6 to 10.5 in.) and attains a maximum length of 1.5 m (4.9 ft.).

Distribution: New South Wales south around the coast to Western Australia.

Biology: *Squatina australis* has been reported from the intertidal zone to a depth of 256 m (840 ft.). It inhabits sand and mud bottoms, often in seagrass beds or ad-

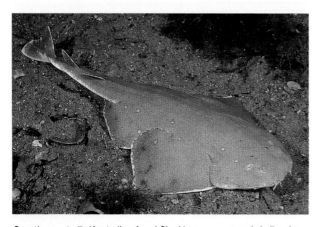

Squatina australis (Australian Angel Shark): uncommon and challenging.

jacent to rocky reefs. It gives birth in the fall, with litters numbering up to 20 young. It feeds on bottom-dwelling fishes, crustaceans, and octopuses. This shark spends its days buried, ingesting anything that moves too close, but it emerges from the sand or mud at night and actively searches for food.

Captive Care: This temperate-water species should be maintained at cooler water temperatures. See the Captive Care section in the family account (page 71) for more husbandry information.

Aquarium Size: 2,850 L (750 gal.).

Water Temperature: 16 to 21°C (61 to 70°F).

Aquarium Suitability Index: 2 (X-large tank required).

Remarks: The Australian Angel Shark is gray to brown overall with no eyespots on its body and numerous small white spots. There are at least three other angel shark species in Australian seas, but *S. australis* is the most common and wide-ranging species.

Squatina californica Ayres, 1859

Common Name: California Angel Shark.

Size, Growth, and Age: This shark is born at a length of 23 cm (9.1 in.) and reaches a maximum length of 1.5 m (4.9 ft.). Males become sexually mature between 75 and 80 cm (29.3 and 31.5 in.), while females reach sexual maturity at lengths of 86 to 108 cm (33.5 to 42.1 in.).

Distribution: Alaska to California on the U.S. coast, south to Baja, the Gulf of California, and all the way to Chile (although this may be a different species).

Biology: This shark is found at depths from 3 to 100 m (9.8 to 328 ft.) off California. In the Gulf of California, *S. californica* has been reported in water as deep as 183 m (600 ft.). This shark often occurs near rocky reefs, where it hides just under the sand or mud. In the winter months, it is known to migrate into deeper water. Females give birth to 1 to 13 young. In California most females pup in March and June, after a 10-month gestation period. They ambush fish and squid that swim by or may hunt and feed on sleeping fish at night. Its color pattern, complete with speckles and mottling, helps it blend in with the substrate. If a prey item passes within a strike zone of 4 to 15 cm (1.6 to 5.9 in.) from the shark's head, it will elicit an attack. If the prey is small enough, the angel shark almost always succeeds in capturing it. California Angel Sharks usually lie adjacent to either rock-sand interfaces or patch reefs. These structures serve as a refuge for many of the prey species that this shark feeds on, so by positioning themselves near these habitats they are more likely to encounter potential meals. It is opportunistic and will take advantage of natural catastrophes to scavenge on dying or dead prey as well. For example, it feeds on Blacksmith (*Chromis punctipinnis*) killed by disease outbreaks and eats dead squid and their egg capsules that result from mass spawning events. Croakers, flatfish, and Corbina (*Menticirrhus undulatus*) have been taken from their stomachs. I examined a specimen in the northern Gulf of California that had eaten hake, croaker, Peppered Shark (*Galeus piperatus*) egg cases, and mantis shrimp. *Squatina californica* will often bury just under the substrate, although it will sometimes sit on top of the sand. They are sometimes found resting in aggregations. At night, *S. californica* does more moving about, with its activity levels peaking at dusk and midnight. The adults are nomadic, spending days in a limited area of 1 to 1.5 km (0.6 to 0.9 mi.), then moving to a new area several kilometers away.

Captive Care: Although *S. californica* is a common species along the west coast of North America, it is less often available than the sympatric Horn Shark (*Heterodontus francisci*) and the Leopard Shark (*Triakis semi-*

Squatina californica (California Angel Shark): a large ambush predator.

fasciata). It is a large species that will require a larger, cool-water aquarium. Public aquarium records indicate that it rarely lives longer than a year in captivity. See the Captive Care section in the family account, page 71, for more husbandry information.

Aquarium Size: 2,850 L (750 gal.).

Water Temperature: 16 to 21°C (61 to 70°F).

Aquarium Suitability Index: 2 (X-large tank required).

Remarks: The California Angel Shark has simple conical nasal barbels and weakly fringed anterior nasal flaps. The skin flaps on the side of its head do not have angular lobes. The eye is large and the distance between the spiracles is less than 1.5 times the eye diameter. The pectoral fins are broad and angular. It has a row of small tubercles on the back, no eyespots on the body, and is gray above with brown flecks of varying size.

References

Clark (1963), Fouts & Nelson (1999), Kuiter (1993), Last & Stevens (1994), Standora & Nelson (1977), Whitley (1940).

BULLHEAD SHARKS
Family Heterodontidae

THIS FAMILY CONSISTS OF ONE GENUS and eight species, all with piglike snouts, spines in front of each dorsal fin, an anal fin, large ridges over the eyes (known as the supraorbital crests), and large molariform teeth in the back of their jaws. The spines are an effective antipredation device, discouraging bony fishes and other sharks from eating smaller specimens. For example, studies conducted on juvenile Horn Sharks (*Heterodontus francisci*) have shown that the spines are effective at deterring Angel Sharks (*Squatina californica*) from ingesting them. Large wobbegongs have been observed attempting to ingest adult Port Jackson Sharks (*Heterodontus portusjacksoni*) without success because of these spines. Bullhead sharks walk about the reef on their large, muscular pectoral fins; if they need to move more quickly, they will swim in a sinusoidal fashion.

These sharks have a respiratory adaptation that facilitates their feeding on infaunal and hard-shelled prey items. The large first gill slit is used for fresh seawater intake, while the posterior gill slits are used for expelling the water. This enables them to respire while they are searching for food in sand or mud, and while handling and ingesting their prey. Those bullhead sharks that have a fondness for eating urchins often have purple pigmentation in their teeth and dorsal spines. The eyes of a bullhead shark are high on the head and well out of the way of an urchin's sharp spines. These are oviparous, producing eggs that are protected by a leathery egg case. The egg case is cone-shaped with an auger-like ridge spiraling around it; the cases of some species have tendrils at one end.

Captive Care

ALTHOUGH MANY BULLHEAD SHARK SPECIES occur in waters cooler than that found in the typical aquarium, most will thrive in captivity. They are sometimes reluctant to feed when first introduced to a tank, but will usually begin eating within a couple of weeks and do well on a diet of crustacean meat and pieces of fresh fish. (An occasional specimen may refuse food for over a month.) At least one species, the Japanese Bullhead shark (*Heterodontus japonicus*) is reported to be very susceptible to thyroid hyperplasia, or goiter (see page 186 for more information on preventing this disorder).

A sturdy ledge or cave, large enough for your bullhead shark to hide under or in, will help it acclimate more readily. Although these sharks can be kept with larger bony fishes, they will eat invertebrate tankmates (from anemones to sea stars and even urchins) and smaller fishes. Be aware that those species regularly available to hobbyists will outgrow many home aquariums, but they will grow slowly if kept at low water temperatures and not overfed. An average annual growth rate of about 5 cm (2.0 in.) was reported for a Crested Port Jackson Shark (*Heterodontus galeatus*) held in captivity for 11 years, but I have seen faster growth rates in captive Horn Sharks (see species accounts

Heterodontus francisci (Horn Shark): juvenile with sharp dorsal spine.

below for more growth-rate information).

Bullhead sharks are candidates for captive reproduction in large aquariums (see page 221 for details).

Species Accounts

Heterodontus francisci (Girard, 1854)

Common Name: Horn Shark.

Size, Growth, and Age: Horn Sharks hatch at 15 cm (5.9 in.) total length and can attain a maximum length of 119 cm (46.9 in.), although most do not exceed 97 cm (37.8 in.). Males mature at 55 to 71 cm (21.5 to 27.7 in.), while females mature at over 60 cm (23.4 in.). An adult can weigh over 10 kg (22 lbs.).

Distribution: Central California to the Gulf of California; may also occur around Ecuador and Peru.

Biology: This species can be found at depths ranging from tidepools in the shallow intertidal zone to 150 m (492 ft.). Juveniles typically inhabit shallower waters than adults, although Horn Sharks of all ages are thought to move into deeper water in the winter months. One study suggested that individuals from 35 to 45 cm (13.7 to 17.6 in.) are found at greater depths than other size classes at all times of the year. Adults and juveniles display different habitat preferences. Adults are usually found on rocky reefs, while juveniles occur on sand bottoms, sheltering near clumps of algae, rocks, debris, or in depressions made in the sand by feeding Bat Rays (*Myliobatis californica*). The spines in front of the dorsal fins of adult Horn Sharks are often abraded as a result of scraping against rocks

in caves and crevices. This shark shows strong site fidelity, in one case having been found at the precise location were it was tagged 11 years previously. During the day, *H. francisci* is usually found in caves or crevices or among dense stands of kelp. It is usually solitary, but groups sometimes gather in caves or crevices. At night it is much more active, using the cover of darkness to ven-

Heterodontus francisci (Horn Shark): hardy and readily available, but will outgrow smaller tanks.

ture into open water, but it moves intermittently and rarely swims more than 2 m (6.6 ft.) above the seafloor. As the sun comes up, Horn Sharks begin searching for their diurnal shelter site. Those that stay in caves and crevices for the night often share their refuge with schools of Blacksmith (*Chromis punctipinnis*, a temperate-water damselfish common off southern California). The Horn Shark has been reported to utilize a home range of about 1,000 m² (10,760 ft.²).

Horn Sharks mate in December and January; egg-laying occurs from February through April. They lay pairs of 10-cm (3.9-in.) auger-type egg cases every 11 to 14 days for about 4 months. In captivity, egg-laying usually occurs 1 to 2 weeks after copulation, but may take as long as 5 weeks. These eggs hatch in 7 to 9 months, depending on the ambient water temperature. The eggs are occasionally preyed upon by gastropods (most likely whelks), which bore through the wall of the egg case.

There is a change in tooth form as the shark develops, which is related to a change in diet. The teeth of juveniles are of the grasping type, with five or six cusps. As the shark grows, the rear teeth become molarlike, losing the cusps and becoming better suited for grinding up invertebrate exoskeletons. Horn Sharks are particularly fond of benthic invertebrates, including sea urchins, worms, crabs, and anemones. When feeding on the Colonial Sea Anemone (*Anthopluera elegantissima*) Horn Sharks will pounce on them, bite off a mouthful of tentacles before the anemones can contract, and then move on. In the case of sea urchins and crabs, they grind up and swallow the entire animal with their molariform teeth, then regurgitate the hard parts later. Captive food-preference studies on juvenile specimens demonstrated that they prefer polychaete parts. In the wild they often feed on polychaete worms that have been exposed, or fragments left behind but not eaten, by Bat Rays. Adult Horn Sharks also eat bony fishes on occasion. They feed on Blacksmith at night when the damsels are resting among rocks, including those individuals with whom they share caves and crevices. Horn Sharks will take advantage of unusual feeding opportunities as well. For example, they have been observed preying upon mating and dying Market Squid (*Loligo opalescens*) and their eggs when these cephalopods form mass spawning aggregations from late October to mid-March. (A single adult Horn Shark may consume as many as six adult squid in one feeding bout.)

Captive Care: Although juveniles can be housed in relatively small aquariums (e.g., 190 L [50 gal.]), adults will need a significantly large tank. The Horn Shark will eat squid and small pieces of fish and will reproduce in captivity. It is possible that amorous males may harass and injure nonreceptive females, so it is best to separate sexually active males from immature females or those females that have already mated. Although the Horn Shark may not be a threat to an active fish during the day, a slumbering fish is potential prey (see the comments about Blacksmith above).

This shark sometimes suffers from acute eye infections, where the eyes become red and then turn cloudy. They will then begin to erode, leaving an empty eye socket. The cause of the condition is unknown at present, but may result from eye trauma (e.g., tankmates nipping the eyes). Over a 4-month time period, shark keeper Kelly Jedlicki had three Horn Sharks suffer from this malady. (A cohabiting male Epaulette Shark sucked the infected eyes from their sockets, she reports.)

Aquarium Size: 912 L (240 gal.).

Water Temperature: 13 to 21°C (55 to 70°F).

Aquarium Suitability Index: 4.

Remarks: This is by far the most commonly encountered bullhead shark in North American fish stores and public aquariums. It has moderately high supraorbital crests, a first dorsal fin that originates over the pectoral bases, small spots on the body (the spots are less than one-third of the eye's diameter, sometimes absent altogether), and lacks light bars between the eyes (such bars are present in the closely related **Mexican Bullhead Shark [*Heterodontus mexicanus*] Taylor & Castro-Aguirre, 1972,** a species rarely, if ever, collected for private aquarists).

Heterodontus galeatus (Crested Port Jackson Shark): this attractive Australian species has very high supraorbital crests that end just behind the eyes.

Heterodontus galeatus (Günther, 1870)

Common Name: Crested Port Jackson Shark.

Size, Growth, and Age: This shark hatches at 17 cm (6.6 in.) and attains a maximum length of 1.5 m (4.8 ft.). However, it rarely exceeds 1.2 m (3.9 ft.) in total length. An average annual growth rate of about 5 cm (2.0 in.) was reported for one captive *H. galeatus*. This same female specimen reached sexual maturity at about 12 years of age.

Distribution: Southern Queensland and New South Wales, Australia.

Biology: *Heterodontus galeatus* occurs from the shallow intertidal zone to depths of 93 m (305 ft.). It is found on reefs, among large macroalgae, and in seagrass beds. The eggs are about 11 cm (4.3 in.) long and of the auger type, with long tendrils extending from one end that can be more than 2 m (6.6 ft.) in length. The eggs are deposited among brown macroalgae or large rocks, around which the tendrils become tangled, at depths of 15 m (49 ft.) or more. The eggs are most abundant in mid and late winter (i.e., July and August); however, oviposition occurs all year round. The eggs hatch in about 5 months, although water temperature affects the incubation period. The Crested Port Jackson will shove its head between rocks in search of sea urchins (which are a major component of its diet), crustaceans, mollusks, and small fishes. The teeth are often stained purple as a result of urchin eating.

Captive Care: This cool-water species is less often encountered than either the Horn or Port Jackson Shark. Its care requirements are similar to these species, but at full size it will require a huge aquarium.

Aquarium Size: 3,135 L (825 gal.).

Water Temperature: 15 to 20°C (59 to 68°F).

Aquarium Suitability Index: 3.

Remarks: This species has very high supraorbital crests that end sharply just behind the eye, and a brown body with several dark bands on the back.

Heterodontus portusjacksoni (Meyer 1793)

Common Name: Port Jackson Shark.

Size, Growth, and Age: This shark hatches at a length of 24 cm (9.4 in.) and attains a maximum length of 1.7 m (5.6 ft.). However, it rarely exceeds 137 cm (4.5 ft.). Males mature at about 75 cm (29.3 in.) at an age of 8 to 10 years, while females are sexually mature at a total length of 80 to 95 cm (31.2 to 37.0 in.) at 11 to 14 years. Annual growth rates for captive Port Jackson Sharks are approximately 5 to 6 cm (2.0 to 2.3 in.) for juveniles and 2 to 4 cm (0.8 to 1.6 in.) for adults.

Distribution: Most common on east and south coast of Australia, but also seen in southern Queensland, Western Australia; a single wanderer was taken near New Zealand.

Biology: The Port Jackson Shark occurs from the intertidal zone to a depth of 172 m (564 ft.). Females migrate to shallow waters in winter to deposit eggs on rocky reefs, then move back to deeper areas in spring. Both sexes also make long-range migrations of up to 850 km (510 mi.) down the coast. During courtship, the male grasps the pectoral fin of the female and wraps the posterior part of his body under hers so a single clasper can be inserted into her cloaca. Egg cases are laid in bays and estuaries, areas used by the juveniles as nursery grounds for the first several years before they segregate by sex and move onto offshore reefs. The egg cases are usually found in reef crevices (although they have also been observed under pipelines and in empty cans), always with the broad end sticking out. The female will take the newly laid egg case in her mouth and insert it under or in a structure on the seafloor. One female was observed to slap an egg case into an interstice with her tail. When the egg case hardens, it is difficult to extract due to its augerlike flanges. Over a breeding season, which lasts 2 to 3 months, a female Port Jackson Shark lays 10 to 16 egg cases in water 1 to 30

Heterodontus portusjacksoni (Port Jackson Shark): hardy species with harnesslike markings.

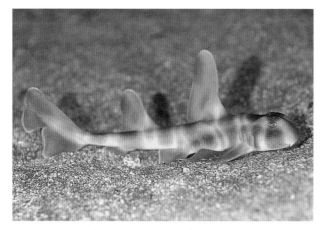

Heterodontus japonicus (Japanese Bullhead Shark): juvenile.

Heterodontus japonicus (Japanese Bullhead Shark): adult specimen.

Heterodontus mexicanus (Mexican Bullhead Shark): note dorsal spike.

Heterodontus sp.(Cortez Bullhead Shark): undescribed Mexican species.

Heterodontus zebra (Zebra Bullhead Shark): temperate-water rarity.

Heterodontus quoyi (Galapagos Horn Shark): seldom-collected species.

m (3.3 to 98 ft.) in depth. The egg cases are about 15 cm (5.9 in.) long and hatch in 9 to 12 months.

Port Jackson Sharks visit specific resting sites on reefs, usually caves or channels, where they are observed singly or in aggregations, some of which can be quite large. They feed on urchins, sea stars, mollusks, crustaceans, and benthic bony fishes. Juveniles have teeth better suited for grasping than those of adults, and they feed more on soft-bodied prey, like shrimp and small mollusks. These nocturnal hunters will rapidly pump water and bottom sediment through their mouths and out their gill slits to excavate buried prey.

Captive Care: This shark is occasionally available in North American fish stores. Like its local cousin, *H. francisci*, it is a good aquarium shark, although acclimation can take several weeks. It is also a cool-water shark that "prefers" to be kept at slightly lower water temperatures than many of the tropical aquarium sharks. *Heterodontus portusjacksoni* will prey on most invertebrates and will also take small fishes at night. It can host a diversity of parasites: copepods, larval isopods, leeches, and small monogenetic trematodes (flukes) have been reported from the mouth and gills, while cestodes and nematodes are frequently found in their intestinal tracts. In the wild, these parasites apparently have little effect upon the well-being of this shark, but in captivity, some of these pests can cause serious problems. The Port Jackson Shark has been reported to reproduce in large public aquariums and has been observed copulating during the day.

Aquarium Size: 2,850 L (750 gal.).

Water Temperature: 14 to 21°C (57 to 70°F).

Aquarium Suitability Index: 4.

Remarks: This species is easily recognized by its unique color pattern, consisting of black harnesslike markings on the back and flanks.

References

Compagno (1984a), Dempster & Herald (1961), Limbaugh (1963), McLaughlin & O'Gower (1971), Strong (1989), Whitley (1951).

COLLARED CARPET SHARKS
Family Parascylliidae

SIX OF THE EIGHT SPECIES IN THIS FAMILY are known to occur on rocky reefs and are anatomically well suited to maneuvering in tight niches and crevices. They have long, slender bodies with a narrow head and an anal fin well in front of the lower tail lobe and partially in front of the end of the second dorsal fin. There are two genera in the family, *Cirroscyllium* and *Parascyllium*. All the species included in this book belong to the genus *Parascyllium* and are limited in their range to the more temperate waters of South and Western Australia. Color pattern is an important feature in identifying the different species. Little is known about their biology; at least some of the species are oviparous and deposit tendril egg cases. They probably feed on worms, crustaceans, and small bony fishes. Because they are nocturnal and hide in caves and among large macroalgae stands during the day, they usually go unnoticed by most divers.

Captive Care

AT LEAST TWO SPECIES FROM THE FAMILY are occasionally collected for the aquarium trade. Their small size (they all attain a maximum length of less than 1.0 m [39.4 in.]) and predilection to dwell in reef crevices and caves make them well suited to life in the confines of the home aquarium, although they need to be provided with plenty of stable hiding places. The *Parascyllium* spp.

would seem to be ideal subjects for captive-breeding programs.

Species Accounts

Parascyllium ferrugineum McCulloch, 1911

Common Name: Rusty Carpet Shark.

Size, Growth, and Age: Hatches at approximately 15 cm (5.9 in.) and attains a maximum length of 80 cm (31.2 in.). Males are mature at a length of 60 cm (23.4 in.)

Distribution: Australia, from Victoria to southwestern Australia.

Biology: *Parascyllium ferrugineum* occurs in beds of macroalgae on rocky reefs and in deeper seagrass meadows at depths of 5 to 55 m (16 to 181 ft.). It tends to inhabit shallower depths around southern Tasmania than in more northerly parts of its range. Spending its days hiding in caves and under ledges, the Rusty Carpet Shark forages for bottom-dwelling crustaceans after dark.

Captive Care: This shark has been reported to appear in the aquarium trade on rare occasions. It is a good aquarium species if kept at lower water temperatures (a chiller will probably be required) and provided with good sheltering places. It may spend much of the day hiding under ledges and in caves, but will gradually spend more time in the open when the lights are on as it adjusts to aquarium living. Its small mature size make it a good candidate for captive-breeding programs.

Aquarium Size: 608 L (160 gal.).

Water Temperature: 14 to 20°C (57 to 68°F).

Aquarium Suitability Index: 3.

Remarks: The Rusty Carpet Shark has an inconspicuous collar around its neck and dark spots on the pectoral fins and body. It also has five or six dusky saddles along the back and on the tail. Those individuals from Tasmania have a greater density of spots on the body.

Parascyllium variolatum (Dumeril, 1853)

Common Names: Necklace Carpet Shark, Varied Carpet Shark, Varied Catshark, Southern Catshark.

Size, Growth, and Age: This species attains a maximum length of 91 cm (35.5 in.). Males are mature at a length

Parascyllium ferrugineum (Rusty Carpet Shark): uncommonly seen by aquarists, but a good potential candidate for captive breeding.

Parascyllium variolatum (Necklace Carpet Shark): not common, but an attractive and hardy choice for a temperate-water aquarium.

of 47 cm (18.3 in.).

Distribution: Australia, from Victoria south to Tasmania, along the southern coast to southwestern Australia. It is reported to be common around King Island.

Biology: A temperate-water, rocky-reef dweller, this species is commonly observed in beds of large macroalgae and in seagrass meadows. Juveniles often hide under flat rocks and debris in shallow water. The Necklace Carpet Shark ranges from the intertidal zone to depths of 180 m (590 ft.). Although little is known about its biology, it is thought to feed on benthic invertebrates like shrimps, crabs, and worms. It is very secretive during the day, making hunting forays into the open after dark. It typically is a solitary shark.

Captive Care: Most of the individuals that enter the aquarium trade come from Western Australia, making it somewhat difficult—but not impossible—to obtain. It is a good aquarium species if kept at lower water temperatures (maintained by a chiller in most cases) and provided with appropriate hiding places. This carpet shark will become quite frenetic if frightened, which may cause it to dash about the tank and collide with decor or jump out of an open aquarium. Its small mature size makes it a good candidate for captive breeding programs.

Aquarium Size: 608 L (160 gal.).

Water Temperature: 14 to 20°C (57 to 68°F).

Aquarium Suitability Index: 3.

Remarks: This species has a distinctive dark brown collar that is peppered with white spots. There is a black blotch on the edge of each fin and white spots all over the body. A similar, undescribed form may occur off southwestern Australia.

References

Kuiter (1993), Last & Stevens (1994), Whitley (1940).

BLIND SHARKS
Family Brachaeluridae

POSSESSING PERFECTLY ADEQUATE EYESIGHT, this very small group is named for the unusual habit of one species, the Blind Shark (*Brachaelurus waddi*), of closing its eyelids when removed from the water. There are just two species in this family, and both make excellent aquarium inhabitants. Unfortunately, neither of these sharks is common in North American aquarium stores, but they do show up from time to time (often under unusual common names).

Captive Care

BECAUSE OF THEIR PREDILECTION for tight spaces and their relatively small adult size, these sharks are ideally suited for aquarium life. If they are to be maintained successfully, however, they must be provided with numerous, securely constructed hiding places. Their only drawback is a secretive nature during daylight hours, and the aquarist may see only their tails protruding from a crevice when bright lights are on. Brachaelurids will accept most fresh and frozen seafood, and will consume small fish and invertebrate tankmates that they can fit into their mouths. Feed them until they are satiated, three times a week. The Blind Shark will reproduce in captivity, and at least one public aquarium has a breeding colony of these fish.

Species Accounts

Brachaelurus colcloughi (Ogilby, 1908)

Common Names: Colclough's Shark, Bluegray Carpet Shark.

Size, Growth, and Age: This shark is probably born at about 16 cm (6.2 in.) and attains a maximum length of

Brachaelurus colcloughi (Colclough's Shark): note juvenile bands.

Brachaelurus waddi (Blind Shark): closes eyes when removed from water.

at least 80 cm (31.2 in.).

Distribution: The range of *B. colcloughi* was once thought to be limited to the south Queensland coast, where it was collected infrequently. However, it is not as rare as was originally believed, having more recently been encountered by divers on rocky reefs off Surfer's Paradise, Queensland, and Forester, New South Wales.

Biology: Colclough's Shark is secretive during the day, hiding between boulders and in reef fissures, on low-profile rocky reefs. I have seen it at depths of 14 m (46 ft.). Because of its cryptic nature, it is often overlooked by aquarium fish collectors. Little is known about its biology.

Captive Biology: Although seemingly rare in the wild, Colclough's Shark occasionally makes an appearance in aquarium stores. Like its more common relative, it is a secretive species that should be provided with suitable hiding places. Time and attention will be needed to ensure that this shark gets enough to eat in an aquarium with elasmobranch or teleost tankmates. It is best to use a small feeding stick to deliver its meals. This shark seems to prefer squid and crustacean flesh.

Aquarium Size: 418 L (110 gal.).

Water Temperature: 18 to 24°C (64 to 75°F).

Aquarium Suitability Index: 4.

Remarks: Colclough's Shark differs from the Blind Shark (*B. waddi*) in the placement of its anal fin (which does not reach back to the origin of the lower tail lobe), in the length of the snout (longer and more rounded), and in the relative sizes of the first and second dorsal fins (the second is noticeably smaller than the first). Juveniles have conspicuous bands on the body and tail that are obscure, or disappear, in adults. There are no white spots. This species was once placed in the genus *Heteroscyllium*.

Brachaelurus waddi (Bloch & Schneider, 1801)

Common Name: Blind Shark.

Size, Growth, and Age: The Blind Shark is born at 17 cm (6.6 in.) and attains a maximum length of 1.2 m (3.9 ft.), but most individuals are much smaller than this. Males and females both mature at over 60 cm (23.4 in.) in total length.

Distribution: Northern Territory to New South Wales, Australia, most often in the more southern part of its range.

Biology: This species ranges from the intertidal zone to depths of 150 m (492 ft.). Juveniles are typically found hiding in crevices or under ledges in shallow, surging waters, while adults hide in caves, under ledges, or in crevices in deeper waters. At night, they move out onto adjacent reef areas and seagrass beds to hunt. This ovoviviparous shark (eggs retained in oviducts until hatching) gives birth to as many as eight pups at a time in the summer months.

Blind Sharks eat sea anemones, cuttlefishes, crabs, and shrimps. Although invertebrates make up their main diet, they will also eat small fishes. An interesting adaptation of Blind Sharks is their ability to live for as long as 18 hours out of the water, which may enable those caught in shallow pools at ebb tide to survive until the tide comes back in.

Captive Care: The Blind Shark is a durable but very secretive aquarium elasmobranch. If kept in a larger aquarium with plenty of hiding places it may be seen only rarely. In time, some individuals may be trained to come out and feed when the lights are on. The best way to observe it is by placing a red light over the tank at night. Finicky specimens should be fed after dark. Unfortunately, this species rarely makes its way into the North American aquarium trade. It has reproduced in captivity.

Aquarium Size: 1,368 L (360 gal.).

Water Temperature: 18 to 22°C (64 to 72°F).

Aquarium Suitability Index: 4.

Remarks: At first glance, the Blind Shark resembles the Nurse Shark (*Ginglymostoma cirratum*), a species familiar to many North American aquarists and divers. It has a stout body, long nasal barbels, predominant grooves along the corners of the mouth, large spiracles, and a short tail. Juveniles are grayish with black bands, while adults are light to dark brown or gray with inconspicuous bands. All ages typically have white flecks on the body and tail.

References

Kuiter (1993), Last & Stevens (1994), N. Marsh (personal communication), Whitley (1940).

WOBBEGONGS
Family Orectolobidae

THERE ARE SIX DESCRIBED SPECIES (and apparently several undescribed forms) within this unusual family, all of which are residents of coral and/or rocky reefs and are popularly known as "wobbies" in their native Australia. They are characterized by a somewhat flattened body, a very broad head with a large mouth positioned near its end, long barbels, and flaps of skin around the mouth. The color pattern, the presence of tubercles (flattened denticles) along the back, and the number of dermal flaps on the upper jaw are features that can aid the aquarist or diver in identifying the various species.

Three genera make up this family. One of these, *Sutorectus*, is represented by a single species known as the Cobbler's Wobbegong (*Sutorectus tentaculatus*). This species, unlike the other wobbegongs, has large, rounded tubercles all over its head and body throughout its life (one species in the genus *Orectolobus* has dorsal tubercles as a juvenile). Cobbler's Wobbegong also has a low first dorsal fin that originates before the midbase of the pelvic fins. This species is reported to be common off South Australia (its range is restricted to Western and South Australia). Not surprisingly, this species does not show up in U.S. fish stores. The genus *Eucrossorhinus* is also represented by a single species, considered to be the most specialized of all the wobbegongs. It is recognized by its very wide head, the edge of which is fringed by a "beard" of dermal flaps. This is the only wobbegong with dermal lobes on its chin. The genus *Orectolobus* is composed of four described and at least two undescribed species.

Natural History

WOBBEGONGS ARE KNOWN TO ambush, stalk, and lure their prey. Ambush (sit-and-wait) predators are those that remain motionless and let their prey venture into striking range. These animals rely on a quick strike to catch their quarry unaware, and are often cryptic in color, form, and behavior. Wobbegongs are adorned with spots, bands, or reticulations that help them to disappear among sun-dappled coral, coralline algae, and larger macroalgae. The flaps of skin around the mouth also help to break up the anterior body outline, enhancing their resemblance to reef substrate. Some ambush predators use anatomical features or specific action patterns to "bait" prey into the strike zone. The wobbegong's dermal flaps, and even its skin patterns, resemble certain calcareous algae and encrusting invertebrates. Numerous bony fishes and some crustaceans feed on these marine plants and animals and may mistake the inactive wobbegong for food-covered substrate. This type of passive luring was first hinted at by the Australian shark expert David Stead. In 1963 he said of the wobbegong, "In front of the jaws are the fleshy lips, which are fringed with seaweedlike dermal

appendages. These are a part of the general get-up of make-believe or camouflage which is this creature's strong point and enables him to live with the minimum of personal effort. Small sea animals actually blunder right up to the mouth, and even inquisitively test these

Eucrossorhinus dasypogon (Tasseled Wobbegong): resting on a large colony of coral in Irian Jaya.

sea-weedy appendages, behind which lurks horrid destruction."

Protective resemblance (when a predator looks like a place to hide) is another way that the wobbegong can dupe potential prey. In reef environments, such hiding space can be a limited resource; a quiescent wobbegong may attract a fish or invertebrate looking for a shelter site.

At night, wobbegongs actively stalk octopuses, squids, crabs, sharks (including other wobbegongs),

Eucrossorhinus dasypogon (Tasseled Wobbegong): extraordinary camouflage allows this species to capture unsuspecting sweepers and cardinalfishes.

rays, and reef fishes. Their jaws are capacious, enabling them to take a larger range of prey. The flattened head of the wobbegong allows it to shove itself into tight crevices to extract hiding cephalopods and crustaceans. When a wobbegong succeeds in capturing a larger prey item, it holds it in its vicelike jaws until the prey is subdued, then manipulates the prey so that it can be swallowed headfirst. Targets of wobbegong attacks have included humans, and it has been suggested that the best way for a person to escape a wobbegong's tenacious grip is to hold still and wait for the shark to be-

gin this manipulation process. When the animal attempts to change its grasp, the victim should quickly pull his or her appendage free.

Wobbegongs probably feed only intermittently. This hypothesis is supported by a study conducted on the food habits of the Japanese Wobbegong (*Orectolobus japonicus*). The stomachs of 330 individuals were examined over a 2-year period: 60 % of individuals from one area and 25% from another had empty stomachs. This high incidence of vacuous stomachs suggests that these fish feed infrequently. (For more on feeding frequency of shark species, see Chapter 6.)

Unlike their close relatives the bamboo sharks (Family Hemiscylliidae), the wobbegongs do not crawl about on their pectoral and pelvic fins; instead, they lift their pectoral fins to their sides and swim in a sinuous fashion, like tadpoles. Individuals have been observed moving from one tidepool to another in water so shallow that their backs were completely exposed. Juvenile wobbegongs lead a very cryptic, reclusive lifestyle, living deep in crevices, under rocks, and in tidepools; it may be that they do this in order to avoid larger conspecifics, which are known cannibals.

These sharks have a dubious reputation. Although many consider them to be harmless unless harassed, there are reports of wobbegongs biting divers without provocation. In fact, Australian shark expert John West reports that 20 to 30% of all the nonfatal shark attacks reported in Australian seas each year are instigated by wobbegongs. Apparently these fishes have relatively poor visual acuity and will strike at any movement near their head; it is unwise to place a hand or foot near the biting end of even a small wobbegong. These sharks may perform a threat display. I, and others, have seen them "cough" (i.e., throw open their jaws) when a diver approaches too closely or before they strike.

Captive Care

WOBBEGONGS ARE IDEAL AQUARIUM SHARKS because of their inactive lifestyle. Being lethargic, they do not need a lot of space in which to move around, but this lack of activity is also considered a negative attribute by some aquarists. Feeding time can provide an explosive display of predatory prowess, but if you need a fish in your aquarium with a vast behavioral repertoire, then a wobbegong is not for you. When the lights are on, most wobbies simply lie under a ledge or in a cave until food comes within striking range. However, with the aid of a red incandescent light, you can watch your wobbegong at night when it is typically more active.

Two other drawbacks to wobbegong ownership are that most species currently available to the aquarist reach over 2 m (6.6 ft.) in length, and they command a high price. The first problem can be curbed, or at least delayed, by not overfeeding. These sharks have low metabolic demands and therefore can be maintained in good condition on two feedings a week. Monitor your shark's condition by visually examining its dorsal musculature. If it appears to be atrophying, feed it more frequently. If you cannot afford a huge tank for your wobbegong, check with your local public aquarium staff before you make your purchase to see if they would be interested in a future acquisition. (Unlike a nurse shark, a wobbegong may be unusual enough to tempt a professional aquarist.) If you cannot find a likely future repository for a larger wobbegong, select a different shark for your home aquarium.

A wobbegong may not eat when initially acquired, and it is not uncommon for this preliminary fast to last as long as 10 to 14 days. When trying to elicit a feeding response in a fasting wobbie, impale a fresh fish on a feeding stick (I use a sharpened piece of rigid air-line tubing), so that you can present it to the animal head-first. Lightly contact the shark's barbels with the head of the food item. If your wobbegong is hungry, it will shoot forward suddenly and devour the offering. Feed juvenile wobbegongs to satiation once or twice a week. Adults should only be fed once a week.

It is important not to feed your wobbie large prey items. If they consume a meal that is too large, they may become bloated and so positively buoyant that they float around the surface of the aquarium like a cork. This condition, apparently caused by a buildup of gas

Orectolobus ornatus (Ornate Wobbegong): handsome but very large.

Ornate Wobbegong: skin flaps help camouflage the predator-in-waiting.

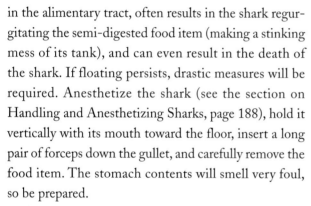

in the alimentary tract, often results in the shark regurgitating the semi-digested food item (making a stinking mess of its tank), and can even result in the death of the shark. If floating persists, drastic measures will be required. Anesthetize the shark (see the section on Handling and Anesthetizing Sharks, page 188), hold it vertically with its mouth toward the floor, insert a long pair of forceps down the gullet, and carefully remove the food item. The stomach contents will smell very foul, so be prepared.

These sharks have enormous mouths and can consume surprisingly large prey. For example, a specimen kept by an acquaintance of mine ate his Yellow Tang (*Zebrasoma flavescens*), a triggerfish, and a Zebra Moray (*Gymnomuraena zebra*). They will even snap at, and occasionally eat, smaller shark and ray tankmates. At Kelly Tarlton's Underwater World in Auckland, New Zealand, a large Ornate Wobbegong (*Orectolobus ornatus*) ate newborn Smooth Stingrays (*Dasyatis brevicaudata*), and photographs exist of the same species consuming a large Southern Fiddler Ray (*Trygonorrhina fasciata*). Because of their rapid feeding response, hand-feeding a wobbegong would be a foolhardy activity indeed.

Fortunately, these sharks are not sensitive to copper-based medications or the more common vitamin deficiencies observed in other elasmobranchs. Wobbegongs are stenohaline (live in a relatively narrow salinity range) and should be maintained at a specific gravity between 1.019 and 1.024.

Wobbegongs are very popular display animals at Australian oceanariums and are gaining popularity with their American counterparts. Ian Gordan, formerly a curator at Manly Marineland in Sydney, told me of an unusual method used by some to collect these sluggish beasts. Some aquarium divers will harass a quiescent wobbegong with a broomstick until the annoyed creature latches on, holding so tenaciously to the piece of wood that it can be pulled up to the surface. In Australian oceanariums, many of the wobbegongs on display are pets donated by aquarists after the animals outgrew their captive environments. While aquarium visitors may appreciate these atypical sharks, some Aussie aquarists loathe them because of their predisposition to bite anything that comes too close to their powerful jaws. One misplaced foot while cleaning the viewing windows or feeding the tank's inhabitants, and the aquarist's metatarsals are suddenly impaled on the needlelike teeth of a hungry shark. (At one aquarium, the term "wobbie-foot" was coined to describe the malady that resulted when a diver accidentally stepped on or near the formidable jaws of a resting wobbegong.) Aquarists have also been bitten when they attempted to hand feed, move, or stroke one of these sharks. Although they appear sluggish, they can move with incredible speed when threatened. One Australian aquarist told me that familiarity should never breed a lack of caution, for wobbegongs are "very unpredictable."

Recently, wobbegongs have been sought out by commercial fisherman for their very palatable flesh, and hand-lining for these sharks has been on the increase along the eastern Australian coastline. The popularity of wobbie flesh became quite apparent to me while visiting the Sydney fish market, where I observed dozens of crates filled with the dressed carcasses of Spotted and Ornate Wobbegongs. Like all sharks, wobbegongs are susceptible to overfishing and, unfortunately for the wobbies, no regulations exist for the fishery.

Species Accounts

Eucrossorhinus dasypogon (Bleeker, 1867)

Common Name: Tasseled Wobbegong.

Size, Growth, and Age: This species is born at about 22 cm (8.9 in.) long, and can reach a maximum length of 1.8 m (6.0 ft.). Reports in the literature of 3 m (9.8 ft.) specimens are erroneous. The minimum size at sexual maturity is unknown.

Distribution: Tasseled Wobbegongs are obligatory coral reef dwellers that occur on the coral reefs off Irian Jaya, Indonesia, Papua New Guinea, and Australia (from Queensland around the northern coast to Western Aus-

tralia). This species has also been observed by scuba divers on reefs of Komodo Island, Indonesia.

Biology: *Eucrossorhinus dasypogon* is observed in reef channels and on the reef front at a depth of 1 to at least 40 m (3.3 to 131 ft.). Unlike many other wobbies, this species is a loner. Solitary individuals are usually found under table corals, among ship wreckage, in caves, or beneath ledges during daylight hours. Based on my observations and those of others, it appears that this fish is site-specific, utilizing several daytime resting sites in a limited home range. There is an anecdotal report of a pair of Tasseled Wobbegongs mating at night in a cave. While at rest in caves, they are often seen with large schools of sweepers and/or cardinalfishes hanging over them; they apparently feed on these fishes at will. At night, they move out onto the reef, where they probably hunt torpid fishes, crustaceans, and octopuses. The flat anterior end of this species would enable it to shove its head deep into narrow crevices to get at its prey. Although data has not been published on its food habits, the Tasseled Wobbegong might also feed during the day on other nocturnal species with which it shares a cave (i.e., squirrelfishes, soldierfishes, and sweepers). The Tasseled Wobbegong may serve as a safe refuge for

Eucrossorhinus dasypogon (Tasseled Wobbegong): hardy in captivity.

The Tasseled Wobbegong: An Angling Shark

A number of bony fish groups are known for actively luring their prey. For example, the frogfishes (Antennariidae) have a modified first dorsal spine that is waved in front of their head, baitlike, to attract potential prey. There are also a couple of elasmobranchs that are thought to attract prey by adopting peculiar body postures. The Nurse Shark (*Ginglymostoma cirratum*) and the Yellow Stingray (*Urobatis jamaicensis*), lift their bodies off the substrate and remain stationary, which may function to draw small, shelter-seeking fishes and crustaceans within striking range (see the species accounts, pages 109 and 151, for more information). Other sharks, including wobbegongs, may passively lure—that is, they simply lie on the bottom and mimic reef substrate but do not engage in any behaviors specifically employed to attract potential prey. But the Tasseled Wobbegong displays the most fascinating elasmobranch luring behavior and is no doubt the Izaak Walton of the shark world.

Some time ago, I acquired a juvenile *Eucrossorhinus dasypogon* from my friend Jim Walters, of Chicago's Old Town Aquarium. Soon after the shark arrived and had acclimated to its new home, my wife, Janine, and I witnessed an amazing sight. When food was introduced to the tank, the wobbie would wag its tail! The entire caudal peduncle (from the pelvic fins back) was held at an angle to the body and then the caudal fin and the

Tasseled Wobbegong appears docile, but is poised to strike with blinding speed when prey ventures near.

posterior portion of the peduncle were slowly thrown from one side of the body to the other. Janine immediately noticed that the lower portion of the caudal fin moved through the water like a small fish and even had an eyespot in the appropriate place! I began digging

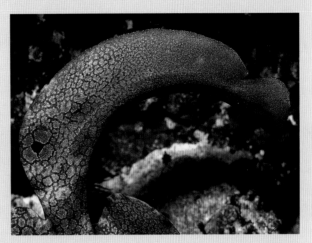

Luring behavior of a Tasseled Wobbie first recorded by the author.

Closeup of the tail, which resembles a small fish, complete with eye.

through the slides I had taken of adult wobbegongs in the wild and ferreting through all my shark books for photographs of *E. dasypogon*. In four of the photographs where the lower caudal lobe was visible, the spot was present.

The Tasseled Wobbegong adopts several unique postures that may be related to this apparent luring behavior. It keeps its tail curled up when in repose on the seafloor, and it will often lie with its head resting on the tank decor (usually against the reef when in the wild) or up against the aquarium glass, so that it is elevated about 50 to 80 degrees to the longitudinal body axis. These postures are rarely if ever seen in other wobbegong species. I decided to collect some quantitative data on *E. dasypogon* to determine how much of the time it adopted these postural characteristics. For 18 days I randomly collected data, recording if the shark's head was elevated or held flat against the sub-

strate, and whether the tail was curled or not (the minimum time that passed between samples was one hour, with a total of 117 data points collected). Over this period, the wobbegong had its head elevated 85% of the time and had its tail curled 98% of the time. Why is this important? I believe that these postures are related to this shark's luring behavior. The head is raised when the shark is in repose so that the tail is brought over the head (and near the mouth) when it is held up and thrown from side to side. By adopting this posture, the shark is able to lure potential predators or aggressors of the "mimic fish" (i.e., the lower caudal lobe) within striking range of its capacious jaws.

Interestingly enough, this wobbegong, like a cartilaginous version of Pavlov's dog, has become conditioned to associating me with food. Every time I enter the room or approach the aquarium, the shark starts wagging its tail.

small shrimps and fishes, like gobies, that are sometimes observed resting on its head. When a predatory fish comes to eat these refugees, it becomes prey for the wobbie. One such fish, the Pacific Trumpetfish (*Aulostomus chinensis*), has been observed sticking out of the mouth of a Tasseled Wobbegong. A small cleaner shrimp, the Red-and-white-spotted Cleaner Shrimp (*Leander urocaridella*), has been observed "cleaning" this wobbegong, with as many as ten of these crustaceans working over a single shark at one time. Other shrimps, like the Boxer Shrimp (*Stenopus hispidus*), occasionally clean this shark as well. I have seen the Blue Streak Cleaner Wrasse (*Labroides dimidiatus*) pick at and enter the gill slits of this species and clean its body and fins.

Captive Care: This is the ultimate wobbegong for the home aquarist. It is a smaller wobbegong that exhibits a pleasing color pattern and some fascinating behaviors (see accompanying box). The Tasseled Wobbegong will readily adapt to captivity, feeding on live, as well as fresh and frozen fish and crustaceans. It has a huge mouth and will consume any fish or crustacean tankmate that it can swallow whole. It is inactive during the day, but will swim about the aquarium after dark. Provide it with a cave, ledge, or some rockwork it can lie in, under, or up against. This species is slow-growing if not overfed. For more information on its husbandry, see the Captive Care section in the family account (page 87).

Aquarium Size: 1,368 L (360 gal.).

Water Temperature: 22 to 27°C (72 to 81°F).

Aquarium Suitability Index: 5.

Remarks: The genus *Eucrossorhinus* is represented by a single species, the Tasseled Wobbegong, which is considered to be the most specialized of all wobbegongs. It is recognized by its very wide head, (the edge of which is fringed by a "beard" of dermal flaps), the presence of dermal lobes on its chin, and by its habit of curling up its tail when lying on the bottom. There are two color patterns observed in this species: one consists of a network of tan lines on a gray background, the other has dark brown lines on a light brown background.

Orectolobus japonicus Regan, 1906

Common Name: Japanese Wobbegong.

Size, Growth, and Age: This shark is born at 20 cm (7.8 in.) in length and can reach a maximum length of at least 1 m (3.3 ft.).

Distribution: The Japanese Wobbegong is known to occur commonly around parts of Japan, and ranges south to Vietnam and the Philippines (where it is apparently rare).

Biology: The Japanese Wobbegong is found on rocky reefs at depths of 8 to 40 m (26 to 130 ft.), often lying among macroalgae or in caves or crevices. The diet of *O. japonicus* has been studied in more detail than that of any other wobbegong. It feeds almost entirely on benthic fishes, including skates, lizardfishes, cutlassfishes, goatfishes, groupers, tilefishes, sandperches, whitings, parrotfishes, scorpionfishes, flatfishes, sea robins, sea breams, and croakers. It also occasionally ingests shark egg cases, cephalopods, and shrimps. Like several other members of this genus, it is reported to be nocturnal. Japanese Wobbegongs make inshore migrations to give birth and to mate. During this reproductive period, adults apparently become anorexic, which may be an adaptation to prevent them from eating the newborn pups.

Captive Care: This is a popular display animal at public aquariums in Asia and has been bred in several oceanariums. Although ideally suited to larger home aquariums, the Japanese Wobbegong is rare in the

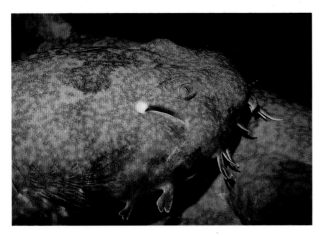

Orectolobus japonicus (Japanese Wobbegong): popular species in Asia.

Orectolobus maculatus (Spotted Wobbegong): grows to 3.2 m (10.5 ft.).

North American aquarium trade. For more information on its husbandry see the Captive Care section in the family account (page 87).

Aquarium Size: 646 L (170 gal.).

Water Temperature: 16 to 25°C (61 to 77°F)

Aquarium Suitability Index: 5.

Remarks: The Japanese Wobbegong has five to six dermal lobes under the eyes on each side of the head, and dark saddles on the back, with a network of dark lines in light areas between the saddles. It is most similar to the Ornate Wobbegong, differing only in its color pattern and size.

Orectolobus maculatus (Bonnaterre, 1788)

Common Names: Spotted Wobbegong, Common Wobbegong.

Size, Growth, and Age: This species is born at 20 cm (7.8 in.) and reaches a maximum length of 3.2 m (10.5 ft.). Males may mature at lengths as small as 60 cm (23.4 in.).

Distribution: This species is probably endemic to Australian waters, but it has also been reported from Japan and the South China Sea (these records probably represent a different species). In Australian waters, it occurs from southern Queensland south to Tasmania and around the southern coast to Freemantle, Western Australia. It is the most common wobbegong in the Brisbane area of Australia, and most juveniles of this species offered in North American aquarium shops are collected from this area. In more southern parts of its range, this species is greatly outnumbered by the Ornate Wobbegong.

Biology: This wobbegong occurs at depths from 1 to 100 m (3.3 to 328 ft.). Juveniles live in estuaries and bays, often hiding in seagrass beds or on low-profile reefs. Adults are found on rocky reefs, often lying among or between smooth boulders encrusted with coralline algae, in caves, under overhangs, in gutters, among ship wreckage, or in beds of macroalgae. They can be solitary or in aggregations of a dozen or more, and are sometimes found lying together with the Ornate Wobbegong or, in northern areas, with the Brownbanded Bamboo Shark (*Chiloscyllium punctatum*). They are a site-attached species, with one individual having been tagged and then recaptured at the same spot 6 years later. Although usually found in repose on the seafloor, the

Spotted Wobbegong occasionally makes short forays well off the bottom. It feeds on crabs, lobsters, octopuses, and bony fishes (including groupers, scorpionfishes, and sea chubs), as well as on other sharks (including bamboo sharks and its own species), and rays. I once observed a 1.5 m (4.9 ft.) specimen capture an octopus that had moved within the shark's strike zone as it was lying among some ship wreckage. The strike was so fast that all I saw initially was a cloud of sediment appear after the mollusk swam into a fissure in the wreck. Upon closer inspection, I found the octopus in the jaws of the wobbegong. The cephalopod was grasping the head of the wobbie with its tentacles to prevent the shark from swallowing it completely. The shark proceeded to spit out and reingest the mollusk eight times over a period of about a minute before it finally succeeded in devouring it.

Captive Care: Although a durable aquarium specimen, the Spotted Wobbegong will outgrow the vast majority of home aquariums. It has two traits that make it unappealing to some shark aquarists: it is inactive during the day, and it is extremely voracious, ingesting any fish or crustacean that can be swallowed whole. It will even consume other elasmobranchs. For more information on its husbandry, see the Captive Care section in the family account (page 87).

Aquarium Size: 11,970 L (3,150 gal.).

Water Temperature: 16 to 25°C (61 to 77°F).

Aquarium Suitability Index: 5 (X-large tank required).

Remarks: The Spotted Wobbegong differs from the Ornate Wobbegong in that it typically has a greater number of dermal lobes on the sides of its head (eight to ten on each side, under and in front of the eyes). These lobes are also longer than those of *Orectolobus ornatus*. In addition, the white rings and saddles on its back are not edged in black, as are those of the Ornate.

Orectolobus ornatus (De Vis, 1883)

Common Names: Ornate Wobbegong, Gulf Wobbegong.

Size, Growth, and Age: This species is born at about 20 cm (7.8 in.) and reaches a maximum size of at least 2.9 m (9.5 ft.). It matures over an unusually large size range; most males mature at around 1.7 m (5.6 ft.), but one male from Queensland was reported to be sexually mature at 65 cm (25.0 in.). Hartley (2000) noted that a pair of copulating Ornate Wobbegongs consisted of a male that was 84 cm (33.0 in.) in total length, and an 86-cm (33.5-in.) female. In his study of the population dynamics of this species, 114 of 135 individuals measured were between 50 and 100 cm (19.5 to 39.0 in.) in length, suggesting the northern population is quite a bit smaller than its southern counterpart. In more southern climes, the majority of *O. ornatus* I have seen have been over 1.5 m (4.9 ft.) in length and ranged up to 3 m (9.8 ft.).

Distribution: Around all of Australia, Papua New Guinea, and Irian Jaya, Indonesia; also reported in Japanese waters, although records from the latter locality probably represent a different species. This is the most abundant wobbegong species in New South Wales, South Australia, and the southern part of Western Australia (south of Perth), and is also seen on rocky and coral reefs in Queensland.

Biology: The Ornate Wobbegong has been observed in such shallow water that its dorsal fins broke the water's surface, but it can also be found at depths of at least 30 m (98 ft.). According to Rudie Kuiter, an Australian fish expert, this species is more abundant in less turbid bays and around offshore islands than the Spotted Wobbegong. On coral reefs, it occurs on the reef flat, where it is sometimes observed in large tidepools (especially juveniles), in reef channels, and on the fore reef. On rocky

Ornate Wobbegong rests with a Port Jackson Shark, a potential victim.

reefs, younger specimens typically hide in crevices or among boulders, while adults lie on smooth coralline algae-encrusted boulders in the open, or in large caves and gutters. In northern New South Wales, solitary individuals often rest in large dish corals.

Orectolobus ornatus occurs singly or in aggregations; sometimes individuals are observed piled on top of one another. In New South Wales, this species is sometimes seen lying among groups of Port Jackson Sharks (*Heterodontus portusjacksoni*), which form large aggregations during the breeding season. Unless disturbed by a diver, the Ornate Wobbegong is rarely active during the day, and often remains in the same spot for months or even years, searching the surrounding reef areas for food at night, then returning to its same diurnal resting place before sunrise. The Ornate Wobbegong eats other sharks, rays, bony fishes, cephalopods, and crustaceans. In New South Wales, schools of bullseye fishes (*Pempheris* spp.), an important food source for this shark, are often found hanging above and around it. The wobbegong can and does feed on these fishes at will, sucking in school members with such great speed that other individuals in the school never learn to recognize

the shark as a threat, and may not even know it is there.

Not only are these small fishes wobbie-fodder, but anything that comes within striking distance is a potential meal, including larger fishes that are trying to prey on the bullseyes. Even if a prey item is too big to eat, the wobbegong may attempt to subdue it. For example, on two separate occasions, an Ornate Wobbegong was observed with the head of an adult Port Jackson Shark in its mouth. In at least one of these episodes, the wobbegong finally gave up and released its oversized victim, which (except for a ring of teeth marks around its neck) was no worse for wear. These sharks are not always unsuccessful in their attempts to consume large prey—one large Ornate Wobbegong was seen with part of a 1.2 m (3.9 ft.) Sandtiger Shark (*Carcharias taurus*) hanging from its mouth, and it was subsequently able to swallow its substantial victim.

I have seen this species with leeches on its body, and it may also occasionally host copepods.

Captive Care: Although hardy and handsome, this is, unfortunately, the largest of the wobbegong species. It is also the most common species in the North American aquarium trade. Adults of this species are highly predatory, feeding on teleost as well as elasmobranch tankmates. (This species has been reported to eat smaller sharks, guitarfishes, and stingrays kept with it.) It is also responsible for numerous attacks on divers in large aquarium display tanks. For more information on its husbandry, see the Captive Care section in the family account (page 87).

Aquarium Size: 11,970 L (3,150 gal.).

Water Temperature: 17 to 26°C (63 to 79°F).

Aquarium Suitability Index: 5 (X-large tank required).

Remarks: The Ornate Wobbegong has only five or six dermal lobes (as opposed to the Spotted Wobbie's eight to ten) under and in front of the eyes on each side of head, and black-bordered saddles and spots. Light areas between the saddles have spots with light centers. The color pattern of this species can vary greatly between individuals, however.

Orectolobus wardi Whitley, 1939

Common Names: Ward's Wobbegong, Northern Wobbegong.

Size, Growth, and Age: This species reaches a maximum size of about 80 cm (31.2 in.), with males reaching sexual maturity at around 45 cm (17.5 in.).

Distribution: Queensland, Australia, around the north coast to Ningaloo Reef, Western Australia.

Biology: Ward's Wobbegong is usually observed on shallow reefs and frequently inhabits tidepools in some areas. It is a solitary species that lies in the open or in reef crevices during the day, at depths of about 1 to 8 m (3.3 ft. to 26.2 ft.). This shark becomes more active at dusk, when it moves about the reef in search of food. It prob-

Orectolobus wardi (Ward's Wobbegong): unusually placid wobbie.

ably catches food items that venture too close during the day as well. Wound patterns on the female's fins indicate that a male will grasp the female's pectoral fin during mating. This is a very docile fish that rarely, if ever, bites.

Captive Care: Because of its passive disposition and its relatively small maximum size, this species is a great choice for the home aquarium. Unfortunately, it is rarely available, except when occasionally collected and exported from northwestern Australia. Ward's Wobbegong should be provided with one or more secure overhangs or caves in which to hide. It may refuse to eat initially, but usually cannot resist a fresh piece of fish, squid, or shrimp presented on a feeding stick. Live food (e.g., fiddler crab or cardinalfish) is also good for coaxing a finicky individual to feed. This is a placid shark that the aquarist can handle without much fear of being bitten. Its small size at sexual maturity makes it an excellent candidate for captive breeding.

Aquarium Size: 418 L (110 gal.).

Water Temperature: 23 to 28°C (73 to 82°F).

Aquarium Suitability Index: 5.

Remarks: This species has two dermal lobes below and in front of the eyes on each side of head, and nasal barbels that are not branched. Its distinctive color pattern consists of large ocellus-like saddles on the back with few spots and no lines between them. A network of light lines on the body resembles the glitter lines cast on the seafloor by the sun, which undoubtedly serves as an effective camouflage for this shallow-water shark.

References

Coleman (1992), N. Coleman (personal communication), Compagno (1984a), I. Gordan (personal communication), Hagiwara (1989), D. Kemp (personal communication), Kuiter (1993), Last & Stevens (1994), N. Marsh (personal communication), Stead (1963), Whitley (1940).

Chiloscyllium punctatum (Brownbanded Bamboo Shark): adapted to tight reef spaces, the hemiscylliids are attractive, adaptable aquarium subjects.

BAMBOO AND EPAULETTE SHARKS
Family Hemiscylliidae

THIS FAMILY HAS 13 SPECIES, at least 4 of which show up in U.S. aquarium stores. Bamboo and epaulette sharks have nasoral grooves, perinasal grooves, small mouths positioned in front of the eyes, no dermal flaps on the sides of the head, and a low, rounded anal fin that is distinct from the caudal fin. They are ideally adapted to life in a highly structured environment: their mus- cular paired fins enable them to walk along the seafloor, and their slender bodies allow them to slip between coral branches and into tight reef fissures.

The hemiscylliids are oviparous, producing egg cases that are sometimes collected for the aquarium trade. Their young are rarely observed in the wild, and apparently live deep within coral crevices and in dense staghorn coral beds, where they are safe from most predators (including other sharks). The color patterns of most of the hemiscylliids change as they grow. Bam- boo shark juveniles usually have distinct bands that fade or disappear with age, while young epaulette sharks have bands that transform into spots. The color patterns of the epaulette sharks provide effective camouflage, especially when they are viewed from above, while the eyespots (ocelli) may function to dupe would-be predators. Predators that approach the bottom-oriented epaulette shark from above see the ocelli as they look down. The paired eyespots may serve to intimidate them by mimicking the head-on perspective of a piscivorous fish. Bamboo and epaulette sharks are harmless to humans, but may bite if harassed.

Captive Care

THE SHARKS OF THE FAMILY HEMISCYLLIIDAE are among those best suited to life in the home aquarium for several reasons. First, the largest member of the family attains a maximum length of only 107 cm (41.7 in.). Second, these sharks occur in tropical areas and therefore thrive in the warmer temperatures (22 to 28°C [72 to 82°F]) maintained in most home aquariums. Finally, the hemiscylliids come from a specialized niche not occupied by many other sharks. They spend most of their time in tidepools, in staghorn coral beds, and under table corals. Because they are accustomed to living in confined areas, they adapt readily to the limited space available in home aquariums. As an added bonus, some of these sharks can also be induced to breed in captive settings. For information on the captive reproduction of bamboo and epaulette sharks, see page 225.

Juvenile hemiscylliids can easily be kept in smaller aquariums, even in tanks as small as the standard 20-gallon long, but the aquarist must be prepared to provide larger quarters as they grow. At maximum size, most bamboo or epaulette sharks could be comfortably housed in a 180-gallon tank. Little information exists on captive growth rates, but a male and female Arabian Bamboo Shark grew from 22 cm (8.9 in.) to 40 cm (15.6 in.) and 45 cm (17.6 in.), respectively, in a 5-year period, while newly hatched Epaulette (*Hemiscyllium ocellatum*) and Brownbanded Bamboo (*Chiloscyllium punctatum*) Sharks have been reported to grow as much as 29 cm (11.3 in.) in a year's time. A newly hatched Whitespotted Bamboo Shark (*Chiloscyllium plagiosum*) was reported to grow from 16.6 (6.5 in.) to 30 cm (11.7 in.) in 1 year. Because these sharks, especially juvenile specimens, spend much of the daylight period hiding in cracks and crevices, some type of aquascaping is needed to make them feel safe. They will appreciate secure ledges and caves, but be advised that hemiscylliids will dig under rockwork to locate food or to create suitable hiding places. An unstable reef structure can end up crushing your shark, so it is essential to build any rockscapes directly on the bottom of the tank—not on a bed of sand in which the sharks may burrow—and to ensure that the rockwork is absolutely secure.

Bamboo sharks are also more likely to suffer from the initial shock of acclimation, and it will often take several days, or even several weeks, before a new specimen starts to eat. If your shark is a reluctant feeder, try introducing food into a darkened tank, or acclimate several freshwater livebearers (e.g., mollies) or grass shrimp to your tank and leave them with the shark to induce a feeding response. A normal feeding regimen for a juvenile hemiscylliid would be to offer it two or three prey items several times a week. All the hemiscylliids have relatively small mouths and teeth suited for grasping, not cutting, so they may have trouble ingesting and chewing larger food items or hard-shelled invertebrates—this is particularly true for smaller specimens. To ensure that the food presented is consumed, chop it into bite-sized pieces, and make sure live prey is small enough to be swallowed whole.

TABLE 4-1.

Some Hemiscylliid Species Not Readily Available in the Aquarium Trade That Would Be Well Suited to Captivity

Species	Total Length	Size at Sexual Maturity	Distribution
Burma Bamboo Shark (*Chiloscyllium burmensis*)	57 cm (22 in.)*	—	Burma ·
Hasselt's Bamboo Shark (*Chiloscyllium hasselti*)	60 cm (23 in.)	Males 44 cm (17 in.)	Thailand, Malaysia, Indonesia
Indian Bamboo Shark (*Chiloscyllium indicum*)	65 cm (25 in.)	Males 39 cm (15 in.)	Arabian Sea to the Solomon Islands, Philippines
Freycinet's Epaulette Shark (*Hemiscyllium freycineti*)	46 cm (18 in.)	Males 37 to 61 cm (14 to 24 in.)	Irian Jaya, Papua New Guinea
Hallstrom's Epaulette Shark (*Hemiscyllium hallstromi*)	77 cm (30 in.)	Males 48 to 64 cm (19 to 25 in.)	Papua New Guinea (south coast)
Hooded Epaulette Shark (*Hemiscyllium strahani*)	75 cm (29 in.)	Males 59 to 75 cm (23 to 29 in.)	Papua New Guinea (north and south coast)
Speckled Epaulette Shark (*Hemiscyllium trispeculare*)	79 cm (31 in.)	Males 51 to 56 cm (20 to 22 in.)	Northern and Western Australia

*Only known from a single specimen.

Be aware that larger bamboo sharks will eat smaller reef fishes kept with them, and all of the hemiscylliids will consume ornamental shrimps. In turn, smaller bamboo and epaulette sharks are sometimes eaten by larger morays and frogfishes. For example, I once saw a Wartskin Frogfish (*Antennarius maculatus*) ingest a juvenile bamboo shark that was at least twice as long as itself.

Although usually passive in nature, mature male bamboo and epaulette sharks have been known to behave aggressively toward consexuals, especially in smaller aquariums. Adult male epaulette sharks have even been implicated in attacks on male sharks of different species. For this reason, caution should be exercised when keeping mature male hemiscylliids with other male sharks in the home aquarium.

How long will these sharks live in the aquarium? The Whitespotted Bamboo Shark (*Chiloscyllium plagiosum*) has been reported to live more than 25 years in captivity. A number of hemiscylliid species that would be suitable for the home aquarium are only rarely seen in the aquarium trade (see Table 4-1, page 99).

Species Accounts

Chiloscyllium arabicum Gubanov, 1980
Common Name: Arabian Bamboo Shark.
Size, Growth, and Age: The Arabian Bamboo Shark hatches at 12 cm (4.7 in.) and attains a maximum length of 78 cm (30.4 in.).
Distribution: Arabian Gulf to India. Reported as being common in the Arabian Gulf, especially in the summer months.
Biology: The Arabian Bamboo Shark has been reported from a depth range of 3 to 100 m (9.8 to 328 ft.). They usually hide in crevices and caves during the day and come out to hunt at night, feeding mainly on crus-

Chiloscyllium arabicum (Arabian Bamboo Shark): reproduces readily.

taceans and mollusks, but also taking fishes (including snake eels) and squids. This shark lays atendril (lacking the two or four typical tendrils) adhesive egg cases that adhere to the coral on which they are placed. Egg laying takes place over a 6-month period. Four egg cases at a time are laid over a period ranging from 20 minutes to 2 days; they hatch 70 to 80 days later.
Captive Care: The species enters the North American trade on rare occasions. It is a hardy aquarium shark that will readily reproduce in captivity.
Aquarium Size: 418 L (110 gal.).
Water Temperature: 22 to 28°C (72 to 82°F).
Aquarium Suitability Index: 5.
Remarks: The Arabian Bamboo Shark has dorsal fins with rounded posterior edges, and the base of the second dorsal fin is longer than that of the first dorsal fin. Juveniles and adults are a uniform brown or tan in color. *Chiloscyllium griseum* (see below) is similar, but its first dorsal base is longer than its second dorsal base, and the distance between the first and second dorsal fin origins is usually more than 9.3% of the total length. *Chiloscyllium arabicum* is synonymous with *Chiloscyllium confusum*.

Chiloscyllium griseum (Gray Bamboo Shark): may be reluctant to feed.

Chiloscyllium plagiosum (Whitespotted Bamboo Shark): ideal species.

Chiloscyllium griseum Müller & Henle, 1838

Common Name: Gray Bamboo Shark.

Size, Growth, and Age: The Gray Bamboo Shark hatches at about 15 cm (5.9 in.) and attains a maximum length of at least 74 cm (28.9 in.) Sexual maturity is attained at a maximum length of 45 to 55 cm (17.6 to 21.5 in.) in males, and about 53 cm (20.7 in.) in females.

Distribution: Arabian Gulf to Papua New Guinea, and north to southern Japan.

Biology: Gray Bamboo Sharks occur on sand and mud bottoms, and have also been reported from coral reef habitats. Euzen (1987) reported the following food-habit frequency in specimens from the Arabian Gulf: bony fishes (including anchovies, catfishes, gobies, flatfishes, and lizardfishes), 50%; shrimps, 33%; worms (other than polychaetes), 32% ; mantis shrimps, 26%; polychaete worms, 26%; mollusks, 22%; and crabs, 20%. Of 88 specimens examined in this study, only 12% of the stomachs were empty.

Captive Care: Although this species is wide ranging in the Indo-west Pacific, it is rarely observed in the aquarium trade. In some cases juvenile specimens may be reluctant to feed.

Aquarium Size: 418 L (110 gal.).

Water Temperature: 22 to 28°C (72 to 82°F).

Aquarium Suitability Index: 4.

Remarks: Dorsal fins with convex posterior margins mark this species. Like *Chiloscyllium punctatum* (see below), juveniles are banded, but the bands are not as dark in the juveniles. These bands fade with age and are almost indistinguishable in adults. This shark is erroneously sold as a "Banded Catshark" in the aquarium trade.

Chiloscyllium plagiosum (Bennett, 1830)

Common Name: Whitespotted Bamboo Shark.

Size, Growth, and Age: The Whitespotted Bamboo Shark hatches at about 15 or 16 cm (5.9 to 6.2 in.) and attains a maximum length of 95 cm (37 in.). The length at maturity is from 50 to 65 cm (19.5 to 25.4 in.) for males and about 80 cm (31.2 in.) for females.

Distribution: From Japan to Indonesia and Thailand to India.

Biology: This species inhabits tropical coral reefs where it haunts crevices during the day and moves out to feed on fishes and crustaceans at night. Two eggs are deposited at a time, with egg deposition occurring every 6 or 7 days on average. The female can store sperm and will keep depositing eggs for 2 to 5 months after copulation. The average hatching period for these eggs is 128 days (incubation times are highly temperature dependent).

Captive Care: This species does well in home aquariums. It mates and spawns readily in larger tanks, with successful breeding programs existing at public aquariums throughout North America.

Aquarium Size: 608 L (160 gal.).

Water Temperature: 21 to 28°C (70 to 82°F).

Aquarium Suitability Index: 5.

Remarks: In this species, the posterior edges of the dorsal fins are rounded, not concave. It has bands and white spots on a gray to dark brown background, and juveniles often have a velvety black appearance. **Hasselt's Bamboo Shark (*Chiloscyllium hasselti*) Bleeker, 1852** is similar, but is uniform in color as an adult, and the distance from the first to the second dorsal fin is less than 9.3% of the total length. The first dorsal height is less than 6.6% of the total length, and the height of the second dorsal fin is less than 5.8% of the total length. The juveniles have black-bordered gray-brown bands. Hasselt's Bamboo Shark has been reported from Thailand, Malaysia, and Indonesia, and may occasionally show up in aquarium stores.

Chiloscyllium punctatum Müller & Henle, 1838

Common Name: Brownbanded Bamboo Shark.

Size, Growth, and Age: The Brownbanded Bamboo Shark hatches at about 16 cm (6.2 in.), and reaches a maximum length of 104 cm (40.6 in.). Males attain sexual maturity at 68 to 74 cm (26.5 to 28.9 in.) in total length.

Distribution: From Japan to Australia, and Indonesia to India.

Biology: This nocturnal shark occurs on tidal flats, sand slopes, fore reef-slopes and among boulders on rocky reefs. The juveniles have also been observed on sand slopes, where they refuge under water-logged palm leaves and manmade debris (e.g., discarded fishing nets) during the day. They have also been reported from deep reef crevices. The juveniles tend to be quite site-attached, having been observed in the same general area (and sometimes in the same refuge) for weeks or even months. Adults hide under table corals or among large

Chiloscyllium punctatum (Brownbanded Bamboo Shark): juvenile form.

Chiloscyllium punctatum (Brownbanded Bamboo Shark): adult coloration.

boulders during the day. At night, they probe the coral rubble and sand with their snouts in search of invertebrate prey.

Captive Care: The Brownbanded Bamboo Shark is one of the most common elasmobranchs in North American aquarium stores. It will readily acclimate to the home aquarium, although it may take a while before newly acquired juveniles begin to feed. This species has been known to reproduce in captivity, laying atendril adhesive egg cases on the bottom or sides of the aquarium. These egg cases are frequently available in the aquarium trade.

Aquarium Size: 646 L (170 gal.).

Water Temperature: 22 to 28°C (72 to 82°F).

Aquarium Suitability Index: 5.

Remarks: In this species, the dorsal fin posterior edges are concave. Juveniles have dark bands on a light background, while in adults these bands are less distinct or absent altogether. An occasional specimen may have black spots scattered over the head and body. This species is often referred to as a "Banded Catshark" in the aquarium trade.

Hemiscyllium ocellatum (Bonnaterre, 1788)

Common Name: Epaulette Shark.

Size, Growth, and Age: This species hatches at 15 cm (5.9 in.) in length and attains a maximum length of 107 cm (41.7 in.). Maturity is reached at 59 to 70 cm (23.0 to 27.3 in.) in males and 60 to 65 cm (23.4 to 25.4 in.) in females. Juveniles grow at a rate of about 5 cm (2.0 in.) a year.

Distribution: Australia (Queensland around the north coast to northwestern Australia) and New Guinea.

Biology: This shark prefers shallow water, from the intertidal zone to 10 m (33 ft.) deep. The Epaulette Shark is very tolerant of low oxygen levels (hypoxia conditions), an adaptation to its inhabiting shallow tidal flats.

One lab study showed that this shark was unaffected when exposed to severe hypoxia (an oxygen level of 0.35 mg/L at a water temperature of 24°C [75 F°]) for 2 hours. It lays atendril adhesive egg cases, which are deposited at night, usually two at a time. This shark breeds in October and November on the southern Great Barrier Reef. An obligatory reef dweller, the Epaulette Shark is most abundant in staghorn coral stands on reef faces and among coral boulders or on sand patches on reef flats (often in tidepools). It feeds mainly on worms and crabs, while shrimps and small fishes are eaten to a lesser degree. Some of these prey items are dug out of the sand or sucked from crevices. It is solitary and primarily nocturnal, although I have observed considerable activity (including mating) in this species during the day. Inactive individuals are sometimes observed hiding with their heads stuck under a ledge. A myxosporean parasite in the genus *Kudoa* has been found within the skeletal musculature of this shark (in some bony fishes, these parasites cause muscle tissue atrophy).

A parasitic ostracod crustacean (known as *Sheina orri*) has been reported from the gills of this shark. Bennett et al. (1997) reported that 17 of 28 Epaulette Sharks examined were host to this parasite. The ostracods use their claws to anchor to the gill lamellae and do cause some damage to the tissues. Gnathiid isopod larvae are also frequently found on *Hemiscyllium ocellatum*. These parasites tend to attach around the cloacae of male and female sharks, but are also found on the gills and in the mouth. They are thought to do relatively little damage to their host. I have seen this shark being cleaned by the Bluestreak Cleaner Wrasse (*Labroides dimidiatus*) in the wild. Isopod larvae like those found on the shark are a preferred prey of this labrid. I once observed the wrasse picking at targets in the shark's gill slits and on its body surface. When the shark opened

A New Epaulette Shark?

In recent years, Sarong, Irian Jaya, has become a popular destination for divers interested in exotic marine life. From these amateur explorers, several photographs have emerged of an epaulette shark that is obviously different from other described species. It is my belief that this is a new species that may represent the adult color phase of a juvenile described in 1983.

In that year, Dingerkus and DeFino published a revision of the Family Hemiscylliidae and recognized 12 valid members of the family, including two new species. They also described a juvenile member of the genus *Hemiscyllium* that they thought might represent a new species. The juvenile shark they described was from Amsterdam Island off Irian Jaya. It was a 14.8 cm (5.8 in.) female collected in 1944. This specimen, which was probably newly hatched, was adorned with alternating white and black bands and a black saddle over the pectoral region, making it very distinct from known juveniles and adults of the described species.

A recent photograph of a live adult specimen of a new epaulette shark, taken by Debra Fugitt, is shown on page 106. It clearly differs in its coloration from the other five members of the genus. Although chromatic characteristics are not always reliable in differentiating fish species, Dingerkus and DeFino relied on color patterns alone to separate the *Hemiscyllium* species. A brief description of those color characteristics follows. (Note: references to the "epaulette" indicate the ocellus, or eyespot, above the pectoral fin.)

Freycinet's Epaulette Shark (*Hemiscyllium freycineti*) (Quoy & Gaimard, 1924): The underside of the head is light in coloration, with no dark spots or bands. The epaulette is clearly discernible from the background coloration. The anterior portion of the head in front of the eyes has spots that are slightly smaller or equal to the eye diameter. There are numerous spots on the anterior portion of the head (in front of the eyes). The background color of the adults is usually tan, with spots that are reddish brown (some have lighter centers). The

Hemiscyllium freycineti (Freycinet's Epaulette Shark)

Hemiscyllium hallstromi (Hallstrom's Epaulette Shark)

Hemiscyllium hallstromi (Hallstrom's Epaulette Shark)

Hemiscyllium strahani (Strahan's or Hooded Epaulette Shark)

body spots are relatively large, exceeding the eye diameter in size. The spots on the body form a honeycomb pattern, and the ventral surface is creamy white.

Hallstrom's Epaulette Shark (*Hemiscyllium hallstromi*) Whitely, 1967: The underside of the head is light in color, with no dark spots or bands. The epaulette is clearly discernible from the background coloration and often has a white margin. The anterior portion of the head, in front of the eyes, is uniformly light in color, with no spots. Some of the spots on the body are equal to or larger than the epaulette (the body spots sometimes have a pale margin). The background coloration of the adult is tan to light brown with dark brown or black spots; the ventral surface is white to creamy white.

Epaulette Shark (*Hemiscyllium ocellatum*) Bonnaterre, 1788: The underside of the head is light in coloration, with no dark spots or bands. The epaulette is clearly discernible from the background coloration. (The epaulette spot varies in size, from one-quarter to one-half the body depth.) The anterior portion of the head, in front of the eyes, is usually uniformly light in color, with no spots (on rare occasions, a few smaller spots are present). All the spots on the body are smaller than the epaulette. The background coloration of the adult is tan to golden brown, with dark brown or black spots. The ventral surface is white to creamy white.

Strahan's or Hooded Epaulette Shark (*Hemiscyllium strahani*) Whitley, 1967: The underside of the head has dark spots or bands. The epaulette spot blends in with the background color making it almost indiscernible. The dorsal background coloration is dark brown to gray, with pale gray to white spots. The ventral surface is white to creamy white, except for the underside of the head, which is dark brown or black.

Speckled Epaulette Shark (*Hemiscyllium trispeculare*) Richardson, 1843: The underside of the head is light in

Hemiscyllium trispeculare (Speckled Epaulette Shark)

Hemiscyllium sp. ("Irian Epaulette Shark"): possible new species.

coloration, with no dark spots or bands. The epaulette is clearly discernible from the background coloration. There are often two or three distinct spots behind the epaulette, all surrounded by a white margin. The anterior portion of the head in front of the eyes has spots that are smaller than half of the eye diameter. The background coloration of the adult is tan to light brown with numerous small dark brown spots. (This shark often has an olive green cast overall.) The spots sometimes coalesce to form saddles on the back and tail. The ventral surface is a uniform white to cream color.

Irian Epaulette Shark (*Hemiscyllium* sp.): This shark is clearly distinct from other members of the genus. The description of its notable chromatic characteristics are based on photographs. **Adult:** The underside of the head is light in coloration, with no dark spots or bands. The epaulette is clearly discernible from the background coloration. The epaulette has an elongated black patch slightly behind and below it. The anterior portion of the head in front of the eyes has

spots that are nearly the same size or slightly smaller than the eye diameter. There is a large spot below and behind the spiracle and another larger dark brown spot even further below on the white ventral surface. The background coloration is tan on the body and slightly darker on the head. Numerous dark brown spots on the body vary greatly in size—from smaller to larger than the eye diameter. Some of the spots are assembled in groups of three. Some of these coalesce to form larger blotches or saddles. There are approximately four dark saddles on the back. The ventral surface is white. **Juvenile:** Bands on the body and a large, saddlelike marking on the back and over the pectoral region. This marking may break up to form the saddle and epaulette of the adult.

In the three species of epaulette sharks where the juvenile is known, the coloration of the adult differs from that of the juvenile. Although likely, it is impossible to tell with certainty that the juvenile pictured in Dingerkus and DeFino represents the juvenile of the Irian Epaulette Shark.

Hemiscyllium ocellatum (Epaulette Shark): standing on its pectoral fins, this shark searches for prey in the shallows on the Great Barrier Reef.

its mouth, the cleaner fish groomed its jaws and oral cavity. The full cleaning session lasted about 8 minutes. This shark is generally considered harmless, but I once saw a specimen bite a diver who was handling it.

Captive Care: This is one of the best sharks for the home aquarium. The Epaulette Shark will readily acclimate to aquarium confines and will mate and lay eggs in the aquarium. Adult males may behave aggressively toward consexuals, as well as toward male sharks of other species. They will also harass females.

Newly collected Epaulette Sharks may be kept with Bluestreak Cleaner Wrasses (*Labroides dimidiatus*), which will help rid the shark of some of the crustacean parasites they are notorious for harboring. Dimilin (di-flubenzuron) can also be used to control parasitic crustaceans.

Aquarium Size: 988 L (260 gal.).

Water Temperature: 22 to 28°C (72 to 82°F).

Aquarium Suitability Index: 5.

Remarks: This species has a swollen snout that is longer than that of any other hemiscylliid shark. It also has a large black spot (usually surrounded by white) just behind the pectoral fins, and numerous dark spots that are smaller than the ocelli. Two color phases have been observed: one has a golden base color, numerous small dark spots, and very pronounced ocelli, while the other is tan with fewer, larger spots and less distinct ocelli.

Hallstrom's Epaulette Shark (*Hemiscyllium hallstromi*)

Whitley, 1967, which is known only from the waters of Papua New Guinea, is similar to *H. ocellatum*. Hallstrom's Epaulette has spots that are equal to or larger than the ocelli, and it has no spots in front of the eyes, whereas *H. ocellatum* may or may not have spots there.

References
Bennett et al. (1997), Dingerkus & DeFino (1983), Dral (1981), Euzen (1987), Heupel & Bennett (1998, 1999), Last & Stevens (1994), Masuda et al. (1998), Soderstrom et al. (1999), West & Carter (1990).

NURSE SHARKS
Family Ginglymostomatidae

THE NURSE SHARKS ARE WELL-KNOWN to divers who frequent the Caribbean and to marine aquarists alike. The Nurse Shark (*Ginglymostoma cirratum*) is one of the most common sharks on reefs in the tropical Western Atlantic, and it thrives in captivity. This family has three genera, each with one species, all of which are rocky and coral reef dwellers. Nurse sharks have nasal barbels, nasoral grooves, small mouths positioned in front of the eyes, fourth and fifth gill-slits that are very close together, a second dorsal fin originating well in front of the anal fin's origin, and a short tail. The nurse sharks are benthic, spending most of their time tucked under ledges or sheltering in caves during the day. By night they prowl the reef in search of a wide variety of invertebrate and fish prey. They are well known for their ability to create a vacuum by rapidly expanding their pharynx, which enables them to suck prey items from crevices or rubble interstices. In fact, the Tawny Nurse Shark (*Nebrius ferrugineus*) has been observed to suck the mantle and innards of tridacnid clams right from their shells. (This Indo-Pacific species also preys on the highly venomous sea snakes.) The jaws and their associated musculature are very strong and, along with multiple rows of functional teeth, are effective at crushing hard-shelled invertebrates. The barbels in front of the mouth are equipped with taste receptors and facilitate food location. When navigating in tight spaces, nurse sharks will "walk" forward or backward on their pectoral fins. Although far from being "man-killers," the nurse sharks may bite if provoked. When they do bite they are often reluctant to let go, hanging on with the tenacity of a pit bull.

Captive Care
NURSE SHARKS HAVE LONG BEEN DISPLAY and experimental animals. This is because they thrive in large public aquariums and, as juveniles, do well in home or laboratory tanks. The only species available in North American fish stores is the Nurse Shark (*Ginglymostoma cirratum*), which is a hardy aquarium species, but it is destined to outgrow even very large home aquariums. For this reason, I do not recommend them to the hobbyist. In a paper on elasmobranch husbandry Juan Sabalones of the National Aquarium in Baltimore states, "The problem with Nurse Sharks, the staple species of many shark displays, is the difficulty in locating proper homes for them when faced with a surplus." Even public aquariums have a problem getting rid of these sharks, so the hobbyist should not expect their local public aquarium to take an oversized nurse shark when it threatens to burst the walls of its aquarium. These animals must never be returned to the wild, leaving as the only alternatives turning one's pet shark over to a fishmonger or taxidermist. If none of these scenarios appeals to you, as they don't to most aquarists, resist ever buying a juvenile nurse shark.

Nebrius ferrugineus (Tawny Nurse Shark): unsuspecting aquarists may purchase members of this family, unaware of the problems that lie ahead.

These sharks eat more, are more active, and grow faster at higher water temperatures. They are reported to remain motionless and cease feeding at temperatures below 20°C (68°F), and one researcher reports that they will stop eating and begin biting one another at temperatures in excess of 30°C (86°F). Nurse sharks relish fresh table shrimp, squid, and fish, and will also make short work of any tankmate (fish or invertebrate) that can be swallowed. They may even nip at larger fishes. They should be fed to satiation two times a week.

Nurse sharks should be kept in water with a specific gravity of 1.018 to 1.024. They can tolerate poor water quality and low dissolved oxygen levels for short periods, and they are not sensitive to copper treatment (levels up to 0.25 ppm). They have been reported to succumb to cestode infestations and can also develop thyroid hyperplasia (goiter). Individuals have been kept alive in public aquariums for over 25 years and have mated in large oceanariums, but their size at maturity precludes their being bred in the home aquarium.

Species Account

Ginglymostoma cirratum (Bonnaterre, 1788)
Common Name: Nurse Shark.
Size, Growth, and Age: A Nurse Shark is born at 28 cm

(10.9 in.) and attains a maximum length of 4.3 m (14 ft.), but most do not exceed 3 m (9.8 ft.). Males reach sexual maturity at about 2.3 m (7.5 ft.), while females are mature at 2.3 to 2.4 m (7.5 to 7.9 ft.). Studies have shown that the Nurse Shark grows 19±5 cm (7.5±2.0 in.) a year in captivity, and slightly less in the wild. It can also put on up to 2.7 kg (5.9 lbs.) of weight per year.

Distribution: The range of this species covers the Western Atlantic from Rhode Island to Brazil, the Eastern Atlantic from Senegal to Gabon, and the Eastern Pacific from southern Baja California to Peru.

Biology: The Nurse Shark occurs on lagoon patch reefs, reef flats, reef faces, and in mangrove swamps, from the intertidal zone to depths of 50 m (164 ft.). It is inactive during the day and often spends daylight hours in aggregations on the seafloor. At night, it hunts benthic invertebrates (including spiny lobsters, crabs, octopuses, and sea urchins), stingrays, and benthic bony fishes (including mullet, catfishes, pufferfishes, surgeonfishes, filefishes, herrings, and parrotfishes). According to Randall (1967), bony fishes make up about 80% (by volume) of a Nurse Shark's diet, and cephalopods account for another 11%. A Nurse Shark will dig under coral chunks with its head in search of concealed invertebrate prey. When it locates its quarry hiding in a crevice or amid coral rubble, the shark places its small mouth near the prey item and inhales it by rapidly expanding its pharynx. Members of this species have also been observed knocking over conchs and sucking them from their shells. Juvenile Nurse Sharks may lure their prey by rolling their pectoral fins under their bodies and resting on them, motionless. The space created under the body by this posture may be mistaken for a home by a shelter-seeking shrimp or fish, and when the prey comes within striking range, the shark pounces on it.

In June this shark forms mating assemblages in

Ginglymostoma cirratum (Nurse Shark): aggressive when food is present.

shallow water. In these breeding areas, observers report seeing as many as five pairs courting at the same time. The Nurse Shark is ovoviviparous. After the eggs are released from the ovaries, they are initially encased in a thin, horny shell. When the embryos reaches about 6 cm (2.3 in.) in total length the egg cases split open. The embryos emerge from the cases when they are 22 cm (8.9 in.) long. Parturition occurs in November and December after a gestation period of about 3 to 4.5 months. Females then go into a resting phase, waiting to mate again until the next summer. Nurse sharks can give birth to as many as 28 young per litter, although litters of 5 to 10 are more common.

Members of this species have a fixed home range, and tagged individuals have been recaptured in the same area even after 4 years at liberty. There are reports of several unprovoked attacks on divers by Nurse Sharks, but in most cases they will not bother humans without provocation.

Captive Care: Although the Nurse Shark is a durable and readily available aquarium fish, it will outgrow home aquariums. (See the Captive Care section in the family account.) It is highly predaceous, consuming fish and crustacean tankmates and is an aggressive feeder that will hamper your attempts to get food to more reclusive elasmobranchs. It often spends its days resting on the aquarium bottom, although it will quickly spring into action if an attractive stimulus presents itself. In tight confines, it is a clumsy shark that will knock over or rearrange aquarium decor when rooting around looking for food or shelter.

Aquarium Size: 18,240 L (4,800 gal.).

Water Temperature: 22 to 28°C (72 to 82°F).

Aquarium Suitability Index: 5 (X-large tank required).

Remarks: The Nurse Shark has rounded pectoral and dorsal fins, and the second dorsal fin starts in front of the anal fin's origin. It also possesses long barbels, which extend to the mouth. Individuals are tan to dark brown in color, and juveniles have numerous small black spots.

References

Carrier et al. (1994), Carrier & Luer (1990), Castro (AES Meeting), Clark (1963), Gonzalez (AES Meeting), Pratt & Carrier (1995), Randall (1967).

ZEBRA SHARKS
Family Stegostomatidae

THE ONLY MEMBER OF THIS FAMILY, the Zebra Shark (*Stegostoma varium*), is a resident of coral and rocky reefs in tropical to warm-temperate regions. It is characterized by a tail almost as long as its body, ridges on the sides of the body, and a small mouth. The color of individuals over about 90 cm (35.1 in.) varies from a yellow to cream background color, with black dots or open dark circles. Smaller individuals have yellow to white bars and spots over a dark brown background. Albinism has also been reported in this species. Some ichthyologists include this in the Family Rhincodontidae, along with the whale and nurse sharks (Family Ginglymostomatidae).

Captive Care

THE ZEBRA SHARK IS A WONDERFUL display animal that has been reported to live for lengthy periods in public aquariums. It readily feeds on snails, clams, and fish flesh, and is less of a threat to fish tankmates than its cartilaginous cousins. (On occasion, it will eat fishes that can be swallowed whole when they settle on the bottom or are torpid and resting on aquarium decor after dark.) The Zebra Shark has been reported to reproduce in captivity, and both juveniles and egg cases are occasionally available in the aquarium trade.

The amateur aquarist should resist the temptation to purchase one of these beauties because they will outgrow any typical home system. For example, an adult individual would require a tank or pool at least 6.5 m (21 ft.) long and 4.3 m (14 ft.) wide. If you don't have the space or money to set up such a system, don't buy a Zebra Shark.

Species Account

Stegostoma varium (Seba, 1758)

Common Names: Zebra Shark, Variegated Shark, Monkey-mouthed Shark.

Distribution: Samoa to Australia, north to Japan in the Pacific, and from Indonesia to South Africa in the Indian Ocean, as well as the Red Sea.

Size, Growth, and Age: This shark hatches at 25 cm (9.8 in.) in length and is reported to attain a maximum length of 3.5 m (11.5 ft.), although they rarely exceed 2.3 m (7.5 ft.). Males mature at a length between 147 and 180 cm (57.3 to 70.2 in.), while females are reproductively ripe at a length over 170 cm (66.3 in.).

Biology: The Zebra Shark is observed in lagoons, reef channels, and on reef faces, at depths from the shallow intertidal zone to 65 m (213 ft.). The gorgeous juveniles of this species are rarely encountered and may occur in deeper water (greater than 50 m [164 ft.]),

Stegostoma varium (Zebra Shark): a wonderful display animal for public aquariums, but an unwise choice for hobbyists tempted to buy a juvenile.

although there are old accounts of the young of this species inhabiting shallow bays. Adults and subadults usually rest on sand or coral rubble substrates, sometimes standing on their pectoral fins with their open mouths facing into the current. This behavior probably facilitates respiration while the animal is at rest. Occasionally, this species will also bask just below the water's surface. At night, the Zebra Shark hunts the reef and adjacent sand flats or slopes, and feeds primarily on snails, clams, and mussels. It crushes these armored invertebrates with its flattened, three-cusped teeth, which, along with short jaws, operate like a pair of pli-

ers to grip and pulverize the prey. It also eats crabs, shrimps, and bony fishes on occasion. The long, flexible body and tail of the Zebra Shark enable it to enter reef crevices and caves to capture concealed prey.

It is usually solitary, but will aggregate during the reproductive season. Members of these aggregations often swim high above the substrate and have been observed to follow one another and to nip at each other's tails. Although copulation has not been observed in the wild, aquarium observations indicate that the amorous male bites the female's pectoral fin before and during mating (see Chapter 8 for more on the reproductive behavior of this species). A female may lay as many as four atendril adhesive egg cases at one time. These egg cases, which can be brown or purple with longitudinal striations, measure 13 to 20 cm (5.1 to 7.8 in.) in length, 8 cm (3.1 in.) in width and are 5 cm (2.0 in.) thick. The time of hatching for the deposited egg case is 170 days (about 5.5 to 6 months). It is highly temperature dependent.

These sharks are often accompanied by discfishes and are also cleaned by the Bluestreak Cleaner Wrasse (*Labroides dimidiatus*). Even so, they often have clumps of parasitic copepods on the end of the snout (an area that discfishes apparently overlook). This shark is very inoffensive, never having been reported to attack a scuba diver, even when harassed.

Captive Care: The Zebra Shark is a great display animal for large public aquariums. Its imposing maximum size, however, makes it unsuitable for the home aquarium, despite the fact that juveniles carrying hefty price tags are occasionally available to hobbyists. This shark has been known to reproduce in large public aquariums.

Aquarium Size: 23,560 L (6,200 gal.).

Water Temperature: 22 to 28°C (72 to 82°F).

Aquarium Suitability Index: 4 (X-large tank required).

Remarks: This species is sometimes called the Leopard Shark (this causes confusion because *Triakis semifasciata* is also called the Leopard Shark). The name *Stegostoma fasciatum* (Hermann, 1783) is often used for this species, but this is a junior synonym of *S. varium* (see Randall, 1986). This species is sometimes sold under the erroneous name "Angel Shark" in the aquarium trade.

References

Bass et al. (1975), M. Carl (personal communication), K. Kunze (personal communication), Randall (1986).

CATSHARKS
Family Scyliorhinidae

CATSHARKS MAKE UP THE LARGEST shark family, with 15 genera and more than 103 described species. They have retractable protective (nictitating) membranes protecting elongated eyes that suggest a feline appearance to many observers. Their first dorsal fin originates over or behind the pelvic fins, and they have no precaudal pit, a strongly developed lower caudal lobe, and large spiracles. Although many catshark species occupy deepwater habitats (deep-water ghost catsharks, genus *Apristurus*, comprise about one-third of the family), a number of these sharks are reef dwellers, and at least one species regularly makes appearances in North American aquarium stores. The reef-dwelling species (e.g., *Atelomycterus* spp.) have elongate bodies and narrow heads that allow entry into small interstices in which they hunt and take refuge. A number of catsharks are nocturnal, spending their days resting on the seafloor, and many reef varieties bear attractive color patterns consisting of stripes, spots, saddles, and/or blotches, which disrupt the catshark's outline against the varied background of the reef, effectively camouflaging it.

The reef-dwelling species feed on a wide range of food items, including worms, snails, crustaceans, bony fishes, and elasmobranchs. Swell sharks, genus *Cephaloscyllium*, wedge themselves into reef crevices and inflate their abdomens by swallowing large volumes of water, making it difficult for large predators to extract and eat them. This strategy does not always work, however, as in the case of a Balloon Shark (*Cephaloscyllium sufflans*) that was taken from the stomach of a Coelacanth (*Latimeria chalumnae*).

While the majority of catsharks are egg layers, a few are ovoviviparous, but none of the shallow reef-dwelling species are live-bearers. Copulation has been observed in several species. In many catsharks, males have longer teeth than females, which is probably an adaptation to aid them in biting and holding a prospective mate.

Captive Care

THESE BOTTOM-DWELLING SHARKS do well in large home aquariums. Catshark specimens have been kept for more than 20 years in public aquariums, and their husbandry is similar in many respects to that of the hemiscylliids. They should be given adequate daytime hiding places, but too much decor will impede their ability to move around in the tank. Unlike bamboo and epaulette sharks, these fishes do not crawl on their paired fins, and thus are not as well adapted to maneuvering in tight spaces. Their temperature preferences vary from one species to the next. Temperate-water forms, such as the Swell Shark (*Cephaloscyllium ventriosum*) and the Smallspotted Catshark (*Scyliorhinus canicula*), should be kept at lower water temperatures (less than 18°C [64°F]), while coral-reef-dwelling forms can be kept in the tropical aquarium (temperatures above 22°C [72°F]). Catsharks may refuse to eat for a week or more after their initial purchase. They should be provided with a ledge under which to hide and a varied diet of fresh seafood. If necessary, introduce live shrimp into the tank at night to induce a feeding response. Most catsharks will eat any fish or invertebrate they can fit into their mouths, and the mouths of some, like the Swell Shark, are relatively huge. For information on the captive reproduction of catsharks, see page 227. A number of catshark species that would be suitable for home aquariums are not yet available in the aquarium trade (see Table 4-2, page 116).

Species Accounts

Atelomycterus macleayi Whitley, 1939
Common Name: Marbled Catshark.
Size, Growth, and Age: This shark hatches at 10 cm (3.9 in.) and attains a maximum length of at least 60 cm (23.4 in.). Males become sexually mature at 48 cm (18.7 in.), while females are mature at 51 cm (20.0 in.).
Distribution: Western and northern Australia. It has been reported from Queensland, but this record may be erroneous.

Atelomycterus macleayi (Marbled Catshark): desirable aquarium species.

Biology: Little is known about the biology of this species. It occurs in tide pools, sometimes at water temperatures in excess of 32°C (90°F). It probably feeds on small, benthic invertebrates.
Captive Care: This wonderful little shark is not common in the aquarium trade at this writing. This is unfortunate as its small size makes it ideal. Provide it with a stable ledge or cave in which to hide.
Aquarium Size: 266 L (70 gal.).
Water Temperature: 22 to 30°C (72 to 86°F).
Aquarium Suitability Index: 4.
Remarks: *Atelomycterus macleayi* is medium brown on the dorsum, with 7 gray saddles and a number of large, black spots. The ventral surface is pale. It has larger anterior nasal flaps that partially overlap the mouth, and long labial furrows.

Atelomycterus marmoratus (Bennett, 1830)
Common Name: Coral Catshark.
Size, Growth, and Age: This species hatches at about 10 cm (3.9 in.) and reaches a maximum length of 70 cm (27.3 in.). Maturity is attained at a maximum length of 47 to 62 cm (18.3 to 24.2 in.) in males and 49 to 57 cm (19.1 and 22.2 in.) in females. Mature males are easy to recognize, as they are endowed with extremely long claspers.
Distribution: Pakistan to New Guinea, the Philippines, Thailand, China, and southern Japan. Commonly observed on Indonesian reefs at night.
Biology: The Coral Catshark is a shallow-water coral reef species with an elongate body that allows movement into reef crevices and among branching corals, but it does not move on paired fins like the bamboo sharks. It occurs at depths of at least 10 m (33 ft.). I encountered an individual in Indonesia that spent the day under a sunken tree trunk. It would hunt on the sur-

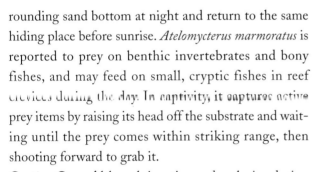

Atelomycterus marmoratus (Coral Catshark): note feline look of the eye.

Atelomycterus marmoratus (Coral Catshark): interesting color variant.

rounding sand bottom at night and return to the same hiding place before sunrise. *Atelomycterus marmoratus* is reported to prey on benthic invertebrates and bony fishes, and may feed on small, cryptic fishes in reef crevices during the day. In captivity, it captures active prey items by raising its head off the substrate and waiting until the prey comes within striking range, then shooting forward to grab it.

Captive Care: Although inactive and reclusive during the day, this species is very energetic in the dark. When the lights go out in the aquarium, the Coral Catshark will often stick its nose in the corner of the tank and begin swimming, resulting in the displacement of large quantities of substrate from the aquarium corners. Coral Catsharks are more voracious than bamboo sharks and will attempt to eat fishes kept with them, even if they are too large to swallow whole. For example, I had a specimen that chewed off the end of a moray's tail, and a friend reported having a specimen eat a pufferfish. Even so, it often takes some time before this nocturnal shark starts to feed in captivity. This shark will breed in captivity, with females laying two tendril egg cases at a time.

Aquarium Size: 418 L (110 gal.).

Water Temperature: 22 to 28°C (72 to 82°F).

Aquarium Suitability Index: 5.

Remarks: This shark has nasal flaps that reach the mouth, light spots and bars on a dark background, a white belly, and dorsal fins that are usually white-tipped. It has no nasoral grooves or distinct saddles. Male members of this genus have very long, narrow claspers. The color pattern of this species is extremely variable, and two color forms are commonly encountered in U.S. fish stores, which may actually represent two distinct species. The Australian Marbled Catshark (*A. macleayi*) differs in color, having gray bands (or saddles) with spots in the light areas between them.

Cephaloscyllium ventriosum (Garman 1880)

Common Name: Swell Shark.

Size, Growth, and Age: This shark hatches at 14 cm (5.5 in.) and attains a maximum length of 1 m (39.4 in.). Males attain maturity at 82 to 85 cm (32.0 to 33.2 in.).

Distribution: Central California to southern Mexico; also reported near central Chile. Along the California coast, this species has disappeared from areas where it

TABLE 4-2.

Some Catshark Species Not Available in the Aquarium Trade That Would Be Well Suited to Captivity

Species	Maximum Length	Size at Sexual Maturity
Australian Spotted Catshark (*Asymbolus analis*)	61 cm (24 in.)	Males 55 cm (21 in.); Females 57 cm (22 in.)
Gulf Catshark (*Asymbolus vincenti*)	56 cm (22 in.)	Males 38 cm (15 in.); Females 45 to 53 cm(18 to 21 in.)
Blackspotted Catshark (*Aulohalaelurus labiosus*)	67 cm (26 in.)	Males 54 to 62 cm (21 to 24 in.); Females 67 cm (26 in.)
Lined Catshark (*Halaelurus lineatus*)	56 cm (22 in.)	Males 48 to 56 cm (19 to 22 in.); Females 46 to 52 cm(18 to 20 in.)
Tiger Catshark (*Halaelurus natalensis*)	47 cm (18 in.)	Males 42 to 45 cm (16 to 18 in.); Females 47 cm (18 in.)
Puffadder Shyshark (*Haploblepharus edwardsii*)	60 cm (23 in.)	Males 42 to 51 cm (16 to 20 in.); Females 41 cm (16 in.)
Brown Puffaddershark (*Haploblepharus fuscus*)	73 cm (28 in.)	Males 63 to 69 cm (25 to 27 in.); Females 60 to 73 cm (23 to 28 in.)
Dark Shyshark (*Haploblepharus pictus*)	56 cm (22 in.)	Males 56 cm (22 in.); Females 53 cm (21 in.)
Pyjama Catshark (*Poroderma africanum*)	101 cm (39 in.)	Males 58 to 78 cm (23 to 30 in.); Females 65 to 72 cm (25 to 28 in.)
Leopard Catshark (*Poroderma pantherinum*)	84 cm (33 in.)	Males 54 to 59 cm (21 to 23 in.); Females 58 to 61 cm (23 to 24 in.)
Cloudy Catshark (*Scyliorhinus torazame*)	48 cm (19 in.)	Males 41 to 48 cm (16 to 19 in.); Females 39 cm (15 in.)

*This size is for Mediterranean specimens; grows larger in British and North Sea.

Haploblepharus edwardsii (Puffadder Shyshark): African native.

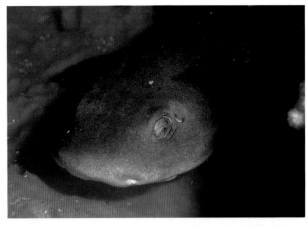

Haploblepharus fuscus (Brown Puffadder Shyshark): South African fish.

Poroderma africanum (Pyjama Catshark): from South Africa, Madagascar.

Poroderma pantherinum (Leopard Catshark): native of African waters.

Asymbolus vincenti (Gulf Catshark): native of Australia and Tasmania.

Scyliorhinus retifer (Chain Catshark): captive-breeding candidate.

once was common, possibly as a result of changes in sea temperatures.

Biology: *Cephaloscyllium ventriosum* is a rocky reef dweller that occurs at a depth range of 5 to 457 m (16 to 1,499 ft.), but is most common between depths of 5 to 37 m (16 to 121 ft.). It is most often encountered among coralline encrusted boulders and in rocky crevices in kelp forests. This shark often occurs singly or in small aggregations. The Swell Shark is oviparous, with females laying amber or green tendril egg cases that hatch in 7.5 to 10 months. Developing embryos are occasionally consumed by snails that bore through the protective casing. Grover (1972) reported that 65% of the egg cases he collected had been robbed of their contents, probably by hungry gastropods. Young have enlarged denticles along the back that allow them to escape through the small egg case exit with minimal energy expenditure. The posteriorly pointing denticles catch the edge of the egg case and give the shark leverage to push itself progressively forward and out by successive lateral movements. The denticles are lost by the time the juvenile reaches 30 cm (11.7 in.) in length.

Cephaloscyllium ventriosum is a sit-and-wait predator that takes up a nocturnal ambush site on the sandy bottom, adjacent to the reef, where Blacksmith Damselfish (*Chromis punctipinnis*) aggregate. The Swell Shark will employ two different feeding techniques to capture these refuging fish. One is the "gulp": the inactive Swell Shark rapidly opens its mouth and expands its gill and mouth cavities to suck in a Blacksmith that has come within reach. The second technique is the "yawn": when a drifting Blacksmith moves toward the Swell Shark the predator will slowly open its mouth and wait until the prey fish recklessly swims into its gaping jaws. The Swell Shark is reported to feed on bony fishes and crustaceans, although its food habits have not been studied

Cephaloscyllium ventriosum (Swell Shark): a favorite in public aquariums, but one requiring a good-sized tank and a chiller to keep water cool.

in detail. There are two ecologically similar species in this genus whose diets have been investigated extensively. I studied the Draughtsboard Shark (*Cephaloscyllium isabellum*) off southern New Zealand and found that it eats a wide range of fishes (including spiny dogfish, cod, sand perch, blennies) and invertebrates (octopuses, squids, snails, krill, hermit crabs, brachyuran crabs, spiny lobster). Some of the more unusual things that it consumes include the innkeeper worm, which the shark sucks from the worm's U-shaped burrow, and a species of stalked tunicate, known as the Sea Tulip (*Pyura pachydermatina*). The smaller Japanese or Blotchy Swell Shark (*Cephaloscyllium umbratile*) also has a very polyphagous diet, with teleost fishes being its primary prey. This sluggish-looking shark was reported to feed on 50 species of bony fishes, including morays, snake eels, conger eels, sardines, lanternfishes, lizardfishes, mackerel, dragonets, coffinfishes, scorpionfishes, flatfishes, and a species of trunkfish. Cephalopods, including squids, cuttlefishes, and octopuses, were also important prey, comprising 31% of the diet by occurrence, while other elasmobranchs made up 13.6% by occurrence. The Blotchy Swell Shark feeds on members of its own species, several other catsharks and their egg cases, the Deep-water Lanternshark (*Etmopterus unicolor*), and the electric Japanese Numbfish (*Narke japonica*). The swell sharks have a tremendous appetite. For example, a 103 cm (40.2 in.) *C. umbratile* was found to contain 10 fishes of 6 species and about 15 squid.

Captive Care: This unusual elasmobranch has long been a reliable species at public aquariums. It is a hardy shark that does best at lower temperatures than those maintained in most home aquariums. In fact, the aquarist will need to invest in a chiller to keep this shark successfully. As field studies of other swell shark species indicate, this fish cannot be trusted with invertebrate or fish tankmates. (Captive Draughtsboard Sharks have been observed to ingest spiny lobster tankmates and swim around with the antennae sticking out of the jaws for hours.) It may even eat smaller sharks, including members of its own kind. The Swell Shark will readily mate and lay eggs in captivity. The eggs are best removed from the tank after deposition, and the young sharks must be raised in a separate tank.

Aquarium Size: 988 L (260 gal.).

Water Temperature: 16 to 19°C (61 to 66°F).

Aquarium Suitability Index: 4.

Remarks: This species has nasal flaps that reach the mouth and a spotted ventral surface. Its extremely large jaws are proportionally wider than those of the Great White Shark (*Carcharodon carcharias*). The larger size of the jaws and oral cavity allows it to create a greater vacuum when inhaling prey. The dentition consists of up to 70 rows of multicuspid teeth in the upper jaw and 65 rows in the lower jaw. The greater number of small, multipronged teeth help the sharks to grasp slime-coated fishes.

Scyliorhinus canicula (Linnaeus, 1758)

Common Name: Smallspotted Catshark.

Size, Growth, and Age: This shark hatches at a length of 10 cm (3.9 in.). It attains a maximum length of 1 m (3.3 ft.) in the British Isles, while in the Mediterranean it only reaches 60 cm (23.4 in.) in length. In the Mediterranean, males become sexually mature at a length of 39 cm (15.2 in.), while females mature at 44 cm (17.2 in.).

Distribution: Eastern North Atlantic: Norway, British Isles, Mediterranean, to Ivory Coast.

Biology: This is a common temperate-water shark that inhabits rocky reefs, sand, and mud bottoms. It ranges from shallow tidepools to depths of at least 400 m (1,312 ft.). Juveniles tend to occur in shallower water than adults. Adults segregate by sex. In at least some populations, females move into nearshore habitats in the winter and are then joined by males in the spring. Toward the end of the summer months, both sexes disperse into deeper water. This shark is oviparous. It lays two tendril eggcases (4 to 7 cm [1.6 to 2.7 in.] long) at a time and 18 to 20 per breeding season. The female will swim around algae, or other suitable anchoring sites,

Scyliorhinus canicula (Smallspotted Catshark): hardy in cool water.

until extruding tendrils catch and the egg is pulled from the cloaca. The eggs hatch in 5 to 11 months, depending on water temperature. (See page 227 for additional information on the mating behavior of this species.) This catshark is inactive during the day and hunts at night. The primary components of its diet are mollusks (including squids, whelks, scallops, and clams) and crustaceans (including hermit crabs, swimming crabs, lobsters, and shrimps), but it also feeds on a variety of bony fishes (including seahorses, dragonets, goatfishes, hake, gobies, and flatfishes), polychaete worms, and sea cucumbers. Larger sharks feed more on cockles and hermit crabs, while younger sharks eat more polychaete worms. *Scyliorhinus canicula* employs an interesting behavior when feeding on shelled invertebrates: it knocks them over with its snout, grasps the animal's body in its jaws, then rips it out of its protective home by shaking its head vigorously from side to side before the upended invertebrate has a chance to retract. Most of the fishes that this shark eats are also bottom-dwellers, but more active species are also taken (e.g., herrings, pilchards, cod, jacks, and mackerels). This relatively sluggish shark may ambush these fishes as they swim past.

Captive Care: This cool-water species is sometime kept by European aquarists and by public aquariums in North America. It is a very hardy captive species that readily breeds in aquarium confines. As with some other catsharks, it must be kept at lower water temperatures and a chiller will most likely be needed.

Aquarium Size: 988 L (260 gal.).

Water Temperature: 14 to 19°C (57 to 66°F).

Aquarium Suitability Index: 4.

Remarks: In *Scyliorhinus canicula*, the second dorsal fin is smaller than the first, there are no upper labial furrows, no nasal barbels, and the nasal flaps are broad and extend to the mouth. It has many small dark and sometimes light spots over the body; eight to ten dusky saddles are often present on the back.

References

Compagno (1984b), Grover (1972), Last & Stevens (1994), Taniuchi (1988), Uchida et al. (1990).

SMOOTHHOUND SHARKS
Family Triakidae

WITH THE CLASSIC FORM and swimming style most people associate with sharks, the smoothhound family is composed of 9 genera and 38 species. Family members have well-developed dorsal fins, with the first dorsal fin positioned well ahead of the pelvic fins, elongated eyes, nictitating eyelids, no precaudal pits, and short anterior nasal flaps that are not barbel-like (except in the Whiskery Shark, *Furgaleus macki*). Most smoothhounds are drab in color and without markings, but there are some exceptions.

Although most smoothhounds occur near continental coastlines, few are indigenous to reef environments. These active sharks spend most of their time swimming just above the bottom, occasionally resting motionless on the ocean floor, but only for short periods. Members of the genus *Mustelus* are either viviparous or ovoviviparous, while those of the genus *Triakis* are ovoviviparous. Most of these sharks form large reproductive aggregations at specific times of the year, usually in shallow inshore waters. In an old account, captive male Dusky Smoothhounds (*Mustelus canis*) were observed trying to mate with each other in the absence of females. In this same study, males were reported to insert both claspers simultaneously during copulation, a rare practice in elasmobranchs. Several smoothhound species are commonly preyed upon by other sharks (e.g., Broadnosed Sevengill Sharks and Great White Sharks).

Captive Care

MANY SMOOTHHOUND SHARKS are considered good for aquarium displays. Juvenile smoothhounds do well in medium-sized tanks (70 gallons or larger), but will outgrow most home aquariums in time. Growth rates have been shown to be relatively rapid for members of the genus *Mustelus*. For example, in the wild, newborn Spotted Estuary Smoothhounds (*Mustelus lenticulatus*) grew 8 cm (3.1 in.) in as little as 6 months, and studies on the Gray Smoothhound (*Mustelus californicus*) indicate that it can grow 20 cm (7.8 in.) in 1 year's time. If a smoothhound is overfed, it may grow at an even greater rate. Males and females of most smoothhound species grow at the same rate for the first 2 to 4 years of life, but females grow faster from that point on. Depending on the species, males reach sexual maturity at an age of 1 year and 4 months to 5 years, while females mature between 2 years and 6 years 10 months.

Some of the *Mustelus* species do not exceed 100 cm (39.0 in.) in length and could be housed in larger home aquariums indefinitely. They are more active than many of the aquarium sharks, so a larger tank is a prerequisite to ensure proper care. Smoothhounds ship well, accept fresh crustaceans, fishes, and scallops (often without hesitation), and have been reported to live as long as 20 years in captivity. Fiddler crabs and small crawfish are ideal food items for these sharks. Just crush the carapace or the claws of these crustaceans before dropping

them into the aquarium so that their body fluids leak into the water. It may take a minute or more for the shark to locate the crustacean, but when it does, it will circle the prey, pick it up in its jaws, and usually swallow it whole. If the item is too large, however, the shark will rasp it against the bottom to break it into smaller morsels. The Brown Smoothhound (*Mustelus henlei*) has been observed "disarming" large cancrid crabs by grasping a claw in its mouth and shaking it free from the body of the crab. At least some members of this family are

Mustelus antarcticus (Gummy Shark): smoothhounds demand ample swimming space.

prone to thyroid hyperplasia, or goiter. Larger individuals of several species will eat juvenile sharks and rays. They will also eat lobsters, hermit crabs, crabs, mantis shrimps, shrimps, worms, snails, bivalves, and small bony fish tankmates. (Remarkably, they will swallow hermit crabs and snails shell and all.) On the other hand, I have seen smaller smoothhounds that were

Mustelus californicus (Gray Smoothhound): minimal aquascaping is the rule for these active sharks, which are athletic swimmers—and jumpers.

mauled, or even swallowed whole, by moray eels.

Because smoothhounds are more active than many aquarium elasmobranchs and generally haunt sandy areas and mudflats, which are devoid of structure, one special requirement for these sharks is that they be kept in tanks with a maximum of swimming space and no, or minimal, aquascaping. Smoothhounds are the escape artists of the shark clan: they will jump out of even the smallest opening in an aquarium top if the aquarist hasn't covered it properly. Most smoothhounds inhabit temperate seas and therefore prefer cooler water than that normally found in the tropical home aquarium; in many cases, a chiller is a prerequisite for maintaining optimal living conditions. In large public aquariums,

these sharks often fall prey to their larger relatives, and they are best housed with smaller sharks and rays. They are often hosts to copepod parasites that attach to head, body and fins. In some cases, large numbers hang on the posterior margin of the fins. The abundance of these parasites on their hosts is reported to vary from one season to the next in California waters. For example, in one study 61% of the Leopard Sharks (*Triakis semifasciata*) observed in October were parasitized by copepods, while only 7.5% of specimens examined in April hosted these crustaceans. Leeches have also been found in the mouth, claspers, and fins of these sharks (reported on 24% of 45 Leopard Sharks examined, with as many as a dozen on the claspers of a single shark).

Species Accounts

Mustelus californicus Gill, 1864

Common Name: Gray Smoothhound.

Size, Growth, and Age: The Gray Smoothhound is born 20 to 30 cm (7.8 to 11.7 in.) long and reaches a maximum length of 120 cm (46.8 in.). Males mature from 15 to 33 months, at between 57 to 65 cm (22.2 to 25.4 in.) in total length, while females reach maturity in about 25 months, at about 70 cm (27.3 in.). Males live to a maximum of about 6 years, while females reach 9 years.

Distribution: Northern California to the Gulf of California.

Biology: The Gray Smoothhound occurs in coastal waters, often in shallow intertidal areas, although it has been taken as deep as 90 m (295 ft.). Along the California coast, it inhabits estuaries and shallow muddy bays, at least during certain times of the year. During the summer months, it migrates from south to central California. Gray Smoothhounds are viviparous, giving birth to 2 to 16 young at a time. They feed primarily on crabs. Juveniles eat more grapsid crabs, while adults feed more heavily on cancrid crabs. These sharks also eat innkeeper worms, squids, shrimps, mantis shrimps, and bony fishes (e.g., midshipmen, croakers, and herrings). They apparently dig prey out of the substrate less often than does the related Leopard Shark (*Triakis semifasciata*). In California estuaries, what is thought to be this species has been observed hurling itself out of the water onto the shore in an attempt to catch shore crabs. In the Gulf of California, I examined Gray Smoothhound stomachs that were packed with krill, apparently captured by the shark taking "bites" out of krill aggregations. Talent (1982) reported the following food-distribution frequency in the Gray Smoothhound diet: crustaceans (primarily cancrid crabs, but also shrimp), 97%; innkeeper worms, 8%; fishes (including midshipmen and herrings), 7%.

Captive Care: This active shark requires an aquarium with plenty of swimming room and cooler water temperatures. This species is also likely to do better in a circular or oval-shaped tank, if space or financial limitations mean a smaller holding facility is required. It is also a master of escape and will jump out of an open aquarium.

Aquarium Size: 6,460 L (1,700 gal.).

Water Temperature: 11 to 21°C (52 to 70°F).

Aquarium Suitability Index: 3 (X-large tank required).

Remarks: The Gray Smoothhound has its first dorsal fin positioned closer to its pelvic fins than to its pectoral fins. The dorsal fins are triangular, and the ventral lobe of its tail is poorly developed. The shark has no spots and is uniformly gray in color, although some albino specimens have been reported.

Mustelus henlei (Gill, 1863)

Common Name: Brown Smoothhound.

Size, Growth, and Age: Birth size is about 20 cm (7.8 in.), with maximum lengths of 95 cm (37.1 in.) having been reported. Males mature between 52 and 66 cm (20.3 and 25.7 in.); females, between 51 and 63 cm (20.0 and 24.6 in.). Males of this species are reported to live to 7 years, while females live much longer, attaining approximately 13 years of age.

Distribution: The Brown Smoothhound ranges from northern California south to the Gulf of California, Ecuador, and Peru.

Biology: The Brown Smoothhound occurs at a depth range of less than 10 cm (3.9 in.) to 200 m (656 ft.). Although it is an active, temperate-water shark most often found over muddy or sandy substrates, it occasionally visits rocky reefs. This shark is found in San

Francisco Bay in the summer time, but in the cooler winter months it migrates to deeper, offshore waters. It returns to the Bay in May. Brown Smoothhounds occur as solitary individuals or in large schools. They are viviparous, giving birth to three to nine pups per litter. Over much of its range, crabs are this shark's primary food, but it also eats shrimps, mantis shrimps, squids, tunicates, and bony fishes (adults eat more fishes than do juveniles). In a study I carried out, 97% of the stomachs of 37 individuals examined contained large numbers of krill. Talent (1982) reported the following food-habit frequency of the Brown Smoothhound off Northern California: crustaceans (primarily crabs, but also some shrimps), 97%; bony fishes (including anchovies, gobies, and flatfishes), 36%; cephalopods (squids), 9%. My own observations in the Gulf of California found these feeding frequencies: krill, 97%; bony fishes (including hake, croakers, scorpionfishes, and sardines), 49%; mantis shrimps, 32%; squids, 16%; shrimps, 6%. In another study it was reported that of 154 individuals, only 11% had empty stomachs. This suggests that this species may feed more regularly than many tropical sharks.

Mustelus henlei (Brown Smoothhound): needs cool water, room to swim.

Captive Care: This active shark requires an aquarium with plenty of swimming room and cooler water temperatures. If space or financial limitations dictate a smaller holding facility, this species is reported to do better in a circular or oval-shaped tank that allows an uninterrupted swimming pattern. This species is more likely to suffer from shipping stress than its more sedentary relatives. It will jump out of an open aquarium. See the Captive Care section in the family account, page 121, for more husbandry information.

Aquarium Size: 4,560 L (1,200 gal.).

Water Temperature: 12 to 21°C (54 to 70°F).

Aquarium Suitability Index: 3 (X-large tank required).

Remarks: This species is similar to the Gray Smoothhound, but the posterior edges of its dorsal fins are frayed and the origin of the first dorsal fin is over the pectoral fins. It is bronze to gray above, lighter below, and has no spots.

Triakis semifasciata Girard, 1854

Common Name: Leopard Shark.

Size, Growth, and Age: This shark is born at 20 cm (7.8 in.) and while most specimens do not exceed 160 cm (62.4 in.), females are reported to attain a maximum length of 180 cm (70.2 in.). Females are sexually mature at 110 to 129 cm (42.9 to 50.3 in.). Males, by comparison, attain a total length of 150 cm (58.5 in.) and mature between 70 and 119 cm (27.3 and 46.4 in.).

Distribution: Oregon to the central coast of Mexico.

Biology: The Leopard Shark occurs at a depth range from the intertidal zone to 90 m (295 ft.). It gives birth in spring to 4 to 29 young at a time after a gestation period of 12 months, with coastal bays serving as nursery grounds. Although little information exists on its reproductive behavior, courting males are known to bite females. This shark usually occurs in coastal areas, fre-

Triakis semifasciata (Leopard Shark): unusual color variant (juvenile).

Triakis semifasciata (Leopard Shark): adult, suited to very large systems.

quenting rocky reefs as well as muddy and sandy bays. They often aggregate in shallow waters, sometimes in mixed schools with smoothhound sharks and Spiny Dogfish (*Squalus acanthias*). They will rest on the bottom, but usually swim just above it. Their diet includes crabs, shrimps, clams, innkeeper worms, octopuses, bony fishes (anchovies, herrings, surfperches, gobies, rockfishes, sculpins, and flatfishes), fish eggs, and juvenile elasmobranchs (smoothhounds, guitarfishes, and bat rays). Russo (1975a) found the following food-distribution frequencies in a study of Leopard Sharks: bony fishes (including Shiner Perch [*Cymatogaster aggregata*], anchovies, gobies, and flatfishes), 19%; fish eggs, 17%; shrimps, 17%; innkeeper worms, 16%; crabs, 16%; clams (necks only), 9%; elasmobranchs (newborn smoothhounds and bat rays), 5%. They feed on several types of invertebrates that bury in the substrate, such as innkeeper worms that are sucked from their U-shaped burrows in the mud. These soft-bodied worms are usually found completely intact in the sharks' stomachs. They also bite off clam siphons, or "necks," which protrude from mud or sand bottoms.

Captive Care: This shark is long-lived in captivity, with longevity reports of over 20 years. However, Leopard Sharks may show signs of discomfort and may even die at higher water temperatures (i.e., 28°C [82°F]), and are apparently intolerant of hypoxic (low oxygen) conditions. They can be kept at a salinity of 26 to 34 ppt. They readily accept crustacean meat: live fiddler crabs and small crayfish make great first foods. Newborn *T. semifasciata* are seasonally available, usually from mid-April to September. Some wholesalers have told me that the collection of this shark for the aquarium trade has been outlawed recently due to unscrupulous collection practices. It seems a number of collectors were taking gravid females, killing them, and removing the near-term young from their uteri for sale to aquarists who were unaware of the irresponsible and repugnant fishing methods used to procure their specimens. The Leopard Shark was already under fairly heavy fishing pressure for its flesh, and the demand for small individuals for the aquarium market put even greater pressure on the reproductive stocks. I have been told by other aquarium fish distributors that if a collector has a permit, this shark is legal to collect and sell.

Aquarium Size: 17,100 L (4,500 gal.).

Water Temperature: 13 to 21°C (55 to 70°F).

Aquarium Suitability Index: 4 (X-large tank required).

Remarks: The color of the Leopard Shark is distinctive: black saddles and spots on a gray-bronze background. Occasionally an anomalous specimen is encountered. One of these has small, numerous black spots on the flanks and larger saddles, like those found on "normal" specimens on the dorsum. Another unusual color form is silver and grayish brown overall, with some saddles on the back that merge, and others with dark outlines. One albino specimen has also been reported.

References

Compagno (1984b), Francis (1981), Limbaugh (1963), Russo (1975a, 1975b), Talent (1982), Yudin & Cailliet (1990).

REQUIEM SHARKS
Family Carcharhinidae

THIS FAMILY IS FAMILIAR TO DIVERS because a number of its well-known members are encountered on coral reefs. Although the term "requiem" generally means a religious mass or dirge for the dead—adding a sinister flavor to the reputation of this group—the word may simply come from the French *requien*, meaning shark. Features shared by all 58 described species of the 13 genera include a circular eye, nictitating eyelids, a first dorsal fin positioned well ahead of the pelvic fins, precaudal pits, and a well-developed lower caudal lobe. Most of these sharks are active predators on large invertebrates, bony fishes, and/or other elasmobranchs. They are viviparous (placental viviparity) except for Tiger Sharks (*Galeocerdo cuvier*), which are ovoviviparous (yolk sac viviparity). They range in length from 70 cm (27.3 in.) to over 5 m (16.4 ft.) and a number of requiem sharks reach over 2 m (6.6 ft.) in length. Many of these sharks make long, seasonal migrations, moving to warmer waters in cooler months. Because of the large size of these sharks and their affinity for areas frequented by humans (i.e., tropical, shallow, coastal areas), they are probably responsible for more attacks on people than any other family of sharks.

Captive Care

THE REQUIEM SHARKS ARE NOT SUITABLE for the home aquarium. There are a number of these fishes that are kept in public aquariums, although they vary in their adaptability. Some, like the Lemon Shark (*Negaprion brevirostris*), Whitetip Reef Shark (*Triaenodon obesus*), Blacktip Reef Shark (*Carcharhinus melanopterus*), Bull Shark (*C. leucas*), and Sandbar Shark (*C. plumbeus*) do well in immense shark tanks. Others, like the Tiger Shark (*Galeocerdo cuvier*), have greater difficulty acclimating to captive life. The home aquarist should not even entertain the idea of keeping a small carcharhinid (such as the Blacktip Reef Shark) unless you have a tank at least 7.9 x 3.0 x 1.8 m (20 x 10 x 6 ft.), or a circular tank that has a diameter of at least 4.6 m (15 ft.). (Some of these sharks can be kept in smaller enclosures as juveniles.) Most of us do not have the space or the finances required to set up and maintain a system of this size. I include these species here, not to recommend them, but because they are often kept in public aquariums, where amateur aquarists may see how their challenging husbandry requirements are being met by professionals. They are occasionally available in the aquarium trade; an elite minority of hobbyists have the resources and dedication to take in these big sharks.

It has been suggested that these sharks must be housed in a circular or oval tank if they are going to survive in captivity. Although there are some advantages to a tank of this shape, if space is limited, carcharhinids can be successfully housed in rectangular aquariums. What is imperative is that they have enough room to beat their tails several times and then glide for several body lengths before they have to divert their course (the critical part of the swimming cycle is the glide period). This is true for the majority of requiem sharks. If they do not have a tank that allows for them to swim efficiently, they use too much energy for locomotion and will soon become fatigued. The carcharhinid aquarium should have little or no decor, as these sharks are apt to collide with it when startled or excited by the presence of food. This is especially important as they get larger and swimming space becomes even more limited. If decor is included, be sure there are uncluttered glide paths.

Some of the carcharhinids can be easily frightened. When startled they will dash about the aquarium and may run into aquascaping or even the sides of the tank. This can cause severe injuries or even death. Requiem sharks with damaged snouts are often seen in undersized tanks or in aquariums with too much decor. These sharks may also swim along the circumference of the aquarium, rubbing their pectoral fins against the sides of the container. If the tank is fiberglass or concrete, this can cause damage to the fins. To prevent this, you can add bumper bars. Take pieces of PVC pipe, wrap them with polyurethane foam of a contrasting color, and place them vertically along the sides of the aquarium at about 1 m (3.3 ft.) intervals. These will act to keep the shark from rubbing against the sides of the tank. It is also a good idea to form polyurethane foam barriers around any aquarium equipment hanging in the tank. This will prevent requiem

Carcharhinus perezi (Caribbean Reef Shark): best viewed in the wild or in spacious oceanariums.

sharks from damaging themselves if they crash into it. Remember, any abrasion or cut caused by such a collision is a site for bacterial infection.

Requiem sharks kept with others of their own species, or with other family members, may exhibit putative intestinal biting syndrome (see page 205). This can lead to the death of those individuals that are bitten. At least some of the species are known to suffer from trematode infestations, nutritional deficiencies, and thyroid hyperplasia. Do not treat carcharhinids with copper. Many of these sharks are highly predatory, capturing and eating any fish tankmates, either bony or cartilaginous, that they subdue. Transporting these sharks can be difficult (it usually requires a large "live well") and very expensive. Some don't fare well during the transport process.

Species Accounts

Carcharhinus melanopterus (Quoy & Gaimard, 1824)

Common Name: Blacktip Reef Shark.

Size, Growth, and Age: The length at birth is 33 to 52 cm (12.9 to 20.1 in.), while adults can attain a maximum length of 180 cm (70.2 in.). In the Indian Ocean, males mature at a maximum length of about 105 cm (41.0 in.), females reach sexual maturation at about 110 cm (42.9 in.) and both sexes grow an average of 2.9 mm (0.1 in.) per month. Off northern Australia, male Blacktip Reef Sharks are sexually mature at 95 cm (37.1 in.), while females are sexually mature at 97 cm (37.8 in.).

Distribution: From the Red Sea east to the Society Islands, north to Japan, and south to New Caledonia and Australia. Also reported from the eastern Mediterranean, emigrating from the Red Sea via the Suez Canal.

Biology: The Blacktip Reef Shark is common around shallow-water reefs in the Indo-Pacific. This is truly a shallow-water shark, occurring at depths of 20 cm (7.8 in.) to 10 m (33 ft.). Females give birth to three or four pups after a gestation period of 8 to 9 months. In northern Australia, this species mates in summer and fall and drops its young in the spring. Surprisingly little is known about the reproductive behavior of this ubiquitous reef dweller. There is one report of a pair of these sharks copulating in a venter-to-venter posture in shal-

Carcharhinus melanopterus (Blacktip Reef Shark): fast and eyecatching.

low water. This species inhabits lagoons and will aggregate in reef channels at low tide, moving onto the reef flat as the tide comes in. It utilizes a limited home range of about 2.5 km² (about 1 mi.²) and feeds on reef fishes (including wrasses, triggerfishes, parrotfishes, goatfishes), squids, octopuses, crabs, and mantis shrimps. In some areas, snakes are an important component of its diet. For example, in northern Australia, 23% of 74 Blacktip stomachs containing food included snake remains. In one food-distribution study of Blacktip Reef Sharks in northern Australia, Lyle (1987) found the following: bony fishes, 67%; mollusks (squids and octopuses), 23%; snakes, 23%; crustaceans (shrimps and mantis shrimps), 5%.

A fast-swimming predator that has been observed chasing down surgeonfishes and stingrays, the Blacktip Reef Shark has also been observed attacking aggregations of spawning surgeonfishes, and groups of these sharks will drive and trap schools of mullet inshore for a feeding assault. There is even one report of Blacktip Reef Sharks chasing schooling fish onto shore and sliding up onto the beach to capture them. This shark is not without its enemies: it is preyed upon by other sharks and large groupers.

Captive Care: The Blacktip Reef Shark makes a good display animal for very large aquariums. (Individuals between 45 and 90 cm [17.6 and 35.1 in.] are ideal for transport and acclimation.) It is handsome, with attractive markings, and it fits the image of the stereotypical shark. Blacktips are more expensive than any other shark normally available to the private aquarist. They are also expensive to ship. Collectors send them in large shipping bags enclosed in wooden crates. The added weight of the crate as well as the large amounts of water needed to sustain the animal during shipping greatly increase the freight costs. This shark has been reported to live in a shipping bag in excess of 24 hours. Captive Blacktip Reef Sharks are easily startled by abrupt movements or the sudden entry of a diver into their tank. In one reported incident, two of these sharks, startled by a careless aquarist, raced across the tank, collided with the aquarium wall, and died. These sharks might also jump out of an open tank if frightened. Entering or approaching a tank that contains one of these sharks should be done very slowly so that the shark can adjust to your presence. It has been suggested that Blacktip Reef Sharks acquired at smaller sizes are less "flighty" as they grow larger.

On one central Pacific island, these sharks were captured using a trained Labrador retriever. The dog would chase the small sharks into shallow water, grab them in her mouth, and carry them to her owner on the shore. The more conventional methods used to capture these shallow-water sharks include cast nets, fishing with barbless hooks, and herding into seines or barrier nets. This shark is host to a monogenetic trematode known as *Dermophthirius melanopteri*. This parasite often causes white patches to develop on the skin of captive Black-

tips. Putative intestinal biting syndrome is also not uncommon in captive colonies of these sharks (see page 205 for more on this malady).

Aquarium Size: 21,850 L (5,750 gal.).
Water Temperature: 22 to 28°C (72 to 82°F).
Aquarium Suitability Index: 4 (X-large tank required).
Remarks: This is a fast-moving, eyecatching shark that always has distinct black markings on the first dorsal and lower lobe of the caudal fin, while the other fins have less defined black tips or margins. There is no interdorsal ridge. The snout is bluntly rounded.

Negaprion brevirostris (Poey, 1868)
Common Name: Lemon Shark.
Size, Growth, and Age: The Lemon Shark is born at a length of 60 to 65 cm (23.4 to 25.4 in.) and attains a maximum length of 3.4 m (11 ft.). This shark is estimated to grow from 10 to 20 cm per year (3.9 to 7.8 in.), although captive specimens have exhibited growth rates as rapid as 70 cm (27.3 in.) per year. Young sharks can double their weight in as little as 100 days if fed 3% of their body weight daily. In the wild, these sharks apparently do not reach sexual maturity until they are at least 12 years of age. It would take over 20 years for this shark to reach maximum size.
Distribution: This common reef-dwelling species is often observed in shallow water in the Caribbean. Its range includes the Western Atlantic from New Jersey to southern Brazil, the East African coast, and the Eastern Pacific from the Gulf of California to Ecuador.
Biology: The Lemon Shark occurs in shallow intertidal areas to 92 m (302 ft.). The females drop their young in shallow bays and lagoons, often in mangrove swamps. The juveniles are common on sand flats and in mangrove lagoons, while adults are also found in lagoons as well as off the fore reef in deeper water. This shark is

viviparous, with litters ranging in size from 4 to 17. When they court, the male swims next to the female and bites her. This is a solitary species that will aggregate in preferred habitats, often in association with schools of jacks. Lemon Sharks cover a home range of from 18 to 93 km² (7 to 36 mi.²), with younger sharks ranging over a smaller area than adults. This shark is most active at twilight. The primary food of juveniles is bony fishes (including toadfishes and pinfishes) and shrimps, while adults feed mainly on bony fishes (including catfishes, mullets, jacks, croakers, spiny boxfishes, and cowfishes) and elasmobranchs (including guitarfishes, stingrays, and other sharks), but also eat crabs, sea birds, and conchs. This species will bite if provoked and is suspected of being involved in unprovoked attacks on humans. They are not generally aggressive toward divers when feeding stimuli are not present, but have been observed carrying out a possibly agonistic display consisting of figure-8 swimming and jaw gaping.

Captive Care: Although a wonderful shark for public aquarium and for use in laboratory studies, this shark gets much too large for home aquariums. Even so, it is occasionally available to hobbyists. Gruber (1980) suggests that up to 1 kg (2.2 lbs.) of Lemon Shark can be housed per 99 L (26 gal.) of water in a well-kept system. This shark will often move around the periphery of the aquarium and may rub its fins against the side or collide with aquarium decor. This can cause injuries, which may result in bacterial infections, fasting, and even death. Therefore, it is best to limit or (even better) to exclude decor in a Lemon Shark aquarium. Also, surround submerged equipment with polyurethane foam to buffer collisions. Feed this shark to satiation every 2 or 3 days. Offer bite-sized pieces of fish to prevent uneaten scraps from decomposing in the tank and causing deadly bacterial blooms. This shark is often host to the monogenetic trematode *Dermophthirius nigrellii*. Trematodes often lead to more virulent bacterial infections. White lesions will appear on the body, which will erupt if left untreated. Death is usually soon to follow. (See Chapter 7 for trematode treatment options.) Gruber (1980) also reports a condition that seems to be unique, or at least much more common, in *N. brevirostris*. The head and anterior portion of the body (i.e., in front of the pectoral fins) will curve to one side. The shark will also swim in circles. The affected animal often continues to feed and may eventually recover. This malady is caused by a lack of vitamin B_1 in the diet. Addition of this vitamin to the food will quickly reverse this condition. Individual may also suffer from putative intestinal biting syndrome, that is, if more than one *N. brevirostris* is kept in the same tank. Individuals suffering from this condition will become paler in color, will

Negaprion brevirostris (Lemon Shark): great subject for professional aquarists.

cease to feed, and will stop swimming. If not treated, they will usually die in 5 to 10 days. This shark will consume ray and bony fish tankmates. It might also bite the aquarist.

Aquarium Size: 37,620 L (9,900 gal.).

Water Temperature: 22 to 28°C (72 to 82°F).

Aquarium Suitability Index: 4 (X-large tank required).

Remarks: The Lemon Shark is easily recognized by its two similar-sized dorsal fins set forward on the body, its broad, rounded snout, and its light, often yellowish, body color. The related **Sicklefin Lemon Shark** (*Negaprion acutidens*) **(Rüppell, 1837)**, from the Indo-Pacific, has more falcate fins, and the teeth of larger individuals are more deeply serrated than those of the Lemon Shark. The geographical ranges of the Lemon and the Sicklefin Lemon do not overlap. *Negaprion acutidens* is also kept in public aquariums.

Triaenodon obesus (Rüppell, 1837)

Common Name: Whitetip Reef Shark.

Size, Growth, and Age: The birth length is 56 cm (21.8 in.), and the maximum length is 2.1 m (6.9 ft.).

Distribution: The Whitetip Reef Shark is a ubiquitous coral-reef dweller found at many popular diving sites in the Eastern Pacific and Indo-Pacific. One world-renowned destination for observing these fish is the Cocos Islands, where they can be seen in large aggregations, sometimes piled next to each other like stacks of wood. They are also frequently observed in the Hawaiian Islands, French Polynesia, Fiji, the Great Barrier Reef, the Maldive Islands, and the Red Sea.

Biology: The Whitetip Reef Shark occurs on coral and rocky reefs from the intertidal zone to a depth of 40 m (131 ft.). It often rests in caves, under ledges, or in reef gutters during the day. On coral reefs, Whitetips are found in lagoons, reef flats, and on the fore reef, where

Triaenodon obesus (Whitetip Reef Shark): common on Indo-Pacific reefs.

they are most abundant. This shark bears from one to five young in a litter after a gestation period of 13 months. These sharks have been observed courting and copulating in the wild and in large oceanariums. Sexually receptive females are followed by 1 to as many as 11 males. The males will bite the gill area of the female and attempt to seize her pectoral fin. When a male succeeds in grasping the pectoral fin, he will twist his body under hers and insert a single clasper. The pair will lie motionless on the seafloor, with their bodies parallel, for 1.5 to 3 minutes.

Whitetip Reef Sharks are most active at night, when they leave their diurnal resting sites to hunt for food. After dark, they ferret about the reef, plunging their heads into cracks and crevices in search of sleeping fishes (including eels, parrotfishes, goatfishes, snappers, damselfishes, surgeonfishes, and triggerfishes), crabs, lobsters, and octopuses. Hungry Whitetips will twist and turn violently in their attempts to penetrate deeper into crevices, with some sharks squirming into a hole in one side of a coral head only to exit through an opening on the other side. They will break off pieces of coral during these zealous forays and sometimes tear their skin and fins. In one observation, Whitetips chased and caught Panamic Soldierfish (*Myripristis leiognathus*) that were feeding over the reef and snapped at Pacific Trumpetfish (*Aulostomus chinensis*) and Pacific Creolefish (*Paranthias colonus*) that had been stirred from slumber by their frenetic activity. Although most hunting activity appeared to occur at night, Whitetips were observed to take advantage of unusual feeding opportunities during the day as well. After their nocturnal forays, individuals often return to the same cave or crevice every day, sometimes for years. Whitetip Reef Sharks range over an area that probably does not exceed several square kilometers (approximately 1 sq. mi.). At Cocos Island, Costa Rica, I observed groups of juvenile Mexican Hogfish (*Bodianus diplotaenia*) picking at the first dorsal fin, head, and probing the gills of resting Whitetip Reef Sharks. Redhead Gobies (*Gobiosoma puncticulatus*) would also inspect and clean their bodies and even swim into their mouths. Sometimes a number of gobies would clean a resting Whitetip in concert with a group of juvenile Mexican Hogfish (*Bodianus diplotaenia*). Whitetips disturbed by the observer while being cleaned would circle and settle in the same spot once the observer left. It may be that these resting areas (sand patches among large boulders) are cleaning stations visited by sharks for the primary purpose of being relieved of parasites. Whitetip Reef Sharks are also cleaned by cleaner wrasses (*Labroides* spp.) and possibly by Golden Jacks (*Gnathanodon speciosus*), which are sometimes seen swimming alongside them or in front of their snouts.

Captive Care: Because of its less active lifestyle and its being adapted to the highly structured coral reef environment, this shark typically does very well in larger aquariums. It can be quite destructive to aquarium decor as it works its way in between or under rocks and/or corals trying to get to hidden food. It often suffers from goiter, if water quality is allowed to deteriorate and/or an iodine supplement is not given. This species has bred in large public aquariums. In fact, one such facility in Japan has raised several generations of Whitetip Reef Sharks. It may be an even better candidate for shipping and acclimating than the Blacktip.

Aquarium Size: 31,920 L (8,400 gal.).
Water Temperature: 22 to 28°C (72 to 82°F).
Aquarium Suitability Index: 5 (X-large tank required).
Remarks: This species has a very broad snout. The pectoral and dorsal fins have pointed tips; the first dorsal and caudal fins have white tips. The dorsal surface and flanks are gray to brown, sometimes with darker blotches.

References

Gruber (1980), Gruber & Keyes (1981), Gruber & Stout (1983), Gruber et al. (1988), J. Hemdal (personal communication), Lyle (1987), Randall (1977), Stevens (1984b), Tricas & LeFeuvre (1985), Uchida (1982).

HAMMERHEAD SHARKS
Family Sphyrnidae

THE HAMMERHEADS ARE CONSPICUOUS members of the shark clan because of the lateral extensions of the head, which form a winglike structure known scientifically as the cephalofoil. Otherwise, these sharks are similar in form to the requiem sharks. There is much speculation concerning the function of the unusual head morphology. It may aid in locomotion, serving as a bow plane to increase lift and maneuverability. It may enhance electroreceptive, olfactory, and visual perception by spreading the sense organs over a broader area. It is also used to pin stingrays to the ocean bottom. There are eight hammerhead species currently recognized that range in size from 1 m (3.3 ft.) to over 5 m (17 ft.) in length. They are found in temperate and tropical coastal habitats, with several species occurring on or near reefs where they take refuge, hunt, and are cleaned by resident cleaner fishes (this has been observed in one species). These sharks are viviparous (placental viviparity); the near-term embryos have flexible "hammers" that are bent back toward the tail to facilitate birthing. Some species move from deeper water into the shallows to give birth. Several species form large schools and undergo long north-south seasonal migrations.

Captive Care

THE HAMMERHEADS HAVE A DUBIOUS RECORD when it comes to captive survival. Most species do poorly in confinement, ramming into the sides of their aquarium homes. They tend to suffer from collecting stress, and often recover only with difficulty. The Bonnethead Shark does do well in larger aquariums, while the larger species suffer capture and handling stress and rarely adapt to life in the oceanarium.

Species Account

Sphyrna tiburo (Linnaeus, 1758)
Common Name: Bonnethead Shark.
Size, Growth, and Age: This species is born at a length of about 37 cm (14.4 in.) and attains a maximum length of 1.5 m (4.9 ft.). Juveniles grow approximately 3 cm (1.2 in.) a month in the first year. Females and males grow at a similar rate initially, but male growth slows at 1+ and 2+ years of age, while females grow more slowly at an age of 3+ to 4+ years. Sexual maturity occurs in males at about 2 years and between 2 and 3 years in females. The natural lifespan has been estimated to be

Sphyrna tiburo (Bonnethead Shark): a hammerhead for expert keepers.

around 12 years for females and about 8 years for males.
Distribution: From North Carolina to Brazil in the Western Atlantic and from southern California to Ecuador in the Eastern Pacific.
Biology: *Sphyrna tiburo* occurs at depths from the intertidal zone to 80 m (262 ft.), although it is most abundant in the shallower portions of this range. It is much more common in shallow bays and estuaries, over sand and mud flats or seagrass meadows. There is one report of a young Bonnethead that was collected in freshwater (salinity 0 ppt) 64 km (38 mi.) up the Trent River, North Carolina. This species gives birth all year round, after a gestation of 4.5 to 5 months, with most parturition occurring in August and September (at least in those populations studied most extensively). Nursery areas are usually in estuaries and shallow bays. The size of their litters vary from 4 to 16 pups, with larger females giving birth to larger litters. Although the Bonnethead's diet can include mantis shrimps, bivalves, barnacles, isopods, squids, octopuses, and fishes (in-

cluding snake eels), it feeds most heavily on swimming crabs and penaeid shrimps. For example, in a study that examined the stomachs of 355 *S. tiburo* individuals, crustaceans (mainly blue crabs) occurred in 88.9% of those containing food. Seagrasses, which are probably taken incidentally with their crustacean prey, were found in 56% of the stomachs. Food-habit studies also suggest that this species feeds more frequently and/or the rate of gastric evacuation is slower than any other shark species studied to date. This species is thought to be equally active during both the day and the night, swimming at a velocity from about 27 cm/sec. (0.36 body lengths/sec.) to about 61.5 cm/sec. (0.82 body lengths/sec.).

This gregarious species typically occurs in small groups (i.e., 3 to 15 individuals), but is also known to form massive migratory schools numbering in the hundreds. Although overt aggression is not common, it does engage in a number of different body postures and action patterns, some of which are agonistic in intent. For example, an individual Bonnethead may swim over the top of another and "hit" the shark below it with the edge of its head. The shark that is "hit" swims off, often bearing a slight contusion in the area where it was struck. A study conducted on a captive colony of Bonnetheads demonstrated that this species forms linear dominance hierarchies, with the size and sex of an individual determining its position in the "pecking order." As the group swam about their enclosure, subordinate individuals would "give way" to dominant specimens (that is, they would change their course to avoid colliding with the dominant shark). In nature, subadult and adult Bonnetheads often aggregate by sex, with females moving into shallower water during the birthing season.

Captive Care: The Bonnethead is occasionally available in the aquarium trade. Although it is a fascinating display animal, it demands an immense aquarium and the sort of expert care offered by good public aquariums. When first added to an aquarium, this shark will often swim near the surface and lift the front of its head out of the water. The shark will discontinue or engage in this behavior less frequently once it has settled in. It is a very active species, perennially cruising around the circumference of its living quarters. It typically occurs in habitats that are devoid of topographical features. If placed in a decor-filled tank it will usually end up injuring itself. The Bonnethead should be fed a diet of fresh squid, shrimp, crab, and marine fish flesh. It is best fed to satiation every other day. An occasional specimen will start to swim in circles in the water column. As time passes, the shark spins in tighter and tighter circles until it finally dies. This unusual behavior often begins weeks after the shark has been successfully acclimated and may go on for as long as a month before the shark perishes. It has been suggested that it results from spinal meningitis brought on by shipping stress.

Aquarium Size: 9,880 L (2,600 gal.).

Water Temperature: 25 to 29°C (77 to 84°F).

Aquarium Suitability Index: 3 (X-large tank required).

Remarks: The Bonnethead Shark has a shovel-shaped head with no indentation. The similar **Scoophead Shark (*Sphyrna media*) Springer, 1940** has a mallet-shaped head, a dorsal fin free tip that is over or behind the origin of the pelvic fin, and unnotched posterior pelvic fin margins. The Scoophead ranges from Panama to southern Brazil in the Western Atlantic and from the Gulf of California to Ecuador in the Eastern Pacific.

References

Carlson & Parsons (1997), Cortés & Parsons (1996), Cortés et al. (1996), Myrberg & Gruber (1974), Parsons & Killam (1991), M. Schuler (personal communication).

GUITARFISHES AND THORNBACK RAYS
Family Rhinobatidae and Family Platyrhinidae

GUITARFISHES HAVE SIMILARITIES to both the sharks and rays and are identified by the placement of the first dorsal fin (which is behind the base of the pelvic fins) and the absence of a lower caudal lobe. There are 43 species in this family, and to casual observers, many of them seem indistinguishable from one another. However, characteristics such as snout shape and length, spiracle shape, nostril morphology, presence or absence of spines along the back and tubercles on the snout, color pattern, and orientation of nostrils relative to the mouth can assist in identification. The largest guitarfishes reach lengths of around 2 m (6.6 ft.), and all are ovoviviparous (yolk sac viviparity). No information is available on their mating behavior, but males have been observed to follow females closely. They spend much of their time lying on sand or seagrass. When startled, they race away, not by undulating the disc like a stingray, but by using lateral, sharklike strokes of their tail fins. Guitarfishes are common near continental coastlines, but rarely near oceanic islands. Several species occur in estuaries and even in freshwater, and some segregate by sex and make seasonal migrations.

APPROXIMATELY FIVE SPECIES ARE IN THE THORNBACK ray family. They are similar in overall appearance to the guitarfishes, but differ in having two slender pieces of cartilage extending from the skull to the tip of the snout (rhinobatids have only one), a broadly rounded snout, and one or three rows of large, curved tubercles (the "thorns") running down the back and the tail. As far as their systematic standing is concerned, thornback rays are thought to be intermediate between the torpedo rays and the guitarfishes. Thornbacks do not exceed 1 m (3.3 ft.) in total length. All of these rays are benthic, occurring on soft sand and mud bottoms. Although at least one species inhabits shallow coastal areas, most occur in deeper offshore waters. They eat infaunal (sediment-dwelling) invertebrates, and most are ovoviviparous (yolk sac viviparity), but there is an unverified report of one species laying skatelike egg cases. They occur in the Eastern Pacific and near Japan, China, India, and West Africa.

Captive Care

ALTHOUGH NONE OF THE GUITARFISHES or thornback rays are common in aquarium stores, a few species do show up occasionally. All of the guitarfishes require generous areas of open space (a tank with a lot of surface area and minimal aquascaping), and most will more readily adapt if provided with sand in which to bury. The guitarfishes are good-sized animals, so an extra-large aquarium is a prerequisite for long-term maintenance. Some specimens require live foods to catalyze a feeding response, while others are less particular. Most do best if there are no decorations in the tank. They may bury near stacks of rocks and coral, causing these decorations to topple on them, or damage their soft undersides when they swim against the abrasive surfaces. These rays will feed on small fishes that they can consume whole, or may maul larger individuals if they can trap them against the aquarium sides or bottom. They should not be housed with angelfishes, pufferfishes, or triggerfishes, as these will nip at their tails and eyes. Thornback rays and several species of guitarfishes do well in large public aquariums, but some guitarfishes fail to adapt to captive confines. Copper is tolerated at low levels but use trichlorfon with caution.

Species Accounts (Rhinobatidae)

Rhinobatos lentiginosus Garman, 1880

Common Name: Atlantic Guitarfish.

Size, Growth, and Age: The maximum length of this species is 76 cm (29.6 in.). Males of about 51 cm (19.9 in.) display well-developed claspers and are thought to be sexually mature.

Distribution: From North Carolina to Yucatan, Mexico, including the Gulf of Mexico.

Rhinobatos lentiginosus (Atlantic Guitarfish): a courting pair off Florida.

Biology: The Atlantic Guitarfish occurs at depths ranging from the intertidal zone to 20 m (66 ft.) and is found on sand and mud bottoms, in seagrass beds, and near lagoon patch reefs. It gives birth to as many as six young at a time. Little is known about the reproductive biology of *R. lentiginosus*; the related Brazilian Guitarfish (*Rhinobatos horkelii*) migrates into shallow water to mate and to drop its young. After parturition and copulation, the females return to deep water in March and April, but the fertilized eggs do not begin to develop until the females return to the shallows the following December. Egg development may be catalyzed by the move into warmer, shallower water and birth occurs 4 months later. *Rhinobatos lentiginosus* feeds on mollusks and crustaceans.

Captive Care: Although uncommon, the Atlantic Guitarfish is one of several guitarfishes in the genus *Rhinobatos* to appear in North American aquarium stores.

Aquarium Size: 760 L (200 gal.).

Water Temperature: 20 to 28°C (68 to 82°F).

Aquarium Suitability Index: 3.

Remarks: The disc of this species is nearly as broad as it is long, the rostral cartilage is expanded at the tip, and the snout has tubercles on its end. The origin of the first dorsal fin is posterior to the tips of the pelvic fins by a distance equal to that between the origin of the first dorsal fin and its free tip. This species is gray to brown dorsally, with many (several hundred) small white spots (rarely, individuals lack spots). The **Southern Guitarfish** (*Rhinobatos percellens*) **(Walbaum, 1792)** is a similar species that has no enlarged tubercles on the end of the snout, and the rostral cartilage is narrower toward the tip. This species may or may not have spots, but when it does, they are fewer (40 to 45) and larger than those of the Atlantic Guitarfish, and occur along each side of the trunk. The Southern Guitarfish ranges from the Caribbean to western Argentina. A third species, the **Brazilian Guitarfish (*R. horkelii*) Müller & Henle, 1841**, is plain in color, has no enlarged tubercles on the expanded snout tip, and the origin of the first dorsal fin is posterior to the tips of the pelvic fins by a distance about equal to the base of the first dorsal fin. The Brazilian Guitarfish ranges from Brazil north to the Lesser Antilles, and might now be seen more often by aquarists because of increased collecting in this area.

Rhinobatos productus Girard, 1854

Common Name: Shovelnose Guitarfish.

Size, Growth, and Age: This species is born at 20 to 24 cm (7.8 to 9.4 in.) and can attain a maximum length of 1.7 m (5.6 ft.), although most do not exceed 1.5 m (4.9 ft.). Large females can weigh over 18 kg (40 lbs.). The males reach sexual maturity at a length of 90 to 100 cm (35.1 to 39.0 in.), at which time their claspers develop quite rapidly. The claspers of mature males usually measure in excess of 13 cm (5.1 in.) and have well-developed spurs. Females reach sexual maturity at a total length of 99 cm (38.6 in.), at an estimated age of 7 years. This species is thought to live to a maximum age of 11 years.

Distribution: Central California to the Gulf of California.

Biology: This species occurs at depths ranging from the intertidal zone to over 13 m (43 ft.). It often occurs in shallow embayments, resting on sandy bottoms (where it often lies partially buried by day), or among seagrass. This ray is a fairly fecund species, with litters numbering from 6 to 16 (some have suggested up to 28). It can be solitary or in aggregates, sometimes in impressive numbers. There is some evidence that suggests that this species segregates by sex. The Shovelnose Guitarfish feeds nocturnally on worms, clams, crabs, and both benthic and midwater fishes. When eating clams, it masticates them, spits out the fragments, then reingests the meat. Juveniles of this species have been taken from the stomachs of large Leopard Sharks (*Triakis semifasciata*). Talent (1982) examined the stomachs of 82 individuals, of which 95% contained food. This suggests that this elasmobranch may feed continuously, rather than intermittently, like many sharks. It is harmless to humans, although there is one report of an apparently amorous male biting a diver.

Captive Care: The Shovelnose Guitarfish will require

Rhinobatos productus (Shovelnose Guitarfish): needs sand for refuge.

an extra-large tank with a 7 cm (2.7 in.) layer of fine coral sand on the bottom. The aquarium should be devoid of aquascaping, allowing plenty of unobstructed swimming room. This species will usually accept fresh fish and has been reported to survive in captivity for 8 to 10 years. *Rhinobatos productus* has been reported to breed in large public aquariums.

Aquarium Size: 3,135 L (825 gal.).

Water Temperature: 13 and 21°C (55 and 70°F).

Aquarium Suitability Index: 3 (X-large tank required).

Remarks: The Shovelnose Guitarfish has a disc that is longer than it is wide, rostral cartilage that is narrow at the tip with no large tubercles, and a row of spines down the middle of its back. It is brown dorsally, with occasional gray spots.

Trygonorrhina sp.

Common Name: Eastern Fiddler Ray.

Size, Growth, and Age: This species is born at about 25 cm (9.8 in.), and is reported to attain a maximum length of 120 cm (46.8 in.), although the largest reliably measured is 92 cm (35.9 in.).

Distribution: Southern Queensland to New South

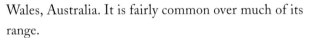

Trygonorrhina sp. (Eastern Fiddler Ray): readily available species.

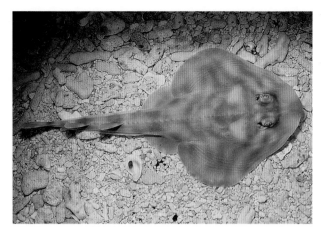

Zapteryx brevirostris (Shortnosed Guitarfish): delightful Brazilian import.

Wales, Australia. It is fairly common over much of its range.

Biology: This fiddler ray occurs from the intertidal zone to depths of 100 m (328 ft.). It is usually found on sandy bottoms and in seagrass beds, sometimes in the vicinity of rocky reefs and jetties. It has also been found in estuaries. The Eastern Fiddler lies on sand or buries underneath it. It is also found on smooth coralline algae-encrusted boulders. This species is ovoviviparous. The egg capsules, which hatch in the uteri, are golden in coloration and contain two or three embryos each. It is reported to feed on mollusks, worms, crustaceans, and fishes.

Captive Care: In recent years, the Eastern Fiddler Ray has become readily available in the North American aquarium trade. It is a durable, handsome species that will thrive in a larger home aquarium. It is not a great threat to teleost tankmates (although it may eat small, slumbering fishes), but it will consume invertebrates. This ray will feed on most foods that reach the bottom of the aquarium, but may have difficulty competing with more nimble bony fishes. It has been known to reproduce in larger public aquariums.

Aquarium Size: 2,128 L (560 gal.).
Water Temperature: 18 to 21°C (64 to 70°F).
Aquarium Suitability Index: 3.
Remarks: This apparently undescribed fiddler ray species is often misidentified as the **Southern Fiddler Ray (*Trygonorrhina fasciata*) Müller & Henle, 1841**. The two are readily distinguished by the distinctive dark triangle or diamond-shaped marking behind the eyes of the Eastern Fiddler Ray. (*Trygonorrhina fasciata* has three pale stripes instead of the dark triangle.) The most highly sought after member of this genus is the **Magpie Fiddler Ray (*Trygonorrhina melaleuca*) Scott, 1954**, which is bluish black on the dorsal with a white or pale disc margin. This rare fiddler has only been reported from St. Vincent's Gulf, South Australia.

Zapteryx brevirostris (Müller & Henle, 1841)
Common Name: Shortnosed Guitarfish.
Size, Growth, and Age: The largest specimen reported in the literature was 54 cm (21.1 in.), but it has been suggested that it can attain a maximum length of about 90 cm (35.1 in.).
Distribution: Endemic to Brazil.

TABLE 4-3.

Size Comparisons of Western Atlantic Guitarfishes

Species	Size at Birth	Maximum length	Male Length at Maturity
Atlantic Guitarfish (*Rhinobatos lentiginosus*)	20 cm (7.9 in.)	76 cm (30 in.)	<51 cm (20 in.)
Southern Guitarfish (*Rhinobatos percellens*)	21 cm (8.3 in.)	99 cm (39 in.)	<56 cm (22 in.)
Brazilian Guitarfish (*Rhinobatos horkelii*)	unknown	~110 cm (43 in.)	>70 cm (27 in.)

Biology: This species is known to be ovoviviparous. No other information is available on its biology.

Captive Care: In recent years, more fishes have been shipped from Brazil, including this ray. It is a delightful aquarium fish and adapts readily if provided with plenty of swimming room and a fine sandy bottom. Live grass shrimp will help induce a feeding response in those specimens reluctant to feed. I have seen this species attract small shrimps by forming a pseudo cave. It did this by lifting its anterior disc margin off the bottom and remaining still. When one of the little crustaceans went to hide under the "overhang," the ray slammed down its disc and consumed the shrimp.

Aquarium Size: 760 L (200 gal.).

Water Temperature: 22 to 27°C (72 to 81°F).

Aquarium Suitability Index: 3.

Remarks: This species is very similar to *Z. exasperata* (see below), but differs in having rostral ridges that converge near the tips, dorsal fin posterior margins that are longer than their bases, and no dorsal bands.

Zapteryx exasperata (Jordan & Gilbert, 1880)

Common Name: Banded Guitarfish.

Size, Growth, and Age: This species is born at a length of about 20 cm (7.8 in.), and attains a maximum length of 91 cm (35.5 in.). Males mature at about 69 cm (26.9 in.).

Distribution: Southern California to Panama.

Biology: The Banded Guitarfish occurs from the intertidal zone to a depth of 22 m (72 ft.). It is common on rocky reefs, where it is found lying on smooth rock substrates, in caves, and under ledges. It has also been reported from tidepools. This species rarely buries in the sand but is often seen with its head under a ledge. Females give birth to 4 to 11 pups per litter.

Captive Care: The Banded Guitarfish is not common in the marine aquarium trade, but it does show up occasionally. It is a relatively hardy fish if provided with fine sand in which to bury, a sturdy ledge under which it can hide, a large tank, and live food (at least initially).

Aquarium Size: 1,140 L (300 gal.).

Zapteryx exasperata (Banded Guitarfish): seldom collected for sale.

Platyrhinoidis triseriata (Thornback Ray): shown feeding on squid eggs.

Water Temperature: 18 to 23°C (64 to 73°F).

Aquarium Suitability Index: 3.

Remarks: Notable features of this species include a moderately rounded snout, parallel rostral ridges that do not converge, prominent spines on the back, and dorsal fins with posterior margins shorter than their bases. The Banded Guitarfish is grayish brown with dark brown bands traversing the dorsum; some specimens have yellow spots, as big as the pupil, outlined in black.

Species Account (Platyrhinidae)

Platyrhinoidis triseriata (Jordan & Gilbert, 1881)

Common Names: Thornback Ray, Thornback.

Size, Growth, and Age: This species attains a maximum length of 91 cm (35.5 in.), and can weigh up to 2.7 kg (6 lbs.).

Distribution: From Central California to Baja California, Mexico.

Biology: The Thornback Ray occurs at depths ranging from the intertidal zone to 50 m (164 ft.). It is found on sand and mud bottoms and sometimes in kelp beds. Diurnally, solitary individuals or small groups are often found partially buried in the substrate; at night, they emerge to feed on worms, mollusks, and crustaceans (including crabs, shrimps, and isopods). This species breeds in August and September.

Captive Care: The Thornback Ray should be housed in a large aquarium with a fine sand substrate and no aquascaping. It will eat invertebrate tankmates and may ingest bottom-dwelling fishes. Its eye may be a target for nipping species, such as puffers and triggerfishes. Use a feeding stick to present it with fresh marine fish flesh, scallops, and shrimp. The sharp thorns along the back are easily entangled in a fish net, so handle with care.

Aquarium Size: 1,368 L (360 gal.).

Water Temperature: 16 to 21°C (61 to 70°F).

Aquarium Suitability Index: 3.

Remarks: Distinguished by a long, rounded snout and three rows of large spines running down its back and tail, the Thornback Ray is brown with no markings.

References

Bigelow & Schroeder (1953), Last & Stevens (1994), Limbaugh (1963), Talent (1982), Timmons & Bray (1997), Villavicencio-Garayzar (1995).

ELECTRIC RAYS
Family Narcinidae

THIS FAMILY OF ELECTRIC RAYS has 9 genera and approximately 24 species. All have oval discs that are usually longer than they are wide; the anterior edge of the disc is broad and rounded. They also have two dorsal fins, a well-developed caudal fin, lateral folds on the tail, stout jaws, and strong labial cartilage. The narcinids possess electric organs and can emit shocks of up to 37 volts, although more provocation is usually necessary to elicit electrical discharge than with the torpedo rays (Family Torpedinidae). They are found on soft mud and sand substrates, but several are residents of, or visitors to, reef environments. Electric rays are ovoviviparous; the uterine wall of the gravid female is covered with villi, minute wormlike processes that secrete uterine "milk" for the developing embryos. Their yolk sacs also provide nourishment.

When threatened, at least one species (the Cortez Electric Ray [*Narcine entemedor*]) is known to arch its back, explode off the bottom, and do a loop in the water column. This is apparently an antipredation strategy that may serve to warn (back arch) and then confuse (loop) a would-be predator. I know of one case where a diver received a mild shock after he provoked one of these rays to do a loop and it landed on his back.

Captive Care

UNFORTUNATELY, DUE TO THEIR selective food habits, electric rays do not fare well in captivity. They feed primarily on annelid worms, both in the wild and in captivity, so unless you have access to a ready supply of these invertebrates, your chances of keeping an electric ray alive are slim. Attempts to get them to eat fresh fishes or shrimps have proved futile in most cases. For those with access to coastal bait shops or a beach, live lug worms and clam worms are good food sources. The best way to feed your ray is to keep worms in the tank so it can feed on them at night. Smaller specimens should be fed worms of 2 to 6 cm (0.8 to 2.3 in.) in length. One Australian species has been kept alive for up to 3 months on a diet of fresh fish pieces and crushed snails.

Electric rays should be kept on a fine sand substrate to avoid abrasion, which will result in inflammation (bacterial infection) of their ventral surfaces. Such infection is usually fatal. In cement enclosures, they have been observed to abrade their disc margins on the sides of the tank with the same unfortunate outcome. This problem may also occur in tanks where decorations such as hard coral skeletons are present. An appropriate electric ray tank should not include any sharp-edged or rough-surfaced decor. When selecting an electric ray, avoid individuals with curled disc margins, pale dorsal coloration, and those that refuse to bury or feed. Captive specimens also fall victim to parasitic monogenetic trematodes (e.g., *Amphibdelloides narcine*) that infest the gills. These can be treated by dipping the infected animal in halquinol (25 mg/L) and formalin (0.17 mg/L). Do not use copper-based medications or trichlorfon on these animals. Also use deionized or RO water in the electric ray aquarium. Individuals can be kept together without concern about aggressive interactions.

Species Accounts

Diplobatis ommata (Jordan & Gilbert, in Jordan & Bollman, 1889)
Common Names: Bullseye Electric Ray, Target Ray.
Size, Growth, and Age: This ray attains a maximum

Diplobatis ommata (Bullseye Electric Ray): can emit up to 37-volt shocks.

Diplobatis ommata (Bullseye Electric Ray): needs live foods to survive.

Diplobatis ommata (Bullseye Electric Ray): color variant, Baja California.

length of just 25 cm (9.8 in.).

Distribution: From the Gulf of California to Panama in the Eastern Pacific Ocean.

Biology: The Bullseye Electric Ray is found at depths from the intertidal zone to 64 m (209 ft.), usually on sandy bays, but also on rubble bottoms near offshore islands. It is usually a solitary species. Inactive and often buried under the substrate by day, it moves on or just over the bottom at night by "hopping" on its pelvic fins. Its diet consists of amphipods, shrimps, and worms.

Captive Care: The Bullseye Electric Ray is seen irregularly in the North American aquarium trade and is difficult to feed. They have been known to eat live annelid worms and small grass shrimp in captivity. For more information on keeping this species, see the Captive Care notes for *Narcine brasiliensis*, page 143.

Aquarium Size: 152 L (40 gal.).

Water Temperature: 22 to 27°C (72 to 81°F).

Aquarium Suitability Index: 2.

Remarks: This attractive species exhibits at least two different color forms. The dorsal color is usually a light brown with many small black spots. It can also be marbled with dark brown, and always has conspicuous ocelli in the middle of its back. Individuals have been taken off Panama that were plain in color except for a black spot in the center of the disc. The dorsal and caudal fin tips are rounded. The **Painted Electric Ray (*Diplobatis pictus*) Palmer, 1950** is a similar species reported from reef habitats near the Atlantic coast of South America—from Brazil to Colombia. This ray has a subcircular disc, a fanlike caudal fin with a distinct upper corner, and sharply pointed dorsal fin tips. The Painted Electric Ray is highly variable in color, but is often tan with scattered brown and white spots. It reaches a total length of 20 cm (7.8 in.).

Narcine brasiliensis (Olfers, 1831)

Common Name: Lesser Electric Ray.

Size, Growth, and Age: The Lesser Electric Ray is born at 11 to 12 cm (4.3 to 4.7 in.) and attains a maximum length of 45 cm (17.6 in.). Males of this species mature at a length of 23 to 25 cm (9.0 to 9.8 in.), while females mature at approximately 27 cm (10.5 in.).

Distribution: North Carolina and the Gulf of Mexico south to Argentina.

Biology: This species occurs at a depth range from the intertidal zone to 40 m (131 ft.). It is most often found resting on or moving over open sand or sand/silt bottoms. *Narcine brasiliensis* feeds almost exclusively on worms, but occasionally eats juvenile worm eels, anemones, and small crustaceans, uncovering infaunal prey by undulating its posterior disc margin to fan away the bottom sediment. This is a nocturnal animal that often buries under substrate during the day. It moves from shallow inshore waters to deeper areas in the winter, where it forms aggregates at preferred sites. The Lesser Electric Ray gives birth to 2 to 17 young per litter. In Florida waters, females move into the surf zone to give birth in late summer.

Captive Care: This ray can be successfully kept if it is provided with a natural food source (e.g., annelid worms). Rudloe (1989a) reports that adult clam worms (*Nereis virens*) and lug worms (*Arenicola cristata*) were a good source of food for adults, while these were often too large for juveniles (less than 25 cm [9.8 in.]). Juveniles were fed lug worms less than 6 cm (2.3 in.) in length or the small oligochaete *Pontodrilus bermudensis*. The Lesser Electric Ray is best kept in an aquarium with a layer (at least 6 cm [2.3 in. deep]) of fine coral sand. If you feed live annelids to your ray you should also place a filter pad or fiberglass screening above the filter plate (if an undergravel filter is installed) to pre-

Narcine brasiliensis (Lesser Electric Ray): gray color variant.

vent the worms from burrowing under it. Although the ray has the ability to shock potential predators or prey, fish tankmates will sometimes pick at its eyes. More than one *N. brasiliensis* can be kept in the same tank, as they do not behave aggressively toward one another. The gills of this fish are sometimes parasitized by the leech *Branchellion ravenelii*, which can be removed with tweezers or the specimen can be given a formalin bath. This fish should be kept at a salinity of 25 to 30 ppt. Below 17°C (63°F) it becomes sluggish, while death results at temperatures of less than 14°C (57°F).

Aquarium Size: 266 L (70 gal.).

Water Temperature: 20 to 28°C (68 to 82°F).

Aquarium Suitability Index: 2.

Remarks: The Lesser Electric Ray often has a readily distinguishable color pattern. The dorsal coloration can be dark brown, grayish brown, orange, or reddish. Some individuals are uniform in color, but most have darker blotches, often with lighter centers and/or bars. Smaller individuals often have dark rings on the body (in many cases the markings become more obscure with age). The ventral surface is white and may have a yellow or greenish cast. It is similar, if not identical, to the **Cortez Electric Ray (***Narcine entemedor***) Jordan & Starks, 1895,** which ranges from the Gulf of California to Panama and occasionally may be found in aquarium stores.

References
Allen & Robertson (1994), Beebe & Tee-Vee (1941b), Rudloe (1989a, 1989b).

TORPEDO RAYS
Family Torpedinidae

THIS FAMILY OF ELECTROGENIC elasmobranchs has 1 genus and approximately 22 species. They are characterized by a round or oval-shaped disc that is quite flabby, two dorsal fins, slender jaws, a straight or notched anterior disc margin, and a short tail with a well-developed caudal fin. Characteristics that can aid in separating the various species include the position of the first dorsal fin relative to the pelvic fins, the presence of papillae on the spiracle margins, the number of spiracle papillae when present, and the color pattern (this may vary in some species).

The torpedoes possess two kidney-shaped electric organs embedded under the skin on each side of the head. These are capable of producing an electrical discharge of over 220 volts in some species. Electrical discharge is used to capture prey, to ward off predators, and possibly to communicate with members of their own kind. People who have contacted these animals while wading or diving have reported that the shock is similar to being punched by a very large fist. Being shocked by a larger species could result in unconsciousness. Torpedoes are found in all temperate and tropical seas, in-shore and offshore, with several species regularly occurring on or near reefs. They are ovoviviparous, being nourished by a yolk sac and secretions exuded by the uteri. In gravid females, the uteri secrete a nutrient-rich liquid (uterine "milk") which is ingested by the developing embryos. No information exists on courtship and mating behavior in these rays.

Fishes make up the bulk of their diets. Dietary studies done on the Marbled Torpedo (*Torpedo marmorata*) have shown it feeds primarily on conger eels, hake, sea bass, goatfish, mackerel, gobies, and soles. It will occasionally eat shrimps and squids. The small jaws are distensible and enable the torpedo rays to eat large prey items relative to their body size. For example, a 1.2 m (3.9 ft.) California Torpedo (*Torpedo californica*) had eaten a 60 cm (23.4 in.) Silver Salmon (*Onchorhynchus kisutch*), while a 41-cm (16.0-in.) Marbled Torpedo contained a 34-cm (13.1-in.) Three-bearded Rockling (*Gaidropsarus* sp.) in its stomach. They employ several strategies to capture prey. Lying just beneath the sand or mud surface, they lunge from the substrate when the victim comes within striking distance. They also stalk their quarry by slowly drifting over the reef or by creeping along the seafloor. Most emit an electrical discharge to immobilize or disorient the prey item just prior to attacking. Despite their strong electrogenic organs, torpedoes are occasionally preyed upon by sharks, including the Broadnosed Sixgill Shark (*Hexanchus griseus*), the Blotchy Swell Shark (*Cephaloscyllium umbratile*), and certain requiem sharks.

Captive Care
THE TORPEDO RAYS CAN BE FASCINATING aquarium inhabitants. Although they spend most of their time buried under the sand, their feeding behaviors provide an engaging show. While many of the torpedoes are

apparently quite hardy, some get much too large for the home aquarium. Species like the Marbled and Atlantic (*T. nobiliana*) Torpedo Rays have been successfully maintained in public aquariums, while others, like the California Torpedo, are reported to be finicky feeders, often refusing to eat in aquarium confines. One species of medium-sized torpedo is being regularly imported from the Red Sea and acclimates well to aquarium life.

Torpedoes should be kept in a tank with no or minimal decor, with a thick layer of fine sand on the aquarium bottom (fine coral sand and/or aragonite sand are good substrate choices). Feeding can be tricky. They will usually take only moving food. Live prey or a piece of fish presented on a feeding stick will usually do. In some cases they may pounce on a food item on the end of a feeding stick, but not ingest it if it immediately stops moving. Live marine fishes (e.g., damselfishes, cardinalfishes) may be needed to get a torpedo to break its initial fast. Care must be taken when handling larger specimens as they can give the aquarist a memorable zap. Do not use copper-based medications or trichlorfon on these animals. Also, use deionized or RO water, not tap water, when topping up the torpedo tank or when mixing-up saltwater for water changes.

Species Account

Torpedo panthera Olfers, 1831

Common Names: Leopard Torpedo, Panther Torpedo Ray, Red Sea Torpedo Ray.
Size, Growth, and Age:. This species is reported to attain a maximum length of around 1 m (3.3 ft.). The size at birth is not known.
Distribution: Red Sea. Reports from other areas in the western Indian Ocean probably refer to the similar Blackspotted Torpedo Ray (*Torpedo fuscomaculata*).

Biology: This is one of a few torpedoes that is commonly found on coral reefs. It usually occurs on reef sand patches on reef slopes or the reef face. It is thought to feed mainly on fishes, like most other members of the family. Preliminary observations indicate that this species may attract prey items by undulating its ante-

Torpedo panthera (Leopard Torpedo): fascinating display animal.

rior disc margin when it is buried just under the sand surface. This may lure potential prey species that are attracted to disturbances in the sand, like wrasses or sea breams. When its quarry moves near the front edge of the disc, the ray erupts from the sand, covering the prey with its disc and shocking it. The Leopard Torpedo will then pivot around on the edge of the disc and often lift its body as it tries to move the prey item toward its relatively small mouth.
Captive Care: This is an interesting display animal. Small individuals (around 25 to 36 cm [9.6 to 14.0 in.]) are available from time to time. Feed this fish at least once a day. Look for signs of malnourishment and in-

crease feeding frequency if necessary. It is best to keep this fish on its own, as it will eat smaller fishes and will not be able to compete with more efficient carnivores.

Aquarium Size: 684 L (180 gal.).

Water Temperature: 22 to 27°C (72 to 81°F).

Aquarium Suitability Index: 3.

Remarks: This species is recognized by the following set of characteristics: The first dorsal fin is only slightly larger than the second dorsal fin, and the tips of both are rounded. The entire base of the first dorsal fin is over or in front of the posterior base of the pelvic fins. The eyes are well in front of the spiracles, and in at least some specimens, they are halfway between the front of the disc and the spiracles. The spiracles have seven papillae. The distance between the dorsal fins is equal to that between the posterior base of the second dorsal fin and the caudal fin origin. Finally, the dorsal coloration is a uniform tan or rusty brown with pale blotches or white spots. It is possible that the **Blackspotted Torpedo Ray (*Torpedo fuscomaculata*) Peters, 1855** may make it into the aquarium trade. This ray is similar to *T. panthera*, but it is known from reefs off South Africa, Zanzibar, the Seychelles, Mauritius, Madagascar, Mozambique, and south-western India. The Blackspotted Torpedo differs in having its eyes much nearer to the spiracles than to the front of the disc, an interdorsal space greater than the distance between the posterior base of the second dorsal fin and the origin of the caudal fin, and a dark brown to light gray dorsum with or without black spots, black lines, or white flecks. The Blackspotted Torpedo is a smaller species, attaining a maximum length of 64 cm (25.0 in.).

References

Belbenoit (1986), Bray & Hixon (1978), Capapé (1979), Compagno et al. (1989), Feder et al. (1974).

STINGAREES AND WHIPTAIL STINGRAYS
Family Urolophidae and Family Dasyatidae

ROUND STINGRAYS AND STINGAREES are similar in morphology to the whiptail stingrays. The most conspicuous difference between the two is the well-developed caudal fin of the stingarees, which is lacking in the whiptails. Also, the urolophids are smaller (the largest species reaches about 80 cm [31.2 in.] in length) and have shorter, broader tails. There are four genera in the family, including *Trygonoptera* (shovelnose stingarees), *Urobatis* (shorttail round stingrays), *Urolophus* (stingarees), and *Urotrygon* (longtail round stingrays). (At least one taxonomist places the *Urobatis* and *Urotrygon* in their own family, the Urotrygonidae.) Of the 36 species in the family, most occur in temperate areas, and a number of these frequent rocky reefs. Stingarees have one or two spines on the tail and are responsible for injuring many bathers each year with this defensive weapon. Some species have even been observed to swim backward toward a potential threat and successfully inflict a sting. Due to their small size, stingarees are probably not responsible for any human fatalities. In addition to defending themselves, females also use their spines to ward off amorous males. There is a report of a Sandyback Stingaree (*Urolophus bucculentus*) that had the broken spine of the same species embedded in its back (the spine had been there long enough to have barnacles growing on it).

These rays are ovoviviparous (uterine viviparity). Males of at least two species have longer tooth cusps than females, apparently to hold a mate during copulation. Stingarees are preyed upon by large bony fishes and other elasmobranchs (e.g., Tiger Sharks [*Galeo-*

Dasyatis americana (Southern Stingray): elegant swimmer, but large tail spines are venomous and can cause excruciating pain in humans.

cerdo cuvier] and other stingarees). These rays do well in captivity, and some species even reproduce in public and large home aquariums.

THE WHIPTAIL STINGRAY FAMILY has 9 genera and approximately 70 species, several of which can be found in aquarium stores. Dasyatid rays are well known because of their interactions, both good and bad, with humans. Popularization of dive sites where large Southern Stingrays (*Dasyatis americana*) envelop divers in their huge pectoral fins and feed from their hands give these animals a positive image. But most of these rays also present a potential hazard. The large spine(s) on the tail, ensheathed in venomous tissue, are used as defensive weapons. When provoked, these fish thrust the tail over

their bodies and into the offender, whether it is a hammerhead shark or an aquarist's hand. The pain is reported to be excruciating. A number of human fatalities have resulted from actual physical injury or loss of blood caused by the sting.

Many whiptail stingrays bury themselves in the substrate, with only their eyes protruding, to conceal themselves from potential predators. They can go unnoticed by waders or even a diver. In all of these rays, a new spine grows periodically in front of or behind the old one, which is then shed. Spine-shedding occurs once a year in at least one species, the Atlantic Stingray (*Dasyatis sabina*).

A number of whiptail stingrays, such as the Feathertail Stingray (*Pastinachus sephen*), migrate up rivers,

Trygonoptera testaceus (Common Stingaree): Australian native.

Trygonoptera sp. (Banded Stingaree): small, attractive species.

Urolophus gigas (Spotted Stingaree): grows to just 60 cm (23 in.).

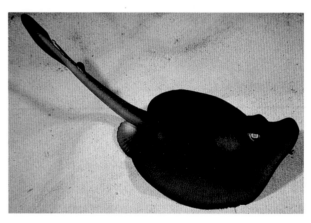

Irygonoptera ovalis (Oval Stingaree): note typical stingaree caudal fin.

Urolophus paucimaculatus (Sparsely Spotted Stingaree): aggressive.

Urolophus cruciatus (Crossback Stingaree): may sting like a scorpion.

and several species are known only from freshwater (e.g., Laos Stingray, *Dasyatis laosensis*).

Whiptail stingrays are ovoviviparous (uterine viviparity). Two different mating postures have been described for these rays: three species have been described as mating venter-to-venter (belly-to-belly), while in another species a male mounted a female dorsally.

These rays eat a variety of invertebrates and fishes, and most dig in sediments for infaunal animals. Stingrays are not considered voracious predators, but some are. For example, the stomach of one Honeycomb Stingray (*Himantura uarnak*) (disc width 145 cm [56.4 in.]) contained eight threadfin breams, three mackerels, eight ponyfishes, eight cardinalfishes, three sardines, three anchovies, two flatfishes, one mojarra, four flatheads, three pufferfishes, five squids, two crabs, and two mollusk shells. Other bony fishes known to fall prey to dasyatids include young eels, scorpionfishes, croakers, damselfishes, wrasses, jawfishes, blennies, gobies (including the sleeper gobies, genus *Valenciennea*), surgeonfishes, and rabbitfishes. Several of the whiptail stingrays visit cleaning stations, where reef fishes remove parasites and ingest the ray's body mucus.

Captive Care

BOTH WHIPTAIL STINGRAYS AND STINGAREES should be kept in aquariums with a sand bottom (so they can bury themselves without getting injured) and minimal rockwork (a ledge to hide under would be utilized by some species). No aggressive or sessile-invertebrate-eating tankmates (e.g., angelfishes, butterflyfishes, pufferfishes, or triggerfishes) should be housed with a stingray. Most rays ship well and, with the exception of the Bluespotted Ribbontail Ray (*Taeniura lymma*), usually feed within days of being purchased. Some will even accept fresh shrimp or fish out of their owner's hand.

The best food to use to stimulate feeding in a finicky stingray is live grass shrimp. The urolophid rays have very small mouths, and the juveniles have difficulty chewing fibrous foods, so these specimens can be fed shelled, finely minced shrimp, mussels, black worms, and small live shrimp. New studies demonstrate that at least one dasyatid, the Atlantic Stingray, feeds almost constantly day and night and consumes large quantities of food. In order to meet the metabolic demands of this species, and perhaps others, it is important to feed them frequently.

In my opinion, the Bluespotted Ribbontail Ray is the most handsome member of the group but also the most difficult to keep. It often goes for a considerable time before it accepts captive fare, and most of the time it never makes the adjustment to aquarium life. For these reasons, this ray is best left in the wild. This ray appears to be very sensitive to copper. (Do not use copper-based medications or malachite green on any of these elasmobranchs; use trichlorfon with great caution.)

Another thing to consider is that whiptail stingrays require more living space than stingarees because most of the former attain greater sizes. Relatively little is known about the growth rate of dasyatids and urolophids. Round stingrays, kept at a water temperature of 19°C (66°F), grew at a rate of about 2.8 cm (1.1 in.) of disc width each year until they reached sexual maturity, at which time the rate of growth decreased.

At least some whiptail stingrays and stingarees will fight in aquarium confines. For example, captive female Atlantic Stingrays (*Dasyatis sabina*) will bite and injure their male counterparts, and Pelagic Stingrays (*Pteroplatytrygon violacea*) have been reported to quarrel in larger tanks. Whiptail stingrays vary in hardiness, but several species have reproduced in captivity.

Species Accounts (Urolophidae)

Urobatis concentricus Osburn & Nichols, 1916
Common Name: Bullseye Stingray.

Size, Growth, and Age: Birth size about 12 cm (4.7 in.); attains a maximum length of at least 60 cm (24.4 in.).

Distribution: Known from the Gulf of California and probably ranges south to Panama and the Galapagos Islands.

Biology: The Bullseye Stingray occurs at depths from the intertidal zone to 20 m (66 ft.), typically on sandy and rocky bottoms in bays and around reefs, feeding on small crabs and worms.

Captive Care: A relatively hardy species that is best kept at water temperatures between 22 and 27°C (72 and 81°F), the Bullseye Stingray is occasionally available to North American aquarists. Like many others in this genus, live grass shrimp are a good first food for this fish.

Aquarium Size: 684 L (180 gal.).

Water Temperature: 22 to 28°C (72 to 82°F).

Aquarium Suitability Index: 3.

Remarks: This handsome ray is characterized by the dark rings around the edge of the disc and dark reticulations on its dorsum.

Urobatis halleri (Cooper, 1863)
Common Names: Round Stingray, California Stingray.

Size, Growth, and Age: The Round Stingray is born at 13 cm (5.1 in.) and reaches a maximum length of 56 cm (21.8 in.). Males and females become sexually mature at a disc width of approximately 15 cm (5.9 in.) or a maximum length of 26 cm (10.1 in.). Both sexes mature by 2 years 7 months of age and grow at an average rate of about 2.8 cm (1.1 in.) in disc width each year until they reach sexual maturity. This species is thought to live about 8 years in the wild.

Distribution: Northern California to Panama.

Biology: This species inhabits depths from the intertidal zone down to 91 m (298 ft.). Over several winters, I studied the mating behavior of this species in the Gulf of California. Most of the year, Round Stingrays, like many elasmobranchs, segregate by sex, with females occupying deeper waters than males. In late winter and spring, the females move into shallow bays to mate, and several months later they return to inshore waters to give birth. This species is usually found on sand and mud bottoms, sometimes around rocky reefs (especially in the Gulf of California). Young stay in inshore waters, occupying a limited area, but as they grow, their

Urobatis concentricus (Bullseye Stingray): hardy and handsome small ray.

Urobatis halleri (Round Stingray): requires a cool-water system to thrive.

home range extends to include deeper water. The movements of adults are also limited. The longest movement reported for 39 tagged and recaptured rays was 7.7 km (4.7 mi.) after a maximum of 208 days at liberty. Round Stingrays forage mostly during the day, feeding almost exclusively on worms, bivalves, and crustaceans. In a study by Babel (1967) off the southern California coast, the volume distribution of Round Stingray foods was as follows: clams, 42%; polychaete worms, 30%; crustaceans (including shrimps, amphipods, isopods, and mysids), 21%. (Nematodes, bony fishes, echinoderms, and sea spiders were all under 1% of stomach volume.) Juveniles feed mostly on crustaceans and annelid worms, with few bivalves being consumed. Adults bite off the extended siphons of certain bivalves, and they crush clams with thin to moderately thick shells. When hunting, they dig large holes (up to 13 cm [5.1 in.] deep) in the mud looking for prey and pick small crustaceans off eel grass.

Captive Care: The Round Stingray is most commonly collected from the southern coast of California. This is a hardy aquarium species best kept at water temperatures between 12 and 22°C (54 and 72°F). Unhealthy specimens will appear listless and lose weight, their overall color will fade to light gray, and their markings will become less distinct. Small specimens will have trouble masticating fibrous foods and should therefore be fed finely chopped shrimp, frozen mysid shrimp, live brine shrimp, and live black worms. Although newly acquired individuals can be easily startled by loud noises or sudden movement, after some time in captivity they become quite tame.

Aquarium Size: 684 L (180 gal.).

Water Temperature: 12 to 22°C (54 to 72°F).

Aquarium Suitability Index: 3.

Remarks: The Round Stingray has a tail that is shorter than the disc length, a smooth back, and no dorsal fin. Although the dorsal color is variable, it is usually plain brown with yellow spots and vermiculations.

Urobatis jamaicensis (Cuvier, 1817)

Common Name: Yellow Stingray.

Size, Growth, and Age: This stingray attains a disc width of 36 cm (14.0 in.) and a maximum length of 67 cm (26.1 in.). Males apparently reach sexual maturity at a disc width of about 15 cm (5.9 in.).

Distribution: North Carolina and the Gulf of Mexico throughout the Caribbean to Trinidad.

Biology: *Urobatis jamaicensis* is found in harbors, bays, and lagoons (often near coral reefs) at depths ranging from the intertidal zone to at least 20 m (66 ft.). It is found on sand and mud bottoms. The mating period is in spring, and litter size ranges from two to four pups. It hunts by undulating the anterior disc margin to excavate holes in the sand and expose buried prey, reportedly feeding on shrimps, but probably also eating small fishes, clams, and worms. Individuals have also been observed to lift the front of the disc margin and remain motionless, forming a pseudo "cave" to attract potential prey; when a small fish, shrimp, or crab enters this

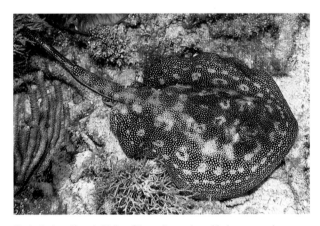

Urobatis jamaicensis (Yellow Stingray): may breed in large aquariums.

apparent hiding place, the stingray slams down its disc margin and consumes the duped prey.

Captive Care: The Yellow Stingray is the most common member of its family in the North American aquarium trade due to its distribution. This is a good aquarium fish that will acclimate readily if provided with enough space and nonaggressive tankmates. It will, however, eat small fishes if it can catch them. A Yellow Stingray I once kept mauled a large wrasse as the fish slept under the sand, and a friend of mine had a specimen that caught and ate a Blue Green Chromis (*Chromis viridis*) that it trapped in the corner of the aquarium. This species will breed in larger aquariums.

Aquarium Size: 684 L (180 gal.).

Water Temperature: 22 to 28°C (72 to 82°F).

Aquarium Suitability Index: 3.

Remarks: This species has a tail that is not as long as its disc, low tubercles along its back from the front of the eyes to the tail spine (not present in juveniles), a pointed snout, and a disc that is slightly longer than wide in adults. It has no dorsal fin. The dorsal color consists of a dark reticulated pattern and yellowish spots on a pale background.

Urobatis maculatus Garman, 1913

Common Names: Cortez Round Stingray, Spotted Round Stingray.

Size, Growth, and Age: *Urobatis maculatus* attains a maximum length of 42 cm (16.4 in.).

Distribution: Magdalena Bay on the west coast of Baja California, Mexico, and throughout the Gulf of California.

Biology: This species is found at depths ranging from the intertidal zone to 20 m (66 ft.). Mating is probably similar to that of the Round Stingray (*U. halleri*) but it has never been documented. I did observe a female of this species being bitten and held by two male Round Stingrays, suggesting that these two species may hybridize, or that *U. maculatus* is simply a color variant of *U. halleri*. In the activity I witnessed, the female *U. maculatus* thrust her spine at the two courting males and was able to escape. This ray occurs on shallow sand and mud bottoms, in seagrass beds, near rocky reefs, and in bays, where it hunts for worms and crustaceans. Like the Round Stingray, it forages primarily during the day.

Captive Care: This is an ideal aquarium ray because of its smaller size and durability. It is also a good candidate for captive breeding.

Aquarium Size: 684 L (180 gal.).

Water Temperature: 22 to 28°C (72 to 82°F).

Aquarium Suitability Index: 3.

Remarks: This species is similar to the Round Stingray, but with conspicuous black spots on the back and ventral surface. Some, called Chocolate Chip Rays, are cream-colored with jet black spots.

Urobatis maculatus (Cortez Round Stingray): an ideally sized aquarium ray.

Species Accounts (Dasyatidae)

Dasyatis americana Hildebrand & Schroeder, 1928

Common Name: Southern Stingray.

Size, Growth, and Age: This species is born with a disc width of 20 cm (7.8 in.), but can attain a width of 1.5 m (4.9 ft.).

Distribution: New Jersey to Brazil.

Biology: The Southern Stingray is found at a depth range from the intertidal zone to at least 25 m (82 ft.). It occurs on sandy bottoms and in seagrass beds, usually in lagoons, and on reef slopes. This species is observed singly, in pairs, and in aggregations. It will swim over, or rest near, cleaning stations, where it is cleaned by the Bluehead Wrasse (*Thalassoma bifasciatum*) and the Spanish Hogfish (*Bodianus rufus*). Cleaning episodes involving the Bluehead Wrasse may last for less than a minute to as long as 26 minutes. When threatened, the stingray will raise its tail over its body and hold it in this position like a scorpion. It will also bury under the substrate.

The Southern Stingray gives birth to two to ten young (larger females give birth to larger litters) after a gestation period of 135 to 226 days. Males will bite the disc margins of females. The male will flip under the female and the pair will mate in a venter-to-venter orientation. Gilliam and Sullivan (1993) found that 18 *D. americana* fed on 65 different prey items from 15 different families. Crustaceans were the dominant prey (they were present in all stomachs), and included (in order of importance) swimming crabs, penaeid shrimps, pistol shrimps, and mantis shrimps. Teleosts occurred in 83% of the stomachs examined, and included wrasses, gobies, and parrotfishes (others have reported herrings, toadfishes, scorpionfishes, jawfishes, and surgeonfishes).

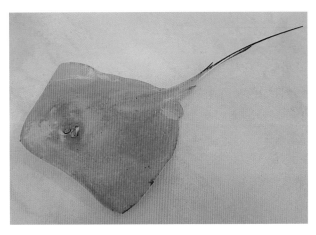

Dasyatis americana (Southern Stingray): a big, voracious predator.

Mollusks (including bivalves, snails, and cephalopods), annelid worms, and plant material were of lesser importance. Bivalves are crushed with the dental plates and most of the shell fragments are spit out. Randall (1967) found the following volume distribution in 25 *D. americana* from the U.S. Virgin Islands: bony fishes, 22%; peanut worms, 21%; crabs, 18%; polychaete worms, 17%; clams, 11%; shrimps, 8%. This species is a voracious, opportunistic predator that feeds throughout the day. Gilliam and Sullivan (1993) found that the average number of prey items per stingray stomach was 31, with 83% of all individuals having over 10 items in their stomachs. Randall (1967) reports one *D. americana*, with a disc length of 30 cm (11.7 in.), whose stomach contained an astonishing 52 penaeid shrimps and 12 portunid crabs. In both these studies, no empty stomachs were reported. The Southern Stingray may feed more heavily at high tide.

Captive Care: Because of its large size, the Southern Stingray should be avoided by the majority of home elasmobranch keepers. It is a voracious predator that will consume any fish or invertebrate tankmate that it can catch. In larger public aquariums, females of this species have been observed biting each other on the disc margins. This species has been known to reproduce in large public aquariums. Maintain the Southern Stingray at a specific gravity of 1.018 to 1.026.

Aquarium Size: 15,960 L (4,200 gal.).
Water Temperature: 22 to 28°C (72 to 82°F).
Aquarium Suitability Index: 4 (X-large tank required).
Remarks: The species is characterized by its rhomboid disc, a row of small tubercles running down the back, a low dorsal keel present on its tail, and a long ventral finfold. In color, it is gray to brown dorsally, without markings.

Dasyatis kuhlii (Müller & Henle, 1841)

Common Names: Bluespotted Stingray, Masked Stingray.
Size, Growth, and Age: This species attains a maximum disc width of 50 cm (19.5 in.) and a total length of 67 cm (26.1 in.). Males reach maturity at a disc width of about 25 cm (9.8 in.), making them ideal candidates for captive-breeding programs.
Distribution: From the Indian Ocean and Red Sea to Samoa, Japan, and Australia.
Biology: The Bluespotted Stingray is found at depths ranging from the intertidal zone to 50 m (164 ft.). It frequents black or white sand flats and slopes adjacent to coastal reefs. It is also found in lagoons, on reef faces or on deep slopes and will move onto the reef flat and into shallow lagoon waters at high tide. It is typically a solitary species, except during the breeding season when it forms aggregations. Male *D. kuhlii* have been observed biting females on the tail at this time. It feeds on crabs and shrimps, digging with the pectoral fins to uncover hidden prey. It is often accompanied by wrasses, goatfishes, and jacks, which pounce on the small prey that the ray flushes out.

Captive Care: This is a hardy aquarium species that usually accepts food within the first 2 or 3 days of captive life if placed in a well-maintained aquarium. It should not be disturbed during the acclimation period, even if it remains buried. The aquarium should have a layer of fine sand on the bottom, at least 5 cm (2.0 in.) deep, so that the stingray can bury itself if threatened. Live grass shrimp are a favorite food in captivity, but it will also take pieces of fresh shrimp and marine fish flesh.
Aquarium Size: 988 L (260 gal.).
Water Temperature: 22 to 28°C (72 to 82°F).
Aquarium Suitability Index: 4.
Remarks: Do not mistake this species for the more commonly available but less hardy Bluespotted Ribbontail Ray (*Taeniura lymma*). *Dasyatis kuhlii* has a rhomboid disc with slightly convex anterior and posterior margins, a short snout, a short dorsal tail finfold, a ventral finfold whose length is 70% of the disc width, and eyes that are slightly smaller than the interorbital width. The dorsal color is reddish brown to olive drab, with blue spots and smaller black spots, and the tail often has white bands.

Dasyatis kuhlii (Bluespotted Stingray): hardy and easily fed in captivity.

Dasyatis sabina (Lesueur, 1824)

Common Name: Atlantic Stingray.

Size, Growth, and Age: Born at a disc width of 9.5 to 13.5 cm (3.7 to 5.3 in.), Atlantic Stingray females attain a maximum disc width of 49 cm (19.1 in.), while the largest male reported was about 32 cm (12.9 in.). Sexual maturity is attained at a disc width of 20 to 25 cm (7.8 to 9.8 in.) for males and about 24 cm (9.4 in.) for females. (Males with claspers measuring about 26% of the disc width are considered to be sexually mature.) It has been estimated that males of this species live only 2 or 3 years in the wild, while females live for 6 years.

Distribution: From the Chesapeake Bay (where it is found only in the warmer months) to Florida, into the Gulf of Mexico, south to Campeche, Mexico.

Biology: The Atlantic Stingray is found at depths from the intertidal zone to 20 m (66 ft.), but is most common at depths of less than 1 m (3.3 ft.) in estuaries and lagoons. It occurs on sand, sand/silt, or seagrass substrates. This species ascends rivers, having been caught 320 km (192 mi.) up the Mississippi River. *Dasyatis sabina* has been reported at water temperatures ranging from 14 to 35°C (57 to 95°F) and a specific gravity of 0.2 to 45 ppt. It has also been reported at dissolved oxygen values of 3 to 9 mg/L, although most occur in waters with readings of 5 to 7 mg/L. Along the Texas coast, *D. sabina* migrates out of shallow bays to deeper coastal water as the water temperatures drop in the winter. In at least some areas, these rays form breeding aggregations. Females give birth to small litters (one to four pups) in late July to September, after a gestation period of 3.5 to 4 months. When searching for food, *D. sabina* digs holes in the sand and mud by undulating its disc margin, usually facing into the current while feeding so that the current carries disturbed sediment away from the feeding depression. It consumes surface,

Dasyatis sabina (Atlantic Stingray): best kept in brackish or saltwater.

infaunal, and tube-dwelling species, including tube anemones, polychaete worms, small crustaceans (including amphipods, isopods, mole crabs, and pistol shrimps), clams, and serpent stars. In one detailed study of this species' food habits, it was determined that amphipods, mysids, isopods, and polychaete worms were their most important prey. The calcified discs of serpent stars were also important during summer months when these echinoderms were full of eggs. (The caloric content of the serpent stars was 16.5% greater during this time of the year because of the nutrient-rich gametes.) This ray actively forages both day and night. The tooth replacement rate is 5.6±0.86 days for males and 7.4±1.17 days for females, with all the teeth in the jaw being replaced in approximately 1 to 2 months.

Captive Care: Although considered an ideal aquarium species because of its small maximum size, Atlantic Stingrays vary in their adaptability to captivity. Dr. Timothy Tricas, who has studied them extensively in the field and the lab, has told me that 50% of the animals they introduce into captivity do not feed, even if supplied with their natural prey. Feed this ray at least once a day. The best foods are fresh or frozen shrimp, clams, crabs, and snails (the latter should be left in their shells). Dr. Tricas reports that overcrowding will increase the incidence of aggression between specimens. Females are more aggressive than males and may severely injure them (inflicting significant abrasions on their fins), especially in smaller tanks. The males will often die of stress. Because of its small size at maturity, this ray is an ideal species for captive breeding. It can be kept at a salinity of 0.2 to 30 ppt and a temperature of 16 to 30°C (61 to 86°F). They are often sold for freshwater aquariums, but are best kept in brackish or marine venues. If your Atlantic Stingray ever suffers from protozoan, fluke, or crustacean infestations, simply drop the salinity over a day or two (depending on where your salinity is to begin with) to eradicate most of these parasites (some flukes and dinoflagellates are euryhaline).

Aquarium Size: 513 L (135 gal.).
Water Temperature: 21 to 29°C (70 to 84°F).
Aquarium Suitability Index: 3.
Remarks: This species has a rhomboid disc, but the anterior margin is concave, while the outer and rear margins are rounded. The snout is long (i.e., the length from the tip to the eyes is longer than the distance between the eyes) and pointed. It has a row of tubercles down the middle of the back, and low dorsal and ventral tail finfolds, the dorsal finfold being inconspicuous, especially in juveniles. It is brown or yellowish brown dorsally, paler toward the edges of the disc, with a white ventrum.

Dasyatis sayi (Lesueur, 1817)

Common Name: Bluntnose Stingray.
Size, Growth, and Age: Born at a disc width of about 15 to 17 cm (5.6 to 6.6 in.), the Bluntnose Stingray attains a maximum disc width of 78 cm (30.4 in.). (There is a questionable report of an individual with a 91 cm [35.5 in.] disc width.) Males attain sexual maturity at a disc

Dasyatis sayi (Bluntnose Stingray): buried with attached Remora.

width as small as 35 cm (13.7 in.), while females are able to reproduce at 50 to 55 cm (19.5 to 21.5 in.) (with females attaining a larger size than males). In males, the claspers greatly increase in length at maturity, with clasper length jumping from 14 to about 30% of the disc width at sexual maturity.

Distribution: Western Atlantic, from New Jersey to southern Brazil.
Biology: The Bluntnose Stingray occurs in inshore coastal waters. Young specimens sometimes occur on shallow shoals in the late fall and winter months (when the sympatric *D. sabina* is absent from this habitat), but move into deeper water in the spring and summer. Adults are rarely seen on the shoals, most commonly frequenting depths greater than 1 m (3.3 ft.). In more northern parts of its range, *D. sayi* migrates out of coastal areas in the cooler winter months; in Florida lagoons, however, it stays the entire year. It occurs at temperatures 12.5 to 32.5°C (55 to 91°F), although it will become lethargic at the lower and upper parts of this range. Although euryhaline, this species occurs at a narrower salinity range (25 to 43 ppt) than *D. sabina*. The Bluntnose Stingray mates between early April and

June, while pregnant females give birth from late May to early June, just before ovulation of the next egg clutch occurs. Litter size ranges from one to six. *Dasyatis sayi* does most of its foraging at night, feeding largely on crustaceans (including pistol shrimps, mantis shrimps, and crabs), but also (to a lesser degree) on annelid worms, squids, small clams, and fishes.

Captive Care: Although slightly larger than the Atlantic Stingray, *D. sayi* is well suited to the home aquarium. It can be kept at water temperatures ranging from 15 to 28°C (59 to 82°F), but prefers water warmer than 19°C (66°F). It is best kept in water with a specific gravity of 1.016 to 1.026. It sometimes suffers from monogenetic trematodes. Use deionized or RO water with these rays and do not treat with copper.

Aquarium Size: 2,128 L (560 gal.).
Water Temperature: 22 to 28°C (72 to 82°F).
Aquarium Suitability Index: 1.
Remarks: The Bluntnose Stingray is sympatric (occupies the same geographical area) with the Atlantic Stingray and occasionally shows up in aquarium stores. This species can be separated from *D. sabina* by its short, rounded snout, which is weakly convex, and its well-developed dorsal finfold on the tail.

Taeniura lymma (Forsskål, 1775)

Common Name: Bluespotted Ribbontail Ray.
Size, Growth, and Age: This species is born at a disc width of about 10 cm (3.9 in.), attaining a maximum disc width of 30 cm (11.7 in.) and a total length of at least 70 cm (27.3 in.). Some authors report that they can reach a disc width of 90 cm (35.1 in.) and a total length of 2.4 m (7.9 ft.), but these figures are apparently erroneous.

Distribution: East coast of Africa (including the Red Sea), east to the Philippines, Australia, Melanesia, and Polynesia.
Biology: The Bluespotted Ribbontail Ray is observed from the intertidal zone to depths of at least 20 m (66 ft.). It is common in lagoons, on tidal flats, and on sand patches on the reef face. At flood tide, it often moves into the tidal zone to feed on worms, shrimps, hermit crabs, and small bony fishes during the day and possibly also at night. It excavates large pits in the sand and mixed sand and coral rubble, and produces huge clouds of sediment as it hunts infaunal prey. It seeks refuge under table corals, staghorn coral beds, and shipwreck debris, but rarely, if ever, buries itself under the sand. I have seen several specimens that have had their tails bit-

Taeniura lymma (Bluespotted Ribbontail Ray): juvenile. Low survivability.

Taeniura lymma (Bluespotted Ribbontail Ray): adult. Expert care needed.

ten off, probably by sharks. Females give birth to up to seven young at a time. Like many of its relatives, it may aggregate in shallow water during the breeding season. For example, in November, near Heron Island, Great Barrier Reef, I observed a group of mature males, with noticeably swollen claspers, patrolling a shallow, sandy area. This ray is frequently groomed by the Bluestreak Cleaner Wrasse (*Labroides dimidiatus*) and will facilitate the cleaning process by lifting its disc up on its pectoral fins and arching its body. This enables the wrasse to pick at the cloaca and the ventral surface. *Taeniura lymma* is sometimes parasitized by monogenetic trematodes. In fact, it is host to a recently described monogenetic trematode known as *Pseudohexabothrium taeniurae*.

Captive Care: Unfortunately, this ubiquitous and attractive ray has a long history of doing poorly in captivity. Often, individuals never accept food; other times they do, but then suddenly die or cease feeding for no apparent reason. Some large public aquariums have successfully kept them for long periods of time, and it may be that these rays need more space and better water quality than can be provided in a relatively small home tank. This species may also be sensitive to low levels of copper and contaminants often present in tap water; only reverse osmosis or deionized water should be used in its tank. If you have an individual that is not eating, an aggressive force-feeding regime may help maintain the ray until it begins to feed on its own. See page 190 for more on force-feeding techniques suitable for sharks and rays.

Aquarium Size: 988 L (260 gal.).

Water Temperature: 22 to 28°C (72 to 82°F).

Aquarium Suitability Index: 1-2.

Remarks: This species has an oval disc and a distinct color pattern, consisting of a yellow-brown dorsum with bright blue spots, and blue lines on the tail.

References

Babel (1967), Bigelow & Schroeder (1953), C. Delbeek (personal communication), Gilliam & Sullivan (1993), Henningsen (2000), Johnson & Snelson (1996), Kajiura & Tricas (1996), Kuiter (1993), Randall (1967), T. Tricas (personal communication), Schwartz & Dahlberg (1978), Snelson et al. (1988, 1989), Teaf (1987).

BUTTERFLY RAYS
Family Gymnuridae

THESE RAYS ARE EASILY RECOGNIZED by their unique kitelike shape. The disc is as wide as it is long and the tail is quite short. Some have a venomous spine near the base of the tail, while others do not. These rays lack a caudal fin and may or may not have a dorsal fin. The butterfly rays are found in temperate and tropical seas around the world. There are 11 species in the genus *Gymnura* and 2 species in the genus *Aetoplatea*. These active rays swim just over the bottom. They are known to use a swim-glide form of locomotion, in which they beat their pectoral fins to gain momentum, then glide for a distance before beating their fins again. They will also rest on the substrate or bury under sand or mud.

Butterfly rays are ovoviviparous. The developing embryos are bathed in uterine "milk"—a nutrient-rich secretion. Projections (villi) from the mother's uterus wall actually enter the spiracles of the embryo and deliver nutrients into the alimentary tract of the developing ray. The young have their pectoral fins folded up underneath them in the uteri. They are unfolded only after parturition occurs. Litters contain 2 to 10 young.

The butterfly rays are active carnivores. Their teeth have relatively large cusps that are good for grasping slippery prey. They feed heavily on bony fishes, as well as on polychaete worms, snails, squids, and crabs. Some bony fishes known to be included in this ray's diet are sardines, herrings, Spot Croaker (*Leiostomus xanthurus*), gurnards, Pigfish (*Orthopristis chrysoptera*), gobies, dragonets, flatfishes, and puffers (*Sphoeroides* spp.). Adults of some of the larger species might also eat small sharks. At least one species (*Gymnura altavela*) has been observed using the tip of its pectoral fin to smack food items in captivity. It has been suggested that they may use this technique to stun live fishes in nature. The Smooth Butterfly Ray (*Gymnura micrura*), on the other hand, is a known ambush predator that lunges out of the sand with incredible speed to capture passing prey. It will pin the prey animal to the seafloor while it manipulates and tries to ingest it. Butterfly rays may occur singly or in large groups.

Captive Care

THE BUTTERFLY RAYS OFTEN DO POORLY in captivity. For example, the Spiny (*Gymnura altavela*), Smooth (*G. micrura*), and California Butterfly Rays (*G. marmorata*) are all reported to be difficult species to feed in the aquarium. They rarely live for more than a month in captive environments, although there has been some recent success with *G. altavela* and *G. micrura*. Most are larger, active rays, that require more swimming space than most hobbyists can provide. It has been suggested that they be housed in a tank suited for more active sharks, rather than for their more sedentary cousins.

Species Account

Gymnura altavela (Linnaeus, 1758)
Common Name: Spiny Butterfly Ray.
Size, Growth, and Age: This ray attains a maximum disc width of 2.6 m (8.5 ft.). The young are born at a disc

Gymnura micrura (Smooth Butterfly Ray): may need live foods to initiate feeding. This species is very similar to *G. altavela* (Spiny Butterfly Ray).

width of approximately 44 cm (17.2 in.). In the Eastern Atlantic, males mature at a disc width of 78 cm (30.4 in.), while females are sexually mature at 108 cm (42.1 in.). In the Western Atlantic, sexually maturity occurs at a disc width of 102 and 155 cm (40.0 and 60.5 in.) for males and females, respectively. Henningsen (1996) provides limited growth rate data on this species. Captive observations of two individuals estimated an annual growth rate of 2.3 cm (0.9 in.) of disc width in a male, 1.1 cm (0.4 in.) in a female. Annual weight gain was predicted to be 3.7 kg (8.1 lbs.) for males and 8.3 kg (18 lbs.) for females.

Distribution: Atlantic Ocean and Mediterranean Sea. Ranges from New England to Argentina in the Western North Atlantic. In the Eastern North Atlantic, it ranges from the Bay of Biscay to the Gulf of Guinea and probably to Angola.

Biology: This species is most common on soft bottoms, at depths of 10 to 100 m (33 to 328 ft.). At times, it may form groups. Its gestation period is 5 to 6 months.

Captive Care: Although this species has long been considered difficult to keep, two individuals were kept for over 18 months using some invasive techniques. As mentioned above, the Spiny Butterfly Ray often refuses food. However, Henningsen (1996) reported that an aggressive force-feeding protocol may keep this ray healthy until it starts feeding on its own. He mixed up a gruel that was fed to the rays through a tube inserted into the esophagus (see page 190 for more on gruel mixtures and force-feeding techniques). The rays were flipped onto their back, which caused tonic immobility. After being force-fed gruel, followed by squid and herring (supplemented with a multivitamin), the rays began to take herring from a feeding pole, 62 and 70 days after being collected. They gradually began taking food from a diver's hand. The rays were fed every 1 to 2 days. The spiracle ventilation rate for the acclimated *G. altavela* ranged from 28 to 32 inhalations per minute.

Schreiber (1997) reports on a Smooth Butterfly Ray (*Gymnura micrura*) that ate live wrasses and mullet housed with it without ever having to be force-fed. It latter accepted krill, shrimp, squid, round scad, and smelt dropped near it when it was buried. (In the end, it was accepting food from the aquarist's hand.) Another specimen he discusses did require the tube-feeding technique described for *G. altavela*.

Aquarium Size: 33,250 L (8,750 gal.).
Water Temperature: 19 to 26°C (66 to 79°F).
Aquarium Suitability Index: 1 (X-large tank required).
Remarks: *Gymnura altavela* has a tail spine; its disc has a relatively straight anterior margin. The **Smooth Butterfly Ray (*G. micrura*) Bloch & Schneider, 1801** is a smaller, sympatric species that may occasionally show up in the aquarium trade as well. It differs from *G. altavela* in having a slightly concave anterior disc margin and a more pronounced snout; it lacks a tail spine. The Smooth Butterfly Ray attains a maximum length of 1.2 m (3.9 ft.) and is born at a disc width of 15 to 23 cm (5.9

to 9.0 in.). It is often found in bays, tidal flats (at flood tide), and in estuaries, where it has been reported from brackish conditions. Its smaller size makes it more suitable for a smaller aquarium (however, it will still outgrow the vast majority of home systems).

References

Bigelow & Schroeder (1953), Daiber & Booth (1960), Henningsen (1996), Schreiber (1997).

EAGLE RAYS
Family Myliobatidae

THE EAGLE RAYS ARE ACTIVE FISHES that move through the water by flapping their pectoral fins. They commonly rest on the seafloor, raising themselves up on their pectoral fins and pushing off the bottom if danger threatens. However, they don't bury under the substrate in the manner of stingrays and stingarees. They can move at great speeds and can even leap clear of the water's surface. They differ morphologically in the formation of the snout (it is a single projecting lobe in eagle rays). Like the two preceding ray families, the eagle rays also possess tail stings (sometimes up to five are present on a single individual) that are used for self defense. There are 23 species and 4 genera in the family. The genus *Myliobatis* has a rostral lobe that is connected to the side of the pectoral fins, while this lobe is not contiguous with the pectoral fins in *Aetobatus*, *Pteromylaeus*, and *Aetomylaeus*. This species has an elongated snout, a narrow subrostral lobe, and rounded pectoral fin tips. The adults are light brown dorsally, while the juveniles have pale and reddish spots. They sometimes school, but usually not in massive numbers like the cownose rays. They are ovoviviparous (uterine viviparity). Courtship and copulation has been reported in two species, and the Spotted Eagle Ray (*Aetobatus narinari*) has bred in large oceanariums. Females of some species are reported to leap out of the sea and slam down on the water's surface to facilitate birthing. Estuaries serve as nursery grounds for some species.

By excavating large holes in the substrate and grubbing with their elongated, flexible snouts, eagle rays capture invertebrates that they masticate with their dental plates. Bat Rays (*Myliobatis californica*), and possibly other eagle ray species, are often followed by bony fishes that consume the small invertebrates the rays dig up.

In the wild and in aquariums, myliobatids, especially young specimens, are commonly eaten by sharks and the Killer Whale (*Orcinus orca*).

Captive Care

EAGLE RAYS OFTEN FARE WELL in captivity, but because of their large size and active lifestyles, they require a very large system to thrive. They should be avoided by the home aquarist, even though at least one species is readily available from some marine fish wholesalers. Some species can be difficult to nourish, requiring special fare to instigate a feeding response. For example, Omaha's Henry Doorly Zoo had a juvenile Spotted Eagle Ray (*Aetobatus narinari*) that for some time would eat only fresh clams on the half-shell before it eventually accepted other foods. These rays will engage in spectacular aerial displays, which can be problematic if they are housed in an open enclosure. They are not a threat to fish tankmates, but are susceptible to being eaten by larger sharks. If these animals are mishandled, their tail stings can cause a painful injury. Some, especially the Spotted Eagle Ray, are very sensitive to trichlorfon.

Species Account

Myliobatis californica Gill, 1865

Common Name: Bat Ray.

Size, Growth, and Age: This ray is born at a disc width of 22 to 31 cm (8.7 to 12.2 in.) and attains a maximum disc width of 1.8 m (5.9 ft.). The males become sexually mature at a disc width of 45 to 62 cm (17.7 to 24.4 in.), at an age of 2 to 3 years. (The claspers undergo a growth spurt at a disc width of about 55 cm [21.7 in.].) Females mature at about 81 cm (31.8 in.) and about 5 years of age. These rays grow about 10 cm (3.9 in.) in disc width for the first several years, after which growth slows considerably. Females grow more slowly than males. The Bat Ray is thought to live at least 24 years.

Distribution: Oregon to the Gulf of California.

Biology: The Bat Ray occurs at a depth range of less than 1 up to 46 m (3.3 to 152 ft.). It is often found in kelp beds and near rocky reefs, and also frequently in bays and estuaries. During courtship, one or more males will follow close behind a female with their rostrums near her vent. Males will also nip the pelvic and pectoral fins of the female. When it is time to copulate, the male moves under the female so his back is against her belly, rotates a clasper up and to the side, and inserts it into

Myliobatis californica (Bat Ray): fascinating animal for huge aquariums.

her cloaca as the pair swims with synchronous beats of the pectoral fins. Parturition and mating occur in the spring and summer months, when this ray forms large breeding assemblages. The litter size ranges from 2 to 12 (there is a direct correlation between the size of the litter and the size of the female). Gestation lasts from 9 to 12 months.

The Bat Ray digs out invertebrates from the sand and mud with its snout and also digs large depressions by lifting its body on its pectoral fin tips and moving up and down. The suction generated by this behavior pulls the sand out from under its body, exposing buried prey. Clams are a major food item of juveniles; as Bat Rays grow, echiuroid worms (weenie worms) become more important in their diet. They also eat polychaete worms, abalones, oysters, snails, shrimp, crabs, and bony fishes. When eating mollusks, the ray ingests the animal whole, crushes the shell, spits it all out, then reingests the soft body parts. It often rests on the seafloor or on kelp. It occurs singly or in schools. In the more southern portions of its range, it has been observed to form mixed schools with Spotted Eagle Rays (*Aetobatus narinari*). The Bat Ray is a major food of the Broadnose Sevengill Shark (*Notorynchus cepedianus*), while small individuals are sometimes eaten by California sea lions.

Captive Care: This is a good aquarium inhabitant if you have a large enough to tank to hold it (few home aquarists do). Mike Shaw, of Sea World in San Diego, was kind enough to share some of his observations on this species. He reports that they have had good success keeping this species and currently have individuals that have been in their facilities for over 10 years. According to Shaw, these rays host an incredible number of parasites when first collected—they are more parasite-ridden than any other fish he has ever seen, excluding the Ocean Sunfish (*Mola mola*). The ray is usually infested with monogenetic flukes, copepods, and leeches (with individual parasites numbering in the hundreds). Quarantine and extensive treatments are required to prepare newly collected specimens before they can be safely introduced to the main display tank. When they are introduced, the flukes are kept in check by keeping low levels of copper (0.05 ppm) in the tank at all times.

Bat Rays readily reproduce in the aquarium, giving birth to three or four litters per year. The males regularly bite the posterior edge of the female's pelvic and pectoral fins. The male's biting results in abrasions that are potential sites of bacterial infections. Amorous males will sometimes even chase the females into the aquarium decor. Because of potential courtship-related injuries, it is best to house a single male in a tank with numerous females (or have females with no males at all). Shaw reports that newborns kept in a shallow, outdoor pool were eaten by seagulls! These rays might also jump out of open enclosures.

Aquarium Size: 18,430 L (4,850 gal.)

Water Temperature: 14 to 21°C (57 to 70°F).

Aquarium Suitability Index: 4 (X-large tank required).

Remarks: The Bat Ray's subrostral lobe is short and rounded. The pectoral fins are broad, with rounded tips, the dorsal fin is small and positioned just behind the tips of the pelvic fins. The dorsal coloration is olive to brown with no markings, while the ventrum is creamy white in color. The Bat Ray can have up to five stings (i.e., tail spines) at the base of its tail.

References

Feder et al. (1974), Limbaugh (1963), Martin & Cailliet (1988a, 1988b), M. Shaw (personal communication), Talent (1982), Tricas (1980).

Myliobatis californica (Bat Ray) swimming through a kelp forest.

CHAPTER 5

Swimming with the Sharks & Rays

Potential Elasmobranch Tankmates—and Livestock to Avoid

I F WE CONSIDER SHARKS TO BE THE APEX PREDATORS OF THE sea, it comes as a surprise to many aquarists that other reef fishes can pose a threat to their captive elasmobranchs. The reality is that triggerfishes, angelfishes, certain wrasses, and puffer-fishes may maim your shark or ray; and morays, frog-fishes, and groupers may eat an elasmobranch if it is small enough to ingest. Of course, sharks and rays are also a threat to certain invertebrates and fishes as well. For these reasons, care must be taken when selecting elasmobranch tankmates. In this chapter we will examine those animals that are and are not compatible with captive sharks and rays.

> *"Care must be exercised when mixing shark species or choosing fishes and invertebrates for the elasmobranch aquarium."*

Dangerous Tankmates

TWO THINGS MUST BE CONSIDERED when we plan the mix of organisms that will find themselves living in close proximity in a marine aquarium: threats and competitors. First, is a particular fish likely to injure or even eat your elasmobranch? I have observed a number of ca-

A school of Golden Jacks or Trevally freely associate with a massive Whale Shark—a filter feeder, not a piscivore—off Western Australia.

sualties and injuries that were inflicted by bony fishes, including a Blue Angelfish (*Holacanthus bermudensis*) that blinded a Horn Shark (*Heterodontus francisci*) by nipping its eyes, a Queen Angelfish (*Holacanthus ciliaris*) that bit and caused the death of a Cortez Round Stingray (*Urobatis maculatus*), and a Regal Angelfish (*Pygoplites diacanthus*) that wounded a Bluespotted Ribbontail Ray (*Taeniura lymma*) by biting it repeatedly. I've also heard reports of butterflyfishes nipping and damaging small wobbegongs in captivity and have seen sharks that had their fins damaged by large pufferfishes. To fish that feed on the ocean bottom, sedentary elasmobranchs are simply an extension of the substrate. Even more, the slime of rays is rich in nutrients and can be an attractive food source for some species. Problems of this nature are more common in the smaller aquariums that one expects in a home or office. Many

TABLE 5-1.

Fish Tankmates that Might Harm a Shark or Ray

Common Name	Family Name
*Scorpionfishes	Scorpaenidae
Butterflyfishes	Chaetodontidae
Large Angelfishes	Pomacanthidae
Filefishes	Monacanthidae
Triggerfishes	Balistidae
Puffers	Tetraodontidae
Porcupinefishes	Diodontidae

* Members of this family may envenom and injure a shark or ray that bumps into their fin spines. The rest of the families represented contain species that have been known to pick at and damage elasmobranchs. However, they may be compatible with a shark or ray in a very large aquarium.

A Regal Angelfish picks at a Bluespotted Ribbontail Ray, a predictable problem that can easily lead to the decline and death of the ray.

species combinations that seem to do well in huge public aquariums would be hard to duplicate in the more limited confines of a standard tank.

Larger piscivorous fishes are also a threat to juvenile sharks. For example, I have seen frogfishes ingest juvenile bamboo sharks, and larger groupers will eat smaller elasmobranchs. I know of several situations where morays have attacked shark tankmates. In one case, a larger Snowflake Moray (*Echidna nebulosa*) captured and swallowed a neonate (newborn) Leopard Shark (*Triakis semifasciata*). In another, an adult Ocellated Moray (*Gymnothorax saxicola*) bit a chunk out of a smoothhound shark's gill region.

Care must also be exercised when mixing shark species in the same tank. Nurse sharks and wobbegongs,

An Ornate Wobbegong attempts to swallow a Port Jackson Shark in the sort of attack behavior that makes "wobbies" untrustworthy tankmates.

Two Port Jackson Sharks shelter in a rocky nook with an Ornate Wobbegong. Many aquarium sharks must have hiding places to feel secure.

for example, will eat other elasmobranchs—even members of their own species—that are small enough to be swallowed. The wobbegongs will even attempt to eat other elasmobranchs that are too large to swallow. For example, the Ornate Wobbegong *(Orectolobus ornatus)* has been observed holding adult Port Jackson Sharks *(Heterodontus portusjacksoni)* by the head, for long periods of time, before releasing them. This shark will also eat small guitarfishes and stingarees. Some of the larger shark species kept in public aquariums are even more notorious for their habit of eating their elasmobranch tankmates. For example, the Sandtiger *(Carcharias taurus)* and the Bull Shark *(Carcharhinus leucas)* will eat any shark or ray that is small enough to subdue.

Food Competitors

THE SECOND THING TO CONSIDER when evaluating potential shark or ray tankmates is: Will they compete unreasonably at feeding times? Although it is possible to keep other predators, such as groupers, with sharks and rays, the lightning-fast feeding behavior of a grouper may hamper the aquarist's attempts to feed a less-ag-gressive elasmobranch. There are, of course, tactics that can overcome this sort of problem. With bamboo, epaulette, or nurse sharks, for example, you can place food in a shallow crevice that the shark's tankmates are unable to enter, or even bury the food lightly in the sand. Because they are very proficient at sucking prey from reef interstices and from the substrate, these sharks have a competitive edge in such situations. Another technique that allows the aquarist to target food intended for a shark is a feeding stick or a pair of long forceps used to present the meal to its proper recipient. In this way you can monitor just how much food your shark is getting while ensuring that no food is left to decompose behind tank decor.

Aggression

ALTHOUGH INTRASPECIFIC AGGRESSION is a relative rarity in wild shark populations, it could be a problem in captivity. This is especially true during the mating season. It has been well documented that male teleost fishes are more belligerent, especially toward consexual competitors, during the breeding period. Although

TABLE 5-2.

Some Potential Fish Tankmates for Sharks and Rays

Common Name	Family Name	Common Name	Family Name
Moray eels	Muraenidae	Snappers	Lutjanidae
Snake eels	Ophichthidae	Jacks	Carangidae
Squirrelfishes	Holocentridae	Discfishes	Echeneidae
Groupers	Serranidae	Monos	Monodactylidae
Batfishes	Ephippidae	Damselfishes	Pomacentridae
Spinecheeks	Nemipteridae	Hawkfishes	Cirrhitidae
Cardinalfishes	Apogonidae	Sand perches	Pinguipedidae
Goatfishes	Mullidae	Gobies	Gobiidae

Groupers

Variola louti (Lyretail Grouper)

Cardinalfishes

Pajama Cardinal (*Sphaeramia nematoptera*)

Squirrelfishes & Soldierfishes

Brick Soldierfish (*Myripristis amaena*)

Damselfishes

Chrysiptera cyanea (Blue Devil Damselfish)

Hawkfishes

Paracirrhites forsteri (Freckled Hawkfish)

Moray Eels

Gymnothorax meleagris (Whitemouth Moray)

there is much less data on elasmobranchs (because they are more difficult to observe in the field), aquarium observations suggest that the same holds true for sharks and rays. For example, adult male wobbegongs are reported to fight during the breeding season, while mature male Sandtiger Sharks have also been reported to behave aggressively toward heterospecific shark tankmates—as well as diving aquarists—during courtship. Mature male Epaulette Sharks (*Hemiscyllium ocellatum*) can be belligerent toward one another, as well as toward other male shark species. Kelly Jedlicki, a serious shark keeper, had a sexually energized male *H. ocellatum* rip part of the lower jaw off of a smaller male Horn Shark (*Heterodontus francisci*). Mitch Carl, aquarist at Omaha's Henry Doorly Zoo reports another observation of possible aggressive behavior within a species. In their largest aquarium, the zoo has a colony of female Southern Stingrays (*Dasyatis americana*) that have been observed to bite each other on the pectoral margins, much the same way that male rays bite females during courtship. Dr. Timothy Tricas also reports that Atlantic Stingrays (*Dasyatis sabina*) display intraspecific aggression in captivity, and that the females are more pugnacious than the males.

In the field, I have observed a considerable amount of intrasexual aggression in male Round Stingrays (*Urobatis halleri*) during the mating period. During this time the males would charge, strike, and nip one another. I also observed an apparent aggressive encounter between a Bluespotted Ribbontail Ray (*Taeniura lymma*) and a Bluespotted Stingray (*Dasyatis kuhlii*) on the Great Barrier Reef. The larger male *T. lymma* was grasping the left pectoral margin of the male *D. kuhlii* and held on tightly as the *D. kuhlii* attempted to escape. After watching for 7 minutes I moved too near the dasyatid duo and the *T. lymma* released its grip.

Triggerfishes, such as this Blueline Triggerfish, have a history of biting captive elasmobranchs.

One group of elasmobranchs that often display aggression toward their shark tankmates are the sawfishes. Dr. David Davies wrote of a Largetooth Sawfish (*Pristis microdon*) kept in the Durban Aquarium: "The sawfish took a violent dislike to the small sharks . . . and lost no opportunity of giving a savage sideways blow with its saw to any shark that came within reach . . . when the sawfish had been in the tank 5

An expert ambush predator, an Australian Angel Shark (*Squatina australis*), explodes out of the substrate to grab a passing fish.

Another Australian Angel Shark retracts back into the substrate with an unsuspectingly engulfed passerby firmly clenched in its mouth.

months there was hardly a shark in the tank which did not bear the marks of the sawfish's teeth." Mike Shaw, curator at Sea World, reported seeing a Smalltooth Sawfish (*Pristis pectinata*) approach a Nurse Shark that was lying on the bottom, and deliver three swift blows with its saw to the shark's dorsum. The Nurse Shark did not respond so the sawfish hit it three more times with its tooth-studded rostrum. Why sawfishes have such disdain for their elasmobranch cousins is not known, but it may be because some sharks prey on smaller sawfishes or because they are potential food competitors. In any case, it is essential that these fishes have plenty of swimming room so they can avoid each other if they are going to coexist in captivity.

Sharks as Predators

THE MORE OBVIOUS THING TO CONSIDER when pondering potential shark tankmates is whether the animal in question is possible prey for your shark. Many sharks simply see smaller fishes as food, and the more-voracious species, such as wobbegongs and nurse sharks, will consume or maul relatively large tankmates like moray eels (another predator often selected to be kept with a shark). Even sharks with relatively small mouths can

TABLE 5-3.

Possible Invertebrate Tankmates for Sharks and Rays

Common Name	Category
Larger cowries	Cypraeidae
Larger conchs	Strombidae
Boxer shrimps	*Stenopus* spp.
Cleaner shrimps	*Lysmata* spp.
Hermit crabs	Paguridae
Decorator crabs	Majidae
Slipper lobsters	Scyllaridae
Spiny lobster	Palinuridae
Linckia sea stars	*Linckia* spp.
Brittle stars	Ophiuroidea
Pencil urchins	Cidaridae

While these invertebrates can be successfully housed with at least some sharks and rays, it is possible that they may occasionally fall prey to a hungry elasmobranch. It is prudent to provide them with a place to hide and to acclimate them to the tank before introducing the shark or ray. Also, make sure you check into the care requirements of whatever invertebrates you plan to acquire before purchasing them.

do damage to larger species that bury in the substrate. I've known a medium-sized Brownbanded Bamboo Shark (*Chiloscyllium punctatum*) to chew the flanks of a larger New Guinea Wrasse (*Anampses neoguinaicus*) when the wrasse was buried under the sand at night. Some sharks kept in public aquariums are notorious for eating any fish that they can swallow whole. The most infamous of these is the Sandtiger Shark (*Carcharias*

taurus). As mentioned above, this snaggle-toothed menace will eat smaller elasmobranch tankmates, but it will also consume any teleost it is able to catch. It will even eat its potential benefactors, the Remoras (*Remora remora*). Although most rays have small mouths and can be kept with a variety of bony fish species, they will occasionally maul a buried fish or pin a fish under their discs, often in the corner of the aquarium, and try to ingest it.

Sharks and Ornamental Invertebrates

MANY OF THE ELASMOBRANCHS AVAILABLE to aquarists feed heavily on invertebrates. Some are more specialized in the types of invertebrates they will eat, while others consume any species small enough to get their teeth around. As a result, care should be exercised when selecting invertebrates to keep with your shark or ray. The obvious thing to do before adding an invertebrate to your elasmobranch tank is to check into the food

Cleaner shrimps will groom aquarium sharks and rays, but should be added to the tank first to reduce the chance of their being eaten.

TABLE 5-4.

Shark and Ray Cleaners

Cleaner Species	Elasmobranch Hosts	Reference
Stripey (*Microcanthus strigatus*)	Zebra Shark	K. Aitken (pers. comm.)
Barberfish (*Johnrandallia nigrirostris*)	Scalloped Hammerhead Shark	Personal observation
Passer Angelfish (*Holacanthus passer*)	Scalloped Hammerhead Shark	Personal observation
Clarion Angelfish (*Holacanthus clarionensis*)	Manta Ray	Personal observation
Longfin Bannerfish (*Heniochus acuminatus*)	Largetooth Sawfish	Davies, 1963
Hogfishes (*Bodianus* spp.)	Requiem sharks, whiptail stingrays	Personal observation
Bluestreak Cleaner Wrasse (*Labroides dimidiatus*)	Epaulette sharks, wobbegongs, Leopard Shark, requiem sharks, Pelagic Thresher Shark, whiptail stingrays, Manta Ray	Personal observation; Keyes, 1982; C. Frew (pers. comm.)
Twotone Wrasse (*Thalassoma amblycephalum*)	Manta Ray	Personal observation
Bluehead Wrasse (*T. bifasciatum*)	Whiptail stingrays, Manta Ray	Personal observation; Snelson et al., 1990
Cortez Rainbow Wrasse (*T. lucasanum*)	Silvertip Shark	F. Bavendam (pers. comm.)
Señorita (*Oxyjulis californica*)	Bat Ray	Limbaugh, 1961
Banded Cleaner Goby (*Gobiosoma nesiotes*)	Whitetip Reef Shark	Personal observation
Randall's Cleaner Goby (*G. randalli*)	Caribbean Reef Shark	Sazima & Moura, 2000

Holacanthus passer (Passer Angelfish): this species has been observed cleaning parasites from large Scalloped Hammerhead Sharks in the wild.

habits of the species you hope to keep. (See the species descriptions in Chapter 4.) Select only invertebrates that are not a normal part of your shark or ray's diet and if still in doubt, stick to the generally "bullet-proof" choices discussed here.

One group of interesting crustaceans that can be successfully housed with some elasmobranchs are the cleaner/boxer shrimps. This group includes the Banded Coral Shrimp (*Stenopus hispidus*) and the Skunk Cleaner Shrimp (*Lysmata amboinensis*). Sedentary sharks will often allow these crustaceans to crawl over their bodies and to pick at their skin. One word of warning—it is usually prudent to introduce the shrimp into the tank before the shark is added. This reduces the likelihood that the crustacean will be eaten as soon as it is added to the tank.

Scavenging crustaceans, such as hermit and brachyuran crabs, can also be kept with some sharks and rays. In fact, these crustaceans will perform a functional role in the elasmobranch aquarium by stirring up the sub-

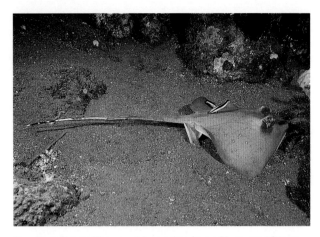
Bluestreak Cleaner Wrasses pick parasites from a Bluespotted Stingray.

strate and eating scraps of leftover food. Beware, however, for large crabs can do damage to sharks and rays. I've seen hermit crabs tenaciously grip the ventrum of both a Leopard Shark (*T. semifasciata*) and a Gray Smoothhound Shark (*Mustelus californicus*). Each continued to swim around with the crustacean hitchhiker attached. In the case of the Smoothhound, the shark had to be removed from the water and the crab forcibly detached by crushing the claws with pliers. I have also seen crabs pinch and pull at the disc margins of buried rays. Be aware that there are also aquarium sharks and rays that love to eat hermit crabs.

It is possible to keep sharks in a very large reef tank that is specifically designed to accommodate them. Bamboo and epaulette sharks, for example, appreciate caves, crevices, and overhangs to hide in or under and will do well in a reef aquarium with a very stable reef structure. Also, plenty of open bottom space should be provided so the shark has room to move (see Chapter 2 for more on shark aquarium decor). While there are no sharks and rays that feed on corals, they can cause mechanical damage by knocking them over and resting on them. Therefore, if you keep corals with these animals,

be sure the corals are firmly affixed to the live rock with underwater epoxy or superglue. Corals should also be positioned well off the bottom. Steer clear of those species of sea anemones and corals that are known to have potent stinging cells (e.g., Elegance Coral [*Catalaphyllia jardinei*]) as they may damage your elasmobranch. Sedentary sharks are likely to rest on the these invertebrates, which can result in eye or skin irritation. Rays, because of their lack of dermal denticles on the ventral surface, are especially prone to being stung by these cnidarians. Larger carpet anemones will even eat smaller elasmobranchs, like juvenile bamboo and epaulette sharks, while smaller sea anemones are fed upon by certain sharks, such as the Horn Shark (*Heterodontus francisci*).

Shark Partners
Remoras and Other Discfishes

SOME SPECIALIZED BONY FISHES feed by picking parasites and necrotic tissue off other fishes, including elasmobranchs. The most widely recognized shark and ray cleaners are the discfishes (Family Echeneidae). These fishes have specialized dorsal fins that they use to adhere to their hosts. The spines in the dorsal fin are split to form movable ridges inside a fleshy disc. The fish presses the disc against the host and moves the ridges like the slats in a window blind to create suction. As juveniles, discfishes can be found in the mouths, gill chambers, and spiracles of sharks and rays. As they grow, they spend more time on the shark or ray's body surface. The discfishes eat parasites, as well as zooplankton, shark feces, and the leftovers from shark feeding events. Their elasmobranch hosts serve as a source of food, transport, and protection.

The discfish family consists of four genera and eight species, three of which are commonly observed associ-

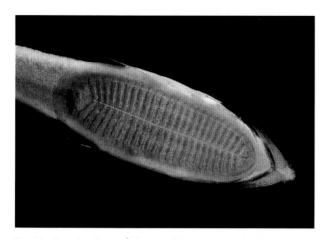

The ridged suction disc, actually a modified dorsal fin, of a Remora.

ating with elasmobranchs. The Remora (*Remora remora*) usually cleans sharks and devil rays, feeding almost exclusively on parasitic copepods, which it scoops from its host with its elongate lower jaw. It rarely cleans parasites from the fins, and concentrates its efforts instead on the host's head, body, and gill chambers. The Shark Sucker (*Echeneis naucrates*) is a common discfish often observed swimming on its own. It will associate with a wide range of hosts, including a number of elasmobranch species. It eats copepods and isopods off sharks and rays, but also scavenges and captures small fishes. In one study, 16% of Shark Sucker stomachs examined contained ectoparasites.

Discfishes are interesting and durable aquarium fishes in their own right and will do well even in the absence of a host shark, although they will greedily eat ornamental shrimps and smaller fishes.

Discfishes can serve a valuable function in the shark and ray tank, controlling crustacean and fluke infestations. I have included them in the home aquarium (to rid sharks and rays of parasites) with varying results. I had a discfish that would clean the monogenetic trematodes off the ventrum of a Bluntnose Stingray (*Dasy-*

atis sayi). When the ray swam above the tank bottom, the discfish would slide along its ventral surface and ingest the trematodes. Because one of the major foods of wild discfishes is copepods, these fishes can also help control crustacean infections in captivity. However, aquarists should be aware that discfishes can irritate their hosts in aquarium confines. For example, the same Bluntnose Stingray would bury itself in an apparent attempt to get away from the discfish, which adhered to and chafed at exposed areas of the ray, causing damage to its epidermis near the disc margins. Obviously stressed, the ray spent more of its time buried and showed an appreciable increase in its respiration rate. Only after the discfish was removed did the ray again behave normally.

Sharks have been observed rubbing against the sub-

A pair of large discfishes hitch a ride on the underside of a Zebra Shark. They make interesting and hardy aquarium fishes in their own right.

strate and leaping out of the water in an attempt to dislodge an annoying discfish. Because these bony fishes can cause stress in certain elasmobranchs, particularly in smaller tanks, it may be best to introduce them for a short period of time only when your shark or ray is showing signs of parasitic infection. Keeping discfishes with more active shark species is less problematic, although the shark will occasionally chafe on the substrate if annoyed by one of these hitchhikers.

Other Cleaner Fishes

OTHER BONY FISHES are also known to pick parasites off sharks and rays (see Table 5-4, page 172), and some of these species can also be useful in ridding elasmobranchs of parasites in the home aquarium. I have seen Bluestreak Cleaner Wrasses (*Labroides dimidiatus*) cleaning the gills and mouth of a Tasseled Wobbegong (*Eucrossorhinus dasypogon*) and an Epaulette Shark (*Hemiscyllium ocellatum*) in the wild. In captivity, the same species of wrasse has been reported to clean the body surface, mouth, and gills of larger requiem sharks. On rare occasions, these wrasses may pick at the eyes of more sedentary sharks. Watch them closely, especially in smaller tanks. Unfortunately, fish mucus is an important component of the cleaner wrasse diet, and they are difficult to maintain long-term in an aquarium that lacks a large number of mucus-laden fishes.

The Longfin Bannerfish (*Heniochus acuminatus*) has also been used to clean a sawfish of flukes in a public aquarium. As with discfishes, these other cleaner species can sometimes be irritants in a home tank. For example, the Bannerfish may persistently pick at the areas around the stingray's eyes, causing irritation and even blindness. If you do house a cleaner species with your shark or ray, keep an eye on the situation and be sure that the cleaner does not become a pest.

Jacks (Trevally)

A NUMBER OF JACK SPECIES associate with elasmobranchs and benefit from these relationships. Jacks have been observed to scavenge on the remains of elasmobranch meals, while some jacks hang over rays as they forage and attack any prey items flushed from the sand. Jacks may also increase their hunting success by using the larger shark or ray as a moving blind to get closer to prey species.

Several jack species are available to aquarists and make attractive shark and ray tankmates. The only potential drawback to keeping them is that they are fast, aggressive feeders and may hamper your attempts to feed the elasmobranch. Two species that are especially interesting are the Pilotfish (*Naucrates ductor*) and the Golden Jack (*Gnathanodon speciosus*).

Pilotfish often associate with open-water sharks, swimming close to their bodies, fins, and snouts. They were originally given their name because it was thought that they led, or "piloted," their host to food; this theory has since been rejected. Instead, it is now believed that Pilotfish derive energy savings by moving within the pressure wave created by their host shark as it swims. They also gain protection against open-ocean predators reluctant to approach a large shark. Pilotfish eat scraps resulting from shark meals and may eat shark feces (this has yet to be confirmed). Whether this association also benefits the shark is not known, but it has been suggested that Pilotfish clean ectoparasites from their hosts. Unfortunately, because of their affinity for open-ocean environments where collection for the aquarium trade is rare, Pilotfish rarely show up in stores.

Juvenile Golden Jacks, sometimes sold as Pilotfish, are reef dwellers that swim with sharks, devil rays, large groupers, and dugongs. Unlike Pilotfish, which are typically observed with active, oceanic species, Golden Jacks

A classic symbiont of sharks and rays is the Golden Jack (*Gnathanodon speciosus*). It will steal bits of food but may offer grooming services in return.

associate with both active and inactive shark species. They have been observed near, or swimming over, Whitetip Reef Sharks (*Triaenodon obesus*) and Tawny Nurse Sharks (*Nebrius ferrugineus*), even when the sharks were lying in a cave or crevice. They apparently benefit in a way similar to the Pilotfish. The advantage to the host shark may include being "cleaned" by the jack—they have been observed to pick at the skin of resting Whitetips. Golden Jacks are often available to hobbyists and make a fascinating addition to the shark tank. One specimen I kept swam continuously near a juvenile Gray Smooth-hound (*Mustelus californicus*) and was observed on several occasions to pick at the shark's skin when it was at rest. They will also help keep the tank clean by feeding on leftovers. The main drawback in purchasing one of these

fish is their potential size—a full-grown Golden Jack can attain a length of 110 cm (42.9 in.).

In short, selecting appropriate species to fit into an aquarium primarily designed to house one or more elasmobranchs can take some thought and investigation. The right tankmates can add significant interest and color to the elasmobranch aquarium, but ill-chosen fishes or invertebrates can easily become expensive targets for a shark or ray or even turn into hazards that impede successful elasmobranch keeping.

References

Cressey & Lachner (1970), Davies (1963), Keyes (1982), Limbaugh (1961), Michael (1993), Nelson (1980), Sazima & Moura (2000), Snelson et al. (1990).

CHAPTER 6

Foods & Feeding

Proper Nutrition for the Captive Elasmobranch

SENSATIONAL MOVIES AND TELEVISION DOCUMENTARIES OUGHT not to be anyone's guide to feeding a captive shark or ray. The image of the all-consuming, eating-machine, maws-of-death predator that has been implanted in the public mind is wildly exaggerated and simply wrong for many, many elasmobranchs. The aquarist who assumes that his or her specimen must be allowed to gorge itself daily is almost certain to create unnaturally rapid growth, water-quality problems, and possibly health consequences for the overfed animal.

> *"Most species kept in home aquariums require much less food than active, 'warm-blooded' species."*

Feeding Frequency

IN NATURE, MOST SHARKS EAT relatively little and grow slowly. Studies conducted on both captive and wild sharks have shown that to maintain good health, a shark eats only 3 to 14% of its body weight per week. As an example, consider Skipper, a 153 kg (337 lbs.) Sandtiger Shark (*Carcharias taurus*) that used to live at the Taronga Park Zoo in Sydney, Australia. This shark ate from 77 to

Not all elasmobranchs share the appetites of a Great White Shark, something aquarists sometimes fail to appreciate.

TABLE 6-1.

Food Consumption by Some Elasmobranch Species in Captivity

Species (Juvenile/Adult)	Food Consumption (% body weight/week)	Reference
Nurse Shark (J)	2.1 - 2.2	Clark, 1963; Schmid et al., 1990
Lemon Shark (J)	9.8 - 21	Clark, 1963; Gruber, 1982
Lemon Shark (A)	3.5	Clark, 1963
Sandtiger Shark (J-A)	1.5 - 2.1	Schmid et al., 1990
Bull Shark (J)	3.3 - 3.9	Schmid et al., 1990
Sandbar Shark (J)	2.1 - 3.7	Early (in Stillwell & Kohler, 1993); Schmid et al., 1990
Southern Stingray (J)	15.75 - 26.6	Henningsen (pers. comm.)

Skipper, a well-studied Sandtiger Shark, ate about 1% of its body weight in food per week, a fraction of the consumption rate of bony fishes.

91 kg (169 to 200 lbs.) of fishes each year, or an average of only about 1% of its body weight in food per week. Skipper's food intake varied from 0.3% body weight per week in the colder months to 3% in the summer. In contrast, a Largemouth Bass (*Micropterus salmoides*) may eat 39 to 59% of its body weight in food per week, while a Variegated Lizardfish (*Synodus variegatus*) may consume 84% of its body weight per week.

Weekly ration sizes ought to vary depending on the species and age of the shark, the ambient water temperature, and the energy value of the food consumed. Active species that maintain their body temperatures higher than the ambient water temperature (e.g., thresher, mako, and Great White Sharks) consume more food due to their higher metabolic needs. For example, it has been calculated that the daily ration for the Shortfin Mako Shark (*Isurus oxyrinchus*) is approximately 3.2% of its body weight. Most species kept in home aquariums, such as epaulettes, bamboos, nurses, catsharks, and wobbegongs, are diurnally inactive, and therefore require much less food than the active, "warm-blooded" species. In colder conditions (as shown by the study of Skipper) sharks eat less and consequently grow more slowly. Young sharks, on the other hand, consume more food due to their greater energy needs for growth. For example, Sandbar Shark pups (*Carcharhinus plumbeus*) were reported to consume 1.43% of their body weight daily, compared to 0.86% of their body weight as larger juveniles and adults. Van Dykhuizen and Mollet (1992) report that the pups of the Broadnosed Sevengill Sharks (*Notorynchus cepedianus*) have a food intake ten times higher than that of the adults. For examples of several shark species' food consumption, see Table 6-1.

Food-habit studies indicate that most sharks feed for a short time, followed by much longer periods during which there is no or limited feeding. For example, Cortes and Gruber (1990) report that captive Lemon Sharks (*Negaprion brevirostris*) feed for approximately 11 hours, then go without feeding for the next 32 hours. It has been suggested that during digestion sharks are less motivated to feed. When examined in studies, a large percentage of sharks have empty stomachs. For example, 25% of Lemon Sharks, 36% of Spiny Dogfish (*Squalus acanthias*), 40% of Shortfin Makos, 50% of Sandbar Sharks (*Carcharhinus plumbeus*), and 60% of Japanese Wobbegongs (*Orectolobus japonicus*) were all observed with empty stomachs in various studies. This data indicates that sharks feed intermittently, and that they may go for days without feeding. Some species, however, have greater rates of prey consumption. In two different studies on the Bonnethead Shark (*Sphyrna tiburo*) only 5% and 7% of the individuals examined had empty stomachs, indicating that this species feeds more frequently. A study of the Smallspotted Catshark (*Scyliorhinus canicula*) demonstrated that it may also

An Epaulette Shark shoves its snout into the substrate in search of food.

Typical hunting behavior of Freycinet's Epaulette Shark.

Live fiddler crab invokes feeding by a captive Gray Smoothhound Shark.

Bluespotted Stingray settles over its prey in a typical hunting pose.

Banded Stingaree roots through the substrate in search of buried prey.

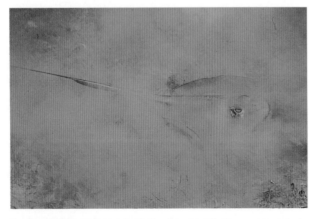
Southern Stingray raises a cloud of sediment hunting in a seagrass bed.

feed more often, or have a slower rate of gastric evacuation: in this study of 2,003 individuals, 90% had some traces of food in their stomachs.

It has been shown that in some species of elasmobranchs there is an inverse correlation between the rate of gastric evacuation (i.e., the amount of time from ingestion until the food exits the stomach) and the return of appetite. Gastric evacuation times are slower in sharks than in most tropical bony fishes, ranging from 24 to 124 hours. The length of time that the food remains in the stomach (which will determine the quantity of nutrients absorbed) will have a direct impact on the quantity of food consumed. Gastric evacuation is dependent on the species in question, the size of the meal consumed, and the water temperature. For example, gastric evacuation in the Smallspotted Catshark (*Scyliorhinus canicula*) was 2.5 times faster when the meal was twice the size, while a Scalloped Hammerhead (*Sphyrna lewini*) evacuated 90% of its meal in 19.7 hours when the water temperature was 27.1°C (80.8°F) and 28.6 hours at 24.0°C (75.2°F). What does this mean for the aquarist? If you keep your sharks at lower water temperatures and feed them larger meals you should not have to feed them as frequently.

Food-habit studies on wild rays demonstrate that these fishes feed continually through out the day and/or night, rather than intermittently as is the case for most sharks. For example, the Southern Stingray feeds on smaller prey items through out the day. Gilliam and Sullivan (1993) found no empty stomachs in their study of this species and the average number of prey items per gut was 31 (compare this to the Lemon Shark, which typically has only 1 or 2 prey items in its stomach at any one time). Of 192 Round Stingrays (*Urobatis halleri*) examined by Babel (1967), only 12 individuals had empty stomachs. He concluded that this species also feeds continually throughout the day on smaller prey items (up to 50 small shrimps were found in the stomach of a single stingray). A recent study on the Atlantic Stingray (*Dasyatis sabina*), conducted by James L. Bradley IV and Dr. Tim Tricas, indicates that this species consumes large numbers of smaller prey items continually, throughout the day and night. (They reported that an individual could consume 15,150 amphipods in a single day!) There is little information available on the consumption rate of rays, but some preliminary studies in the field and captivity suggest that it is probably around 2.5 to 3.0% of their body weight per day. Unlike sharks, it may be best to feed your ray small meals one or more times daily to maintain optimal health.

Feeding Guidelines

How OFTEN SHOULD YOU FEED your shark or ray in the home aquarium? As suggested by some of the data presented above, feeding frequency is somewhat species-specific. Here is a good starting point: the more sedentary, benthic sharks, such as the wobbegongs, should be fed to satiation once or twice a week. Feed the slightly more lively bullhead, bamboo, nurse, zebra, and catsharks two or three times a week. The active species, such as the smoothhounds, requiem sharks, and Bonnethead should be fed at least three times a week. Guitarfishes can be fed daily, while whiptail stingrays and stingarees should be fed at least once a day. Remember, an elasmobranch will need to be fed more if kept at higher water temperatures or if it is still a juvenile. One of the best ways to monitor whether a shark or ray is getting enough to eat is to keep a close eye on the condition of the animal. Signs indicating a protein deficiency include atrophy of the skeletal muscles (especially obvious is the atrophy of the dorsal musculature), a sunken stomach, wrinkled and blotchy skin, tattered

TABLE 6-2.	
Feeding Frequency for Some Elasmobranchs	
Type	**Times per Week**
Bullhead sharks	2-3
Wobbegongs	1-2
Bamboo sharks	2-3
Nurse sharks	2
Zebra sharks	3
Catsharks	2-3
Requiem sharks	3
Bonnethead Shark	3-4
Guitarfishes	7
Electric rays	4-5
Stingrays	7
Stingarees	7

fins, and prolonged inactivity during the day and night. If you observe any of these signs, feed your shark more often, vary its diet, and increase the frequency of vitamin supplementation.

Except for the reporting of accelerated growth rates, no information is available on the effects of overfeeding on captive elasmobranchs. However, this practice has been shown to cause health problems in predatory bony fishes. For example, infiltration of the liver by fatty deposits has been reported in stonefishes that were overfed and not given a varied diet. This condition impairs liver function and can ultimately cause death.

Growth Rates

MANY OF THE SHARKS READILY AVAILABLE through the aquarium trade reach over 1 m (3.3 ft.) in length.

Two female Port Jackson Sharks illustrate age-related size disparity: captive sharks grow more quickly with heavy feeding and warmer temperatures.

Because most aquarists cannot provide suitable confines for such large fishes, many captive sharks inevitably outgrow the aquariums (or wallets) of their owners. In growth-rate studies conducted in the field and in captivity, sharks tended to grow more rapidly in confinement than they did in the wild. Young Lemon Sharks, for example, grew three to nine times faster in captivity than they did in the wild, while captive Sandbar Sharks grew at almost five times the rate, and Gray Reef Sharks grew ten times more rapidly in aquariums than in the field. Accelerated growth rates in captivity probably occur because these sharks eat more (at least some species may be food-limited in the wild), expend less energy locating and capturing their prey, and often live in warmer water than their wild counterparts. Therefore, to reduce the rate of growth in our captive elasmobranchs, we should maintain them at lower water temperatures, feed them less, give them room to move, provide stronger currents for them to swim against, and encourage locomotion by feeding them some live foods. Growth rates also gradually decrease as a shark ages. For example, the yearly rate of growth for the Nurse Shark is 25 cm (9.8 in.) in the first year, 18 cm (7.0 in.) in the second year, and 14 cm (5.5 in.) in the third year.

One fact that the aquarist can use to his or her advantage is the knowledge that many male sharks and rays do not grow as large as the females of their species. For example, male Port Jackson Sharks (*Heterodontus portusjacksoni*) reach 105 cm (41.0 in.) in total length, while females may be 18 cm (7.0 in.) longer. According to the formula for aquarium size selection discussed in Chapter 2, pages 44-45, the tank length for the female would have to be at least 36 cm (14.0 in.) longer than that required by the male. This sexual dimorphism is more extreme in some species than in others. (The condition is reversed in several species, with males growing larger than females, but not in any of the readily available aquarium species.) In some species, the females also grow faster than males, at least until they reach sexual maturity. For information on the specific growth rates of those species commonly kept in aquariums, see the Species Accounts in Chapter 4.

Nutritional Deficiencies

HEALTH PROBLEMS resulting from nutritional deficiencies may be encountered in captive sharks. One of the best ways to ensure that you are meeting the dietary needs of your shark or ray is to feed it a diet as close to its natural fare as possible. If you are keeping a bullhead shark, which normally feeds heavily on crabs and urchins, the primary components of the aquarium diet should, of course, be crabs and urchins. If it is not possible to mimic the normal food habits of the species you intend to keep, use the "shotgun" approach. That

is, provide it with as varied a menu as possible in an attempt to cover all the nutritional bases.

Sharks and rays are typically offered natural foods in one of three states—live, fresh, or frozen. Some live and fresh varieties of seafood, including squid, crab, shrimp, and marine fish flesh are the most nutritious alternative. One problem with using the fresh tissues of certain fishes and invertebrates is that they can contain thiaminase, an enzyme that will catalyze the breakdown of thiamine (vitamin B_1) and contribute to a thiamine deficiency. Some species known to contain thiaminase in the raw state are the Alewife (*Alosa pseudoharengus*), Goldfish (*Carassius auratus*), Smelt (*Osmerus mordax*), Atlantic Herring (*Clupea harengus harengus*), Northern Anchovy (*Engraulis mordax*), Chub Mackerel (*Scomber japonicus*), menhaden (*Brevoortia* spp.), American Lobster (*Homarus americanus*), Giant Scallop (*Placopecten grandis*), Blue Mussel (*Mytilus edulis*), and Softshell Clam (*Mya arenaria*). Thiaminase can be destroyed by cooking the flesh, but this will also decrease its nutritional value. Freezing, on the other hand, does not neutralize this or any other enzyme. If thiamine deficiencies occur, sharks may display de-

Frozen shrimp and krill, with vitamin supplements, make ideal shark fare.

creased appetite, muscular atrophy, convulsions, loss of equilibrium, and edema. (Vitamin supplementation can counteract deficiencies resulting from thiaminase.)

Another problem with live or fresh seafood is that it can transmit infectious disease organisms like *Myobacterium* and monogenetic trematodes. However, this occurs very rarely. Sabalones (1995) reports that the National Aquarium in Baltimore fed fresh seafood to sharks for 13 years without ever having problems with parasite transmission.

Frozen food is probably more frequently used by hobbyists when feeding captive sharks and rays. Because food stored in this way may be stripped of some of its nutritional value during the freezing process, it is imperative to add vitamin supplements. Some symptoms of vitamin deficiencies in elasmobranchs include reduced growth, exophthalmia ("popeye"), ascites (fluid accumulation in the coelomic cavity), and anemia (which results in a decreased oxygen-carrying capacity of the blood). Vitamin B deficiency in Lemon Sharks can result in curvature of the body, slight raising of the head, and continuous circular swimming. This problem can be rectified by placing vitamin B tablets in the ailing shark's food. Multivitamins made for human consumption can be used; even better are vitamins manufactured specifically for sharks (e.g., Purina Mills, Inc. Test Diet Divisions, 505 N 4th St., P.O. Box 548, Richmond, IN 47375). Place one of these multivitamins in a piece of the shark's food once a week. There is also a frozen formula food, produced by Ocean Nutrition, that is specifically made for small sharks and rays. This food contains the flesh of several types of marine organisms and is vitamin fortified.

To use frozen foods, remove them from the freezer and keep them at room temperature until they are thawed. Do not soak the food in water to speed up this process, because the essential vitamins will leach from the tissue. Also, do not refreeze the food once it has been thawed.

Lipid deficiencies can result from offering foods that lack the appropriate fatty acids or that are improperly stored. The lipids most essential in elasmobranch diets are the omega-3 fatty acids, which are abundant in the flesh of many saltwater fishes, like anchovies, mackerel, and tuna, but are less prevalent in freshwater fishes. This is one reason why it is important to feed sharks and rays the flesh of marine rather than freshwater fishes. A lack of these fatty acids can result in fat infiltration of the liver, which can interfere with this organ's function and lead to serious problems.

Mineral Deficiencies

IF WATER CHANGES ARE PERFORMED regularly, mineral deficiencies are generally not a problem. However, thyroid hyperplasia, or goiter, can be a problem in captive sharks. The goiter is a ball-like swelling under the throat that can prevent the animal from feeding and may lead to weakness and even death. In severe cases, the thyroid gland may get up to 300 times its normal size. Some species that are known to suffer from this condition include bullhead sharks, nurse sharks, smoothhound sharks, requiem sharks, and whiptail stingrays. Thyroid hyperplasia results from a lack of iodine, and possibly also the buildup of nitrates. (Crow [1990] reports this condition in sharks at iodide levels of < 0.005 mM and nitrate levels of 111 mM.) If a shark is introduced into an iodine-poor environment, it may take 6 to 16 months before the goiter develops.

Fortunately, if a proper treatment regimen is administered, this condition can disappear in several months. There are several ways to prevent and/or cure thyroid hyperplasia. First, it is important to do regular

TABLE 6-3.

Recommended Shark and Ray Foods

Earthworms	Sardines
Snails	Herring
Clams	Mackerel
Market Squid	Orange Roughy
Krill (Frozen)	Snapper
Table Shrimp	River Smelt
Blue Crab	Plaice
Shark Formula Food (Ocean Nutrition)	

Although the possibility of transmitting certain parasites is greater, fresh seafood is preferred to frozen due to its greater nutritional value.

water changes: in most situations where thyroid hyperplasia is a recurring problem, the water is constantly refiltered and rarely changed, resulting in barely discernable iodine levels. When the aquarist makes 25% water changes every month, his or her captive sharks and rays should not have a problem with goiter. If for some reason you cannot make substantial water exchanges, or the iodine levels in your aquarium are already very low, you can replenish the water with iodine by adding 0.1 mg of potassium iodide (KI) per liter of aquarium water, every 2 weeks. The shark and ray multivitamin tablets mentioned above are also high in iodine and will help prevent this malady, or if your shark is already suffering from goiter you may add KI to its food in a gel cap. Lloyd (1995) recommends adding 6 mg of KI per kilogram of body weight, once a week. (Some professional aquarists recommend up to 15 mg/kg of body weight.) One problem with adding too much iodide to the aquarium is that it will be solvated (bound to other molecules). If the iodide ions should then suddenly become unbound, they could prove lethal to your sharks and rays at such high concentrations.

Fasting

SELF-IMPOSED FASTING is another problem related to nutrition that is especially common in newly acquired sharks or rays. Fasting can have deleterious physiological effects if it goes on too long, including an increase in total body water, a lowering of hematocrit levels (resulting in diminished oxygen-carrying capacity), and hyperglycemia. Therefore, it is important to try to get your shark to eat as soon as possible. If a shark or ray fasts for several weeks, the aquarist may want to intervene and give it an appetite stimulant, such as vitamin B_{12}. This can be administered orally at 0.9 mg/kg body weight, or injected at 0.25 to 0.5 mg/kg body weight.

Force-feeding should always be a last resort: it can be very stressful and can cause internal injury if the animal is handled incorrectly. One way to force-feed is to take a small, whole food fish and insert a plastic knitting needle or sharpened piece of rigid air-line tubing (depending on the size of the shark's mouth) along the spine, from back to front, until the end is pressed up against the inside of the food fish's skull. Lubricate the food fish with some mineral oil or K-Y Jelly, gently pry open the mouth of the shark, then carefully push the food fish into the shark's mouth and down its gullet. In the case of small sharks (under 30 cm [11.7 in.]) a tongue depressor can be used to open the mouth.

One of the most effective ways of getting a shark or ray to feed is to offer it live food. Investigate the food habits of the species you are trying to feed and offer it a prey species that it normally eats. Grass shrimp, fiddler

A feeding stick allows the targeting of food items, ensuring that a captive shark receives its ration.

be tantalizing rather than aggressive in the presentation (don't hit the shark in the face) or the food will be refused. With wobbegongs, lightly touch the barbels in front of the mouth; this will often trigger a feeding response. Many sharks and rays are crepuscular or nocturnal, so presenting food at night may aid in the initiation of a feeding response.

It is not uncommon for some of these animals to go through a settling-in period of 1 or 2 weeks, during which they will not accept food at all. But as long as a specimen is in good health when purchased, it should be able to withstand these moderate periods of fasting. Sometimes feeding cessation will occur in long-term tank residents if water temperature drops. Nurse sharks have been reported to stop feeding if the tank temperature drops below 20°C (68°F), if the water quality deteriorates, or sometimes for no apparent reason at all. There are reports of captive sharks that stopped eating for several months, only to resume feeding as suddenly as they stopped. For example, it has been suggested that the Sandtiger Shark naturally engages in long periods of fasting.

crabs, freshwater crayfish, black worms, earthworms, saltwater annelid worms (often available at bait shops in coastal areas), and freshwater and saltwater fishes are all potential live foods for elasmobranchs. Freshwater fishes are often more likely to elicit a feeding response because of the stress-related stimuli they emit when thrown into a saltwater tank. If using fiddler crabs, it is best to damage the carapace slightly to allow the crab's body fluids to be released into the water. If these delicacies are not eaten, anorexic sharks and rays can be enticed with fresh seafood impaled on the end of a piece of thin, rigid plastic tubing. With inactive species, place the food directly in front of the fish's sensitive nose, but

Handling and Anesthetizing Sharks

SHARKS AND RAYS ARE SENSITIVE to handling stress. If improperly handled, severe and long-lasting physiological disturbances may result, such as the accumula-

TABLE 6-4.

Good Foods for Enticing a Fasting Elasmobranch

Black worms (live)

Lug worms (live)

Other segmented worms (live)

Grass shrimp (live)

Table shrimp (fresh)

Fiddler crabs (live)

Herring (fresh)

Guppies (live)

Mollies (live)

Cardinalfishes (live)

Damselfishes (live)

Plaice (live)

tion of lactic acid, which affects the blood's oxygen-carrying capability. Also, lifting these animals from the water can cause physical damage. Sharks have no ribs to support their internal organs and may injure themselves if they thrash about out of the water. For these reasons, elasmobranchs should be handled as little as possible. If a shark or ray needs to be moved, do it quickly, using a large net with fine mesh and a sturdy handle. The net should also be deep enough to prevent a thrashing captive from flipping out onto the floor. The mesh size of the net is extremely important when handling rays, as the tail barbs can easily be tangled in the netting material. If the spine becomes entangled, you can use a pair of heavy-duty scissors to clip the end of the spine off or just cut the material away that is entangled around the spine. In either case, the old spine will be shed and replaced by a new one. Never pull hard on the netting material to try and free the spine, as you might pull the entire spine off. This will provide a portal for bacterial infection until it heals.

If it is necessary to handle a shark for an extended period of time, it may be best to anesthetize it. This can be done by placing the shark in a large cooler containing tricaine methane-sulfate (trade name MS-222) dissolved in tank water at a concentration of about 100 to 200 mg/liter. You can also mix 1 gram of MS-222 with 1 liter of tank water, place this solution in a plant mister bottle or in a rubber-bulb syringe, and spray it over your elasmobranch's gills. Since you do not want MS-222 in your display tank, you should administer this latter treatment in a cooler full of tank water as well. When the task at hand is completed, carefully lift the shark back into the tank and gently move it back and forth to irrigate its gills with fresh saltwater. One word of caution, the concentration of MS-222 administered seems to be somewhat species-specific. Although I have used it on aquarium sharks with no problems, there are reports of this drug causing cardiac collapse in smaller elasmobranchs. If the spiracles of your shark or ray should stop contracting, or red patches should begin to develop on the ventral surface, immediately transfer the elasmobranch to anesthetic-free tank water. One final note: whenever you handle a shark or ray you should wear clean rubber gloves to prevent the fish from contracting a skin infection.

Some sharks and rays can also be hypnotized, not by having them concentrate on a swinging watch, but by flipping the submerged animal onto its back and gently restraining it. In this position, some species will fall into a trancelike state in which the muscles go limp or rigid, depending on the species, and the respiration rate decreases. This behavior, known as tonic immobility or catalepsy, may be induced in 15 to 45 seconds and last

Elasmobranch Force-Feeding

Although the traditional approach to acclimating newly arrived elasmobranchs has been to minimize stress and handling, some recent findings suggest that more aggressive tactics may be beneficial for certain species that refuse to feed in captivity. Some elasmobranch aquarists are now reporting that force-feeding regimens can increase the survivorship of more-finicky sharks and rays.

Alan Henningsen, aquarist at the National Aquarium in Baltimore, has documented the force-feeding of

Force-feeding a Smooth Butterfly Ray (*Gymnura micrura*), while it is restrained on its back in shallow water at the Florida Aquarium.

a gruel mixture to butterfly rays starting 3 days after they were brought to the aquarium. As a result of his efforts, the rays began to gain weight and finally started feeding on their own. Henningsen says this feeding protocol has also shown promise with the Bluespotted Ribbontail Ray (*Taeniura lymma*), a species that often fails to thrive in home systems.

The easiest way to force-feed an elasmobranch is to create a high-protein gruel. Simply blend a combination of invertebrate flesh (e.g. squid, table shrimp, mysid shrimp), marine fish flesh (e.g. smelt, roughy), an elasmobranch multiple vitamin, and RO or distilled water. Since dehydration can occur in newly acquired elasmobranchs, the gruel mixture should initially be rather thin—up to about 70% water. As time goes on, the

thickness can be increased by reducing the amount of water. The gruel can also be used as a vehicle to administer antibiotics. To feed the shark or ray this ration, you will need a syringe (the size is dependent on the size of the animal) and a rubber tube that will fit on the end of the syringe.

When doing the feeding, it is advisable to have someone assist you. This will reduce the likelihood of injuring yourself or your fish. The procedure involves netting the fish, then lifting it up to just under the water's surface, always trying to keep it submerged.

For sharks, one person should handle the animal, flipping it over on its back and holding it firmly by the back of the head with one hand while grasping the tail with the other hand. The other person inserts the rubber tube in the shark's mouth and slowly pumps in the syringe's contents. Care must be taken when handling wobbegongs, nurse sharks, and any requiem sharks—these are all known biters, with wobbegongs being notorious for this behavior. Being bitten by a pet shark is not a laughing matter. The wobbies and nurse sharks typically hold on tenaciously and may be difficult to remove from a hand or finger, while requiem sharks can inflict painful and potentially serious lacerations.

Stingrays and stingarees present a different challenge. The sting (tail spine) can cause serious puncture wounds or lacerations, which are not only painful but are susceptible to infection. One way to temporarily disable the sting is to put a piece of Styrofoam or cork on the end of it. To do this, you will need a pair of thick neoprene (diving) gloves or even heavy leather gloves. Get the gloves wet before manipulating the animal. Catch the stingray in a large net and hold it just below the water's surface. Use the gloved hand to grasp the base of the tail spine, then gently push the cork or Styrofoam onto its sharp end. Now turn the ray over onto its back to force-feed it. Remove the protective sting cover when the force-feeding is finished.

Stingray and stingaree species differ in their aggressiveness. Some are docile and rarely attempt to sting, even when captured in a net; others will readily put their weapon into play when threatened. In any case, it is always best to assume that these animals will sting if handled. Again, this is not a trivial matter—especially for anyone who may have a bad reaction—and the aquarist should use vigilance to avoid a potentially painful experience. (To disable the tail spine for longer time periods, slip a piece of flexible air-line tubing over it, which will remain in place until it is shed or you cut it off. Be aware, however, that this procedure can cause infection to the surrounding tissue.)

Although such invasive and stressful procedures should be employed only when warranted, force-feeding may be important in maintaining or restoring the health of certain species.

from 30 seconds to 10 minutes, depending on the species, sex, or size of the individual. In some species, it may take several attempts before catalepsy is achieved.

Although not all elasmobranchs are susceptible to this technique, those that are include the Swell Shark (*Cephaloscyllium ventriosum*), Smallspotted Catshark (*Scyliorhinus canicula*), Leopard Shark (*Triakis semifasciata*), Gray Smoothhound Shark (*Mustelus californicus*), Lemon Shark (*Negaprion brevirostris*), Whitetip Reef Shark (*Triaenodon obesus*), Blacktip Reef Shark (*Carcharhinus melanopterus*), Caribbean Reef Shark (*Carcharhinus perezi*), Southern Stingray (*Dasyatis americana*), Round Stingray (*Urobatis halleri*), Clearnose Skate (*Raja eglanteria*), and the Cownose Ray (*Rhinoptera bonasus*). It is easier to force-feed an elasmobranch or examine it closely for parasites while it is in this cataleptic state. Although this may be a sure-fire trick for breaking the ice at parties, it should only be administered when absolutely necessary. Remember, any time a shark or ray is handled, there is a risk of causing physiological disturbances.

References

Babel (1967), Bradley (1996), Branstetter (1987), Carrier & Luer (1990), Clark (1963), Cortes & Gruber (1990), Crow (1990), Dunn (1990), Early (in Stillwell & Kohler, 1993), Gilbert & Wood (1957), Gilliam & Sullivan (1993), Gruber (1980, 1981, 1982), Gruber & Stout (1983), Halver (1989), Henningsen (1994), Jones & Green (1977), Lloyd (1995), Lyle (1983), Martini (1978), McLaughlin & O'Gower (1971), Murru (1990), Pike et al. (1993), Sabalones (1995), Schmid et al. (1990), Schurdak & Gruber (1989), Sims et al. (1996), Spotte (1992), Stillwell & Kohler (1982, 1993), Stoskopf (1990), Sweatman (1984), Uchida & Abe (1987), Van Dykhuizen & Mollet (1992), Wetherbee et al. (1990), Whitley (1940), Whitman et al. (1984), Windell (1978).

CHAPTER 7

Elasmobranch Health

Recognizing and Coping with Common
Disease and Nutritional Problems

WHILE SHARKS AND RAYS ARE NO MORE PRONE TO HEALTH problems than most other groups of marine fishes—and are, in fact, more resilient than many—the prudent aquarist should be ready to deal with possible problems. Just as owning a dog or cat opens the door to occasional veterinary episodes, the keeping of an elasmobranch is likely to present the aquarist with at least minor health issues. Timely and appropriate action can mean the difference between a quick recovery and a loss of the fish.

Parasitic Infestations

AS WITH BONY FISHES, the untimely death of elasmobranchs is sometimes the result of parasitic infestations. Sharks and rays can host quite an array of parasites, including protozoans, trematodes, cestodes, nematodes, leeches, copepods, and isopods. Symptoms of an infestation may include erratic swimming, chafing on the bottom of the tank, frequent yawning, and skin discoloration (white patches and hemorrhaging).

"Reacting in a timely and appropriate fashion can mean the difference between a quick recovery and a loss of the fish."

Researcher carefully supports an adult Colclough's Shark to prevent possible injury from mishandling.

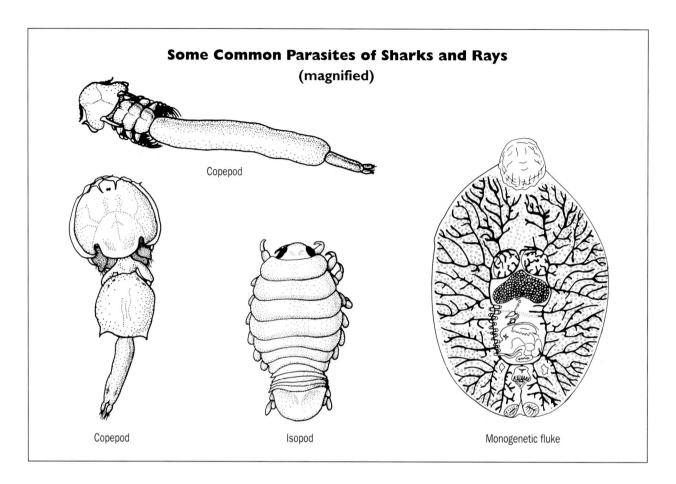

Some Common Parasites of Sharks and Rays
(magnified)

Copepod

Copepod

Isopod

Monogenetic fluke

Protozoans and Dinoflagellates

IN CONTRAST TO CAPTIVE BONY FISHES, elasmo-branchs rarely have a problem with protozoan infestations. However, saltwater ich (*Cryptocaryon irritans*), marine velvet (*Amyloodinium ocellatum*), and possibly *Uronema marinum* have been reported from captive sharks and rays. There are several ways to treat these parasites. If the animal is a euryhaline species (can withstand a wide salinity range), drop the specific gravity to 1.014 for 7 to 10 days to weaken or kill *Cryptocaryon* or *Uronema*. You might also give the elasmobranch a formalin bath (formalin concentration of 200 ppm), although this chemical can cause extreme stress in some

sharks and rays. (Formalin is a carcinogen and so must be used with great care.) Finally, some sharks can be treated with copper sulfate, the common medication employed to treat ich and marine velvet in most bony fishes (see section on Copper Sensitivity, page 198). Sharks have been successfully treated with copper levels of 0.05 to 0.20 ppm for 6 to 8 weeks duration.

Flatworms

THREE MAJOR TAXA IN THIS PHYLUM are known to parasitize sharks and rays: cestodes or tapeworms (Cestoidea), digenetic trematodes (Digenea), and monogenetic trematodes (Monogenea). Although some of these organisms are relatively benign in the effects they have on their hosts, others can cause casualties.

Cestodes (Tapeworms)

The intestinal tracts of sharks and rays are often home to a number of different types of cestodes. For example, a study conducted on the Dusky Smoothhound Shark (*Mustelus canis*) demonstrated that the intestinal tract of a single individual might host up to 4 different species and as many as 166 individual cestodes. Although common, these intestinal parasites are rarely a cause for concern in captive sharks and rays. To eradicate cestodes, you can give your elasmobranch a praziquantel (Droncit) bath. Just add 10 mg of praziquantel per liter (mg/L) of tank water (use a separate container, not the display aquarium) and place the infested animal in the bath for 3 hours.

Digenetic Trematodes

These internal parasites require more than one host to complete their life cycle. The larval phase of all but one species develops in mollusks, while the adult stage is parasitic on vertebrates. These parasites are sometimes found in the stomachs of sharks and rays (they have been reported from bullhead sharks, angel sharks, and torpedo rays) but usually cause their hosts few problems. They should be treated in the same way as cestodes.

Monogenetic Trematodes (Flukes)

These flatworms are primarily ectoparasites of fishes, with many species occupying a specific physical niche on the body surface of their host. The monogenetic trematodes either feed on the blood in underlying vessels or browse on vulnerable integument. (Those in the former group do relatively little tissue damage, while those that display the latter feeding mode can do sig-

nificant harm.) In some elasmobranch species, outbreaks of monogenetic trematodes are not uncommon and can be lethal.

Some flukes are host-specific, only parasitizing a single species in an aquarium. Lemon Sharks (*Negaprion brevirostris*) are the most often-infested shark, but flukes are occasionally found on other species, including whiptail stingrays, round stingrays, bullhead sharks, smoothhound sharks, swell sharks, angel sharks, electric rays, nurse sharks, catsharks, and eagle rays. I've observed them on the disc margin, the tail, and on the ventral surface of a Bluntnose Stingray (*Dasyatis sayi*), where they appeared as opaque flaps of skin, mostly between the gills, but also on the edges of the disc and tail. The skin was red and hemorrhaging where the flukes were attached. In most cases, flukes are difficult to see with the naked eye. Instead, it is usually the manifestations of a monogene infestation, rather than the parasite itself, that the aquarist first notices. Some of these symptoms include chafing against the substrate (flashing), erratic and/or feeble swimming, white lesions on the fins, red or hemorrhaging patches and/or gray patches on the skin, open sores, or ulcerated lesions. Tissue damage caused by the feeding parasite opens paths for bacterial infection, which is usually what ends up killing the host elasmobranch.

Some flukes infest the gills of sharks and rays. To dislodge the parasites, the afflicted animals often swallow sand, which irritates the gills and causes them to hemorrhage. There are several treatment options for dealing with fluke outbreaks. The first thing you can do is to lower the water temperature. For tropical elasmobranchs, drop the temperature to 19°C (66°F). Cheung et al. (1982) reported that by reducing the water temperature from 22 to 19°C (72 to 66°F), sharks infested with flukes seemed less irritated by the parasites,

TABLE 7-1.

Some Symptoms of Parasitic Infestation

Erratic or feeble swimming
Yawning
Sand swallowing
Chafing against the substrate (flashing)
Gray or red patches on skin
Blotchy skin coloration
Scale loss
White lesions or open sores
Labored, irregular ventilation (breathing)
Corneal opacity

Other Signs of Poor Elasmobranch Health

Boils or blisters
Skin blanching or darkening
Reddened ventral surface
Problems with swimming (tail too high, tail too low)
No visual orientation to environment

resulting in less chafing against the aquarium bottom (and hence less damage to the shark).

One anti-fluke medication commonly used in public aquariums is the organophosphate trichlorfon (commercially available as Dylox, Masoten, or Neguvon). Dyacide, manufactured by Aquatronics, is a form of trichlorfon readily available from aquarium fish stores. The problem with trichlorfon is that it is moderately toxic and can be dangerous to elasmobranchs, especially at higher water temperatures; it is also carcinogenic and potentially dangerous to aquarists. (Note: trichlorfon must be used with caution on rays as some, especially Spotted Eagle Rays, are very sensitive to it.) Be sure to follow the manufacturer's instructions carefully. Dylox stored for extended periods of time may also lose its efficacy (one report suggests there is a reduction in effectiveness if not used in 10 days). One effective treatment is 0.2 to 0.25 mg/L trichlorfon for 24 hours. Several exposures may be necessary. You can also dip animals for 1 hour every 5 days at a concentration of 0.25 to 0.5 mg/L until the parasites are gone.

Praziquantel is pricey but the best remedy for trematodes. Use at a dosage of 20 mg/L for a treatment period of 24 hours. Cownose rays immersed in this drug at a concentration of 20 mg/L for 90 minutes were free of all trematodes after the treatment, while the same ray species treated with trichlorfon at 0.7 mg/L for 6 hours and then again 2 days later had lost only 81% of their trematode parasites. Elasmobranchs also display less stress when treated with praziquantel than with trichlorfon. To dissolve praziquantel, place the desired dosage in a mesh bag and knead in a small bucket with a powerhead creating brisk water circulation. Praziquantel can also be administered orally, at a dosage of 400 mg/100 gm of food for 5 to 7 days.

Another procedure shown to be effective in eliminating monogenes is the formalin bath. Unfortunately, formalin can be harmful to the host (sometimes causing gill damage) as well as the parasites and must always be used with vigorous aeration. Sharks placed in seawater with 200 ppm of formalin for 15 minutes were cleaned of flukes, but the procedure was very stressful on the elasmobranchs. When keeping species that can tolerate lower salinity levels, you may be able to reduce fluke problems by lowering the specific gravity to about 1.014 for at least 2 weeks. Freshwater dips (with pH and temperature adjusted to match the tank water) administered for 5 to 7 minutes, 5 to 7 days apart, have been successfully used on some elasmobranchs. (Species vary in their tolerance for freshwater dips. Keep a close eye on the fish and remove it immediately if it shows signs of excessive stress: gasping, frantic escape attempts, going into shock.) Biological control with cleaner species is also an alternative (see Chapter 5).

It is often the bacterial infections associated with fluke infestations that kill the captive shark or ray. These can be treated with topical applications of gentamycin in glycerol (500 mg per 10 ml), or with a solution of 1% methylene green in 70% ethanol.

Nematodes

FIVE OF THE 17 FAMILIES OF NEMATODES (roundworms) are parasites of fishes. In elasmobranchs, these parasites are usually encountered as cysts in the coelomic cavity (the space between the body wall and internal organs), gills, olfactory organs, esophagus, spiral valve, pancreatic duct, skull, and fins. There is, however, one nematode that has been reported from the heart of the Nurse Shark (*Ginglymostoma cirratum*). This nematode, which may be transmitted by a copepod (see the Crustaceans section, below), could cause severe problems in captive specimens. To treat elasmobranchs for nematodes, add cambendazole (three doses, 29 mg/kg of body weight, every 7 days) or mebendazole (three treatments, 20 mg/kg of body weight, every 7 days) to the animal's food. Panacur (fenbendazole) administered at 100 mg/kg body weight can also be effective.

Crustaceans

ALTHOUGH THEY MAY NOT BE AS DEADLY as flukes, crustacean parasites can be a problem if left untreated. These parasites come in many different shapes and

External parasites, such as this copepod attached to a shark dorsal fin, are common on elasmobranchs, but many are relatively easy to treat.

sizes, with copepods being the most common to elasmobranchs: more than 200 species of copepods are known to parasitize them. Most of these (75%) are found only on sharks, with the more active species (e.g., requiem and hammerhead sharks) hosting copepods more often than the benthic, sedentary forms (e.g., wobbegongs and nurse sharks). They will attach to the fins, body, gills, nostrils, eyes, cloaca, and inside the mouths of their hosts, feeding on the skin, mucus, and blood. Copepods erode the tissue around the attachment site, causing it to hemorrhage and opening sites for secondary bacterial and fungal infections. Heavy gill infestation can cause respiratory distress by changing the structure of the gill filaments. Fewer species of copepods parasitize rays, but those that do are often found on the gills.

Copepods can be eradicated by administering praziquantel or trichlorfon (as for flukes), or they can be removed manually with a pair of tweezers (use trichlorfon with caution on rays). The problem with manual removal is that copepods on the gills and in the mouth are often overlooked. Formalin baths (as described above) can also be effective in ridding a shark of copepods. Biological control of crustacean parasites can be accomplished by adding a cleaner wrasse (*Labroides* spp.) or a discfish (Family Echeneidae) to your shark tank (see Chapter 5).

Isopods are less frequently encountered in captive elasmobranchs. One study reported that the commonly kept Brownbanded Bamboo Shark (*Chiloscyllium punctatum*) sometimes hosts isopods on its gills. They have also been reported from the gills of epaulette, cat, smoothhound, requiem, and hammerhead sharks, as well as sawfishes and stingrays. They are sometimes found attached to the heads and around the cloacae of elasmobranchs. One particularly deadly isopod, parasitic on sharks and sawfishes, is known to chew through the side of the body to the heart of its host. Isopods should be dealt with in the same way as copepods.

Dimilin is another drug that has been used to control crustacean parasites on elasmobranchs with varying degrees of success. It works by interfering with the production of chitin, which these parasites need for their exoskeleton development as they grow. Without chitin, the crustaceans (including any ornamental species you may have in the tank with your elasmobranch) will die. Dimilin is available in aquarium stores under the brand name Anchors Away (it is also used for anchor worm infections). Follow label directions.

Leeches

ALTHOUGH RARELY A PROBLEM in captive elasmobranchs, leeches are occasionally observed on the skin, mouth, gills, and cloaca. They have been reported from the Horn Shark (*Heterodontus francisci*), Spiny Dogfish (*Squalus acanthias*), Ornate Wobbegong (*Orectolobus ornatus*), Ward's Wobbegong (*Orectolobus wardi*), Leopard Shark (*Triakis semifasciata*), Brown Smoothhound (*Mustelus henlei*), Shovelnose Guitarfish (*Rhinobatos productus*), numerous skates, Lesser Electric Ray (*Narcine brasiliensis*), Southern Stingray (*Dasyatis americana*), and Bluntnose Stingray (*Dasyatis sayi*), to name a few species. In the Horn Shark, leeches are found singly or in groups of up to five, and most commonly occur on the male's claspers or around the female's cloaca. In wobbegongs, leeches are found on the head, often around the mouth and spiracles. If leeches are present on your shark or ray, they should be carefully removed with a pair of tweezers. Freshwater dips (as described on pages 196-197) are also effective.

Copper Sensitivity

WHEN WE TREAT A BONY FISH for a parasitic infestation, a copper-based medication is often the first choice. Copper, however, can interfere with the feeding behavior of some elasmobranchs, "jamming" their keen electrical senses. The minute pores visible on the underside of an elasmobranch's snout and around the mouth are openings to the small organs responsible for sensing electric fields. These electroreceptors, known as ampullae of Lorenzini, are sensitive to voltage gradients as small as $\frac{1}{5000}$ microvolt per square centimeter. With this sensory capability, a hunting shark can detect the weak electrical field produced by a respiring flounder at a distance of several feet. A metallic ion such as copper overwhelms these electrosensors and causes excess mucus production, which clogs the ampullae. Long-term exposure to copper can also cause changes in blood and liver composition and suppressed immunity.

Not all sharks are sensitive to therapeutic copper levels (0.15 to 0.20 ppm). For example, wobbegongs,

Some Drug and Treatment Regimes for Elasmobranchs

Bacterial Infections

Ampicillin: 10 mg/kg body weight (b.w.) orally or intramuscular (daily).

Endrofloxacin (Baytril): 10 mg/kg b.w. orally (three treatments, every other day).

Endrofloxacin (Baytril): 5 mg/kg b.w. orally (five treatments, every other day).

Gentamycin sulfate (Gentocin): 3.3 mg/kg b.w. intramuscular (seven treatments, every fifth day). (Can be toxic, especially if the animal is dehydrated.)

Kanamycin: 20 mg/kg b.w. orally (daily).

Nitrofurazone (Furacyn): 50 mg/kg b.w. orally (daily).

Nitrofurazone (Furacyn): concentration of 9.0 ppm in aquarium water for 10 days. (Can affect nitrifying bacteria in biological filter.)

Oxytetracycline: 5-15 mg/kg b.w. orally (daily).

Oxytetracycline: 10 mg/kg b.w. intramuscular (daily).

Parasitic Infections

Trichlorfon (Dylox) 0.4 to 2.0 ppm in water for 6 to 8 hours. (Trichlorfon can be dangerous to use on some rays and even on sharks if not administered correctly. May be more dangerous at higher water temperatures. It is also carcinogenic.)

Praziquantel (Droncit) 20 mg/L in water.

nurse sharks, and epaulette sharks can be treated with copper for several weeks with no apparent ill effects. In contrast, at least some of the rays are very sensitive to low levels of copper.

If a tank has ever been treated with copper, some of the copper ions may still be bound to the substrate and filtration media, and if the pH drops in such a system, the copper will be released from the substrate back into solution. A drop of less than 0.2 pH points can cause enough copper to be released to cause a problem for sensitive elasmobranchs. To avoid this complication, it may be prudent to tear the tank down, change the substrate, and cycle the tank again before adding sharks, or especially rays. The other alternative is to run activated carbon continuously and/or make use of a Poly Filter (a contaminant-scavenging pad made by Poly-Bio-Marine Inc.) in an external filter to remove copper if it is released.

Another source of copper ions may be your tap water. In new homes, a relatively large number of these ions may dissolve from the inside of copper pipes. With more sensitive elasmobranch species (especially rays), it is advisable to use deionized (DI) or reverse osmosis (RO) water.

Bacterial Infections

PARASITES ARE NOT THE ONLY PATHOGENS that are dangerous to captive sharks and rays. They may also suffer from, and succumb to, bacterial infections. A whole host of bacteria are found on the skin of sharks, including members of the genera *Aeromonas*, *Proteus*, *Pseudomonas*, and *Fusobacterium*. One genus that is very common on sharks and rays is *Vibrio* (this is the genus that has been erroneously implicated in the "bleaching" and rapid tissue necrosis in certain coral species). These bacteria usually do not cause problems until a portal of entry arises. This could be the wound created by a gill parasite or an ectoparasite (like a fluke or copepod), a wound incurred during handling, or bites or lacerations resulting from aggression or mating activities. Wild sharks are renowned for having remarkable self-healing abilities, but sometimes in the aquarium, because the health of the animal is compromised or the environment is substandard, bacteria will infect open wounds. Bacterial infections often occur because of poor water conditions or sudden changes in environmental parameters. For example, pathogenic bacteria may develop in elasmobranchs when the salinity drops rapidly. To prevent such outbreaks, practice good maintenance habits and avoid any sudden changes in the aquarium's conditions.

The initial signs of possible bacterial infections include lethargy, failure to make eye contact with observers or other aquarium inhabitants, and anorexia. If the infection is not dealt with, disorientation, hemor-

Bacterial infection appears as open sores on a juvenile Leopard Shark. Improving water quality and urgent treatment with antibiotics is needed.

rhaging, congestion, boils, lesions, coma, and death may result. By closely watching your fishes, you can often recognize the early stages of a bacterial infection and initiate treatment before it becomes serious. If you detect the initial signs of infection, first try to improve the animal's external environment by making a partial water change (25%) and replacing any filter media that could be clogged or no longer effective. If the signs do not diminish in the next 12 hours, or if they become more acute, then treat the animal with an antibiotic.

A number of antibiotics have proven effective in treating severe bacterial infections in sharks and rays. These medications can be added directly to the tank water (be aware that some of these drugs can interfere with nitrifying bacteria) or be given orally. The advantage to administering antibiotics orally is that it is less costly, it is most efficacious, and it is less hazardous to the aquarist (some antibiotics can be extremely toxic to humans and must be used with great caution). The subject will often show improvement in 2 or 3 days, which commonly leads the aquarist to discontinue treatment before therapy is completed, thus leaving a small but hardier population of pathogenic bacteria behind. It is best to treat the animal for at least a full week after apparent recovery, observing it closely to be sure that the dosage is not too high and that the "patient" is improving. If not, increase the dose or try a different antibiotic.

One common infection in sharks, shark meningitis (caused by *Vibrio* spp. bacteria), is initially visible as small, white lesions on the skin. These erupt into open sores and, if prompt treatment is not administered, death quickly follows. Species not as well suited to captivity, such as the Spiny Dogfish (*Squalus acanthias*), may be more susceptible to this disease than those sharks that readily adapt to aquarium life. *Vibrio* bacteria have been effectively treated with chloramphenicol or tetracycline. If given orally, the daily dosage is 40 mg of chloramphenicol or 50 mg of tetracycline per kg of body weight. Chloramphenicol must be obtained by a prescription (usually through a veterinarian) and should be handled with extreme care. Be sure to follow the manufacturer's safety precautions about coming into contact with this drug. Oxytetracycline can be used for chloramphenicol-resistant *Vibrio* strains. This should be administered orally at a dosage of 5.0 to 15 mg/kg body weight daily.

Sharks can also develop fin and tail rot, a bacterial infection commonly observed in bony fishes. This is usually the result of a poor environment or improper handling, and can be treated with nitrofurazone (oral dosage 50 mg/kg daily).

Finally, any aquarist using antibiotics should be sure they are never released into the environment—where they might contribute to the creation of resistant bacteria—before being neutralized. Always treat antibiotic-contaminated wastewater before disposing of it. Either circulate it through an ample quantity of fresh, activated carbon for at least 24 hours or treat it with chlorine bleach at a rate of ¼ cup per 5 gallons of antibiotic-contaminated water. In the future, amateur aquarists may have to obtain antibiotics from veterinarians, by prescription, as moves are afoot to ban the sale of over-the-counter antibiotics to prevent their irresponsible dumping into public wastewater systems.

Abrasions and curled disc on a Bluespotted Ribbontail Ray are symptoms of biting by an angelfish.

Oxygen Deprivation

OXYGEN CONSUMPTION RATES are affected by water temperature, locomotor activity, and the amount of food eaten. As water temperature increases, so too does basal metabolism and the need for oxygen. One study suggested that oxygen consumption in some fishes increases by 2.3 times for every 10°C (18°F) increase in water temperature. Locomotion also increases oxygen demands in benthic sharks and rays. Some of the more active species, however, actually consume more oxygen when they are stationary and must actively pump water over their gills. These species use ram-jet ventilation (wherein water is pushed through the mouth, over the gills, and out the gill slits as the fish swims) to irrigate the respiratory

A healthy young Horn Shark crosses its aquarium: the alert keeper observes his or her specimens regularly to catch health problems at an early stage.

organs with oxygenated seawater. This type of ventilation is common in many shark species and some rays.

Subjecting an elasmobranch to excessive activity may build up an oxygen debt, which may be difficult for the animal to pay off, so it is important to avoid any unnecessary handling. If you have to catch a shark or ray, do it as quickly as possible, and resist chasing it around the aquarium with a net. It has also been demonstrated that a fish with a full stomach has a higher oxygen demand than one not recently fed, so

if you feed your elasmobranch frequently, you will increase its oxygen requirements.

Studies have shown that some sharks are not particularly proficient at extracting oxygen from the water. Therefore, it is important to maintain dissolved oxygen levels in the elasmobranch aquarium above 5.5 mg/L. Although rarely a problem in well-maintained aquarium systems, oxygen deprivation may occur for a variety of reasons: inadequate water circulation, poor filtration, a dirty filter, too many fishes, high water tem-

TABLE 7-3.

12 Elasmobranch Health Tips

1. Feed a varied diet, including vitamin supplements.
2. Promptly remove uneaten or regurgitated food.
3. Perform partial water changes on a regular schedule.
4. Regularly check filters and pumps to make sure they are functioning properly.
5. Check for and promptly remove stray parts or pieces of equipment that a shark may ingest.
6. Regularly check to see that rockwork is stable.
7. Regularly check for parasites (especially after a new animal is introduced).
8. If needed, administer drugs promptly, but cautiously.
9. Do not add copper substances to the tank unless you are sure a particular species can tolerate it.
10. Regularly monitor the respiration rate of your elasmobranch.
11. Take time to observe the overall behavior of your elasmobranch.
12. Handle and transport your elasmobranch as infrequently as possible.

perature, overfeeding, or a power failure.

Low dissolved oxygen levels are not uncommon in home aquariums that have tight-fitting covers and are equipped with powerheads to oxygenate the water. In order to achieve maximum aeration, it is important to create turbulence at the water's surface. This can be generated by the output of a powerhead or external filter, one or more airstones, or a surface skimmer (often used with a wet-dry filter). However, if the surface of the aquarium is enclosed and no air is pumped into the tank, the air space between the water's surface and the glass may become oxygen-impoverished. In this situation, surface agitation will enable only minimal gas exchange. An air pump, an adequately sized protein skimmer, or an external filter with a venturi valve to enhance oxygenation will help keep these levels high if the aquarium is tightly sealed to keep your shark from jumping out.

Some telltale signs of oxygen deprivation include increased respiration (the gill movements may be twice as frequent as during "normal" respiration) and blotchy coloration. If your shark or ray displays these signs, measure the dissolved oxygen content of the water, or put an extra air source (e.g., an airstone) in your tank and see how this affects the animal's respiration rate. Because temperature affects the oxygen-carrying capacity of water, it is best to keep the water temperature of your tank at the lower end of the recommended range.

To avoid problems with bacterial blooms (which can quickly deplete dissolved oxygen), it is important not to overfeed. Remove uneaten food immediately and offer only bite-sized pieces. If a food item is too large to be ingested in a single bite, a shark will often bite it and shake off a mouthful, resulting in smaller fragments of food tearing loose and falling to the bottom, where they may not be eaten. Remove these small pieces with a net and add scavengers to help clean up the leftovers (see Chapter 5). Oxygen-starved elasmobranchs often regurgitate, causing more bacterial growth and compounding the problem of oxygen depletion.

I recently witnessed what a long-term (more than 24-hour) power outage can do to captive fish populations. A storm in my area caused damage to numerous power lines and transformers, leaving many residents of the city without power. Several individuals I know lost most of their fishes—to cold and/or oxygen starvation—during this episode. If you have a valued collection of fishes, it's a good idea to have a gas or propane-powered electricity generator on hand in case such emergencies arise.

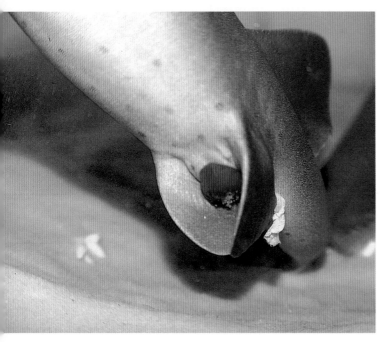

Rectal eversion in a nurse shark: this condition is natural and temporary, but the animal may be vulnerable to biting by its tankmates.

Miscellaneous Problems

BESIDES DEATH DUE TO DISEASE, oxygen depletion, and nutritional problems, shark mortalities may result from physical damage caused by aquarium equipment and/or decor. For example, smaller sharks can be injured or killed by being sucked into filter intake tubes. In order to prevent this, it is important to place strainers on siphon tubes. Because they are available at small sizes and are of a slender build, juvenile bamboo sharks are especially prone to this type of accident. I have also heard of nurse sharks getting their heads lodged in filter intake openings in poorly designed public aquariums. Powerheads should be tightly affixed to undergravel uplift tubes, or, if they are placed in the tank for circulation, they should have a sponge filter attached to the intake opening. On one occasion, I had a small Epaulette Shark (*Hemiscyllium ocellatum*) swim into the powerhead intake, where it was crushed by the impeller.

Unstable ledges or caves can result in a shark being crushed. Some of these animals, such as epaulette, bamboo, and nurse sharks, are proficient diggers and can topple poorly structured rockwork. Rocks or corals can be strapped together with long nylon cable ties to ensure that they will not tip over, or lighter weight, imitation coral pieces can be used. Caves can be formed by drilling holes in the rock and using PVC pipe as a hidden framework for support. Sharks can also get wedged between an undergravel uplift tube and the side of the aquarium, or between decorations, which can result in physical injury or physiological disturbances (e.g., lactic acid buildup) as the animal struggles to get free.

Sharks will sometimes ingest pieces of aquarium equipment carelessly left in the tank, which can impede feeding or prevent the passage of materials through their digestive tracts. I once had to extract a heater suction cup from the gullet of a nurse shark. If foreign material enters the gastrointestinal tract, it may be necessary to anesthetize the shark, place a piece of PVC pipe in its mouth, and carefully remove the object with long forceps. It is best to have a veterinarian perform this procedure, because an endoscope is often needed to locate the swallowed object. Metal objects can be removed in a similar manner using a magnet attached to a flexible rod.

TABLE 7-4.

Conversion Factors

Dry Medications

mg/L	×	3.785	=	mg/gal.
mg/L	×	0.001	=	gm/L
mg/L	×	0.0038	=	gm/gal.
mg/L	×	1.0	=	gm/m^3
mg/L	×	0.0283	=	gm/ft.^{3}

Liquid Medications

ppm	×	0.001	=	ml/L
ppm	×	0.0038	=	ml/gal.
ppm	×	1.0	=	ml/m^3
ppm	×	2.83	=	ml/ft.^{3}

English Units to Metric Units

pounds	×	0.454	=	kilograms
kilograms	×	2.20	=	pounds
gallons	×	3.785	=	liters
liters	×	0.264	=	gallons
U.S. fl. oz.	×	0.0296	=	liters
liters	×	33.8	=	U.S. fl. oz.
dry oz.	×	0.0284	=	kilograms
kilograms	×	35.3	=	dry ounces

Temperature

degrees Centigrade (°C) = 5/9 (°F) - 32

degrees Fahrenheit (°F) = 9/5 (°C) + 32

Another unusual cause of death in sharks, documented in public aquariums, is the laceration of the intestine by other sharks, known as **putative intestinal biting syndrome**. How does one shark bite the intestine of another? In an effort to flush out debris and possibly parasites, a shark will sometimes evert the posterior portion of its intestine from its cloaca. This has been reported for those shark species with a scroll-valve intestine, such as requiem sharks and hammerheads. Species with a ring valve intestine will sometimes evert the rectum. For example, a small (40 cm [16 in.]) nurse shark I once kept everted its rectum about 2 to 3 cm (about 1 in.). Other sharks sometimes bite this protruding organ, and this can be a concern for the aquarist who keeps more than one shark in the same aquarium, especially those with a scroll-valve intestine. A shark that has had its intestine lacerated will often stop eating suddenly, and the prolapsed intestine may protrude from the cloaca and appear hemorrhagic. Intramuscular injections of gentamycin sulfate (3.3 mg/kg body weight) have proved effective in treating this condition.

Toxic compounds can also cause elasmobranch mortality in captivity. For example, dissolved organic solvents (e.g., acetone), PVC cement, paint fumes, and other airborne contaminants (e.g., cigarette smoke) have all been suggested as possible causes of shark and ray mortality in closed systems. Appropriate measures should be taken to screen out such substances. For example, if you use PVC in the aquarium plumbing, be sure the cement has ample time to dry, run freshwater through the system for several hours, drain the tank, then add the seawater. Allow any dry salt mix plenty of time to dissolve before introducing it into a tank that contains an elasmobranch or before adding these fishes to a tank of newly mixed saltwater. Airborne contaminants can be removed by an air purifier that employs activated carbon.

Shipping Sharks and Rays

AS FOR MOST MARINE FISHES, small aquarium sharks or rays can be shipped in large plastic shipping bags in a Styrofoam cooler. For each elasmobranch, use several

TABLE 7-4.

Sizing Up Your Shark or Ray

When feeding a shark or ray it is helpful to know the approximate weight of the animal, and when preparing to give medication it may well be essential.

The time-honored method is to catch, restrain, and weigh the specimen, and this may be unavoidable if knowing the exact weight is important, as when administering a powerful antibiotic. However, elasmobranchs are stressed by such exercises, and careless handling can result in serious injury to the animal.

To obtain an estimated weight for routine care and diet planning, it is possible to arrive at a reasonably good calculated number if you know the length, sex, and species of the shark or ray. See below for a number of equations that relate the length and weight of a number of species.

Unfortunately, equations such as these are not available for many of the species kept by amateur aquarists, but included on the facing page are representatives of some of the more commonly kept elasmobranch groups. In most cases, there are equations for both males and females of the species, as females generally tend to weigh more than males of the same length.

Example: You have a 70 cm (27.6 in.) female Nurse Shark, and you want to feed it 10% of its body weight in food each week.

To estimate the weight of the animal, you must first obtain a length measurement in centimeters. To do this, simply hold a tape measure against the aquarium glass when the specimen is close to a viewing pane. Note the total length from the tip of the snout to the tip of the tail. (For a ray, you will need to get an approximate measure of the disc width from fin tip to fin tip.)

Next, you will need a scientific calculator to run this equation:

$$W = 4.093 \times 10^{-6} \, (TL^{3.037})$$

where

W = weight (in kilograms)

TL = total length (in centimeters)

The step-by-step procedure is as follows. First, take 70 cm raised to the 3.037 power (the factor for a female Nurse Shark). Punch 70 into your calculator, hit the "y^x" button and then enter 3.037. Hit the "=" button. The result should be 401,386.487.

Multiply this times 0.000004093 (or 4.093×10^{-6}). This gives your shark an estimated weight of 1.6 kilograms. Convert kilograms to pounds by multiplying by 2.2, which gives you 3.5 pounds. Thus to provide a weekly food ration equal to 10% of the shark's body weight, you will need to offer 0.16 kilograms or 0.35 pounds (5.6 ounces) of food per week.

Known Length/Weight Equations

W = weight in kilograms

TL = total length in centimeters

DW = disc width in centimeters

Bamboo Sharks

Gray Bamboo Shark (*Chiloscyllium griseum*)

male	$W = 1.357 \times 10^{-5} \, (TL^{2.7390})$
female	$W = 1.607 \times 10^{-5} \, (TL^{2.7205})$

Nurse Sharks

Nurse Shark (*Ginglymostoma cirratum*)

male	$W = 3.44 \times 10^{-5} \, (TL^{2.595})$
female	$W = 4.093 \times 10^{-6} \, (TL^{3.037})$

Smoothhound Sharks

Spotted Estuary Smoothhound
(*Mustelus lenticulatus*)

male	$W = 7.305 \times 10^{-6} \, (TL^{2.859})$
female	$W = 1.855 \times 10^{-6} \, (TL^{3.173})$

Requiem Sharks

Sicklefin Lemon Shark (*Negaprion acutidens*)

male & female	$W = 1.205 \times 10^{-6} \, (TL^{3.29})$

Blacktip Reef Shark (*Carcharhinus melanopterus*)

male	$W = 1.004 \times 10^{-6} \, (TL^{3.39})$
female	$W = 3.25 \times 10^{-7} \, (TL^{3.649})$

Whiptail Stingrays

Atlantic Stingray (*Dasyatis sabina*)

male	$W = 1.64 \times 10^{-5} \, (DW^{3.340})$
female	$W = 1.94 \times 10^{-5} \, (DW^{3.277})$

Eagle Rays

Bat Ray (*Myliobatis californica*)

male & female	$W = 8.2 \times 10^{-9} \, (DW^{3.096})$

heavy plastic shipping bags. To reduce visual stress during shipping, nestle each bag in a black plastic bag or surround it with a black plastic bag liner. The airspace in each bag must be filled with pure oxygen. Fill about one-third of the bag with water (so it completely covers the elasmobranch) and the rest with oxygen. (Hobbyists may need to seek the assistance of a local aquarium shop.)

It is imperative that a shark or ray not be fed for at least 4 days before it is to be placed in a shipping bag and transported so that its digestive system is empty of solids. I have lost sharks in transit after they evacuated their wastes in the confines of a shipping bag. (This rule, obviously, does not apply to short local trips, as from retail shop to home.) A study of the Lemon Shark (*Negaprion brevirostris*) demonstrated that it takes about 2 days for this species to digest and pass a meal, while in the Smallspotted Catshark (*Scyliorhinus canicula*), a temperate-water species, it may take as long as 8 days.

As with all marine fishes, sharks and rays may live for years in an aquarium with no noticeable health problems when proper water conditions and dietary requirements are met. If trouble arises, a prompt response by the aquarist, at least to seek the advice of other elasmobranch keepers or to discuss the problem with the shop where it was purchased, is always recommended.

References

Adamson & Caira (1991), Benz (1980), Bird (1981), Brett & Groves (1976), Cheung (1992), Cheung et al. (1982), Cisio & Caira (1993), Crow & Brock (1993), Crow et al. (1991), Gruber (1980, 1981), Gruber & Keyes (1981), Laird (1951), LaVerane & Mesnil (1901), Leibovitz & Leibovitz (1985), Moss (1984), Murru (1990), Ross (1999), Schmahl & Mehlhorn (1985), Stoskopf (1990, 1993), Strong (1989), Thoney (1989), Whitley (1940).

CHAPTER 8

Captive Reproduction

Advice for the Would-be Elasmobranch Breeder

HOME AQUARISTS HAVE A TREMENDOUS ADVANTAGE OVER field biologists when it comes to observing breeding behavior, with a 24-hour-a-day, 365-days-a-year window on the private lives of their subjects. In fact, there is precious little scientific information available on the reproduction of sharks and rays, and much of what is known has come from aquarium observations.

Although we still have few details on the breeding of most species, certain smaller sharks and rays are actually reasonably good candidates for the aquarist with a larger home aquarium and an interest in captive propagation. Several elasmobranch species available to aquarists have mated in captivity, and although most of these mating events have occurred in large oceanariums, some species have reproduced in relatively small tanks, even 513 L (133 gal.) systems.

One of the best prospects for captive breeding is the Epaulette Shark (*Hemiscyllium ocellatum*), which has reproduced frequently in a number

> *"Amateur aquarists have an exciting opportunity to help lead the way in the captive breeding of these animals."*

Candling reveals a Swell Shark embryo growing in its egg case. Captive breeding of smaller sharks is becoming a reality.

Mating rituals in the wild: male Epaulette Shark grasps the pectoral fin of a female in a characteristic courtship behavior seen in many other species.

Maneuvering through thickets of branching *Acropora* coral, the female puts the biting male through a prolonged chase before allowing copulation.

of public aquariums. Several of the bamboo shark species have also mated and laid their leathery egg cases in captivity with regularity. In fact, there is a surplus of Whitespotted Bamboo Sharks (*Chiloscyllium plagiosum*) in North American public aquariums as a result of captive breeding. The Yellow, Round, and Cortez Round Stingrays (*Urobatis jamaicensis, U. halleri, U. maculatus*) do well in captivity, mature at smaller sizes, and are good candidates for aquarium reproduction as well. (For a list of elasmobranchs known to breed in captivity, see Table 8-1.)

Recently, there has been growing worldwide concern about shark fisheries. In contrast to most bony fishes, sharks are slow to mature and live long lives. As a result, they produce relatively few young. Because of this life-history pattern, heavy fishing pressure usually leads to a rapid depletion of shark populations. In the case of reef sharks, aggressive collection for the aquarium trade could have a similar effect in areas of intense exploitation. The number of such sharks being caught to supply aquarist's demands is relatively small at this writing, but it is important for serious shark keepers to ini-

tiate captive-breeding programs to relieve potential pressure on natural populations of the most-desired species. Finally, some species most suited to home-scale aquariums are found in areas not regularly fished, and captive breeders could easily find a very receptive market for these currently rare and hard-to-get animals.

Reproductive Behavior

ALL SHARKS AND RAYS PRACTICE internal fertilization. The medial edges of the male's pelvic fins are modified to form claspers, tubelike organs designed to deliver sperm into the female's reproductive tract. Males of some species possess terminal hooks and spines that help secure the clasper in the female's cloaca during copulation. Before mating, the clasper is rotated into position (the direction varies depending on the mating posture of the species) and inserted into the female's cloaca. In most sharks and rays, only one clasper is inserted at a time. However, there are a few reports of two claspers being inserted simultaneously. For example, a male Flapnose Ray (*Rhinoptera javanica*) was observed to insert both of its claspers during one mating bout.

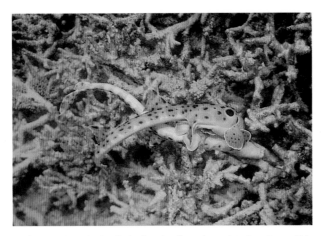

Finally going into a body roll, the female allows the male to insert one of his semen-and-serotonin-conducting pelvic clasper fins into her cloaca.

A leathery Epaulette Shark egg case: hatching can take 18-19 weeks at 25°C (77°F). Live egg cases are often collected for the aquarium trade.

In male sharks, a pair of siphon sacs (located on the abdomen just under the skin) are connected to the claspers by way of small openings. The siphon sacs range from small capsules just under the skin beneath the claspers (e.g., Horn Sharks), to structures that extend all the way to the pectoral fins (e.g., epaulette sharks). These sacs are filled with seawater prior to copulation, possibly by repeated flexing of the clasper or by swimming forward with the clasper flexed. Water, copious secretions from the sac (including serotonin, a smooth-muscle contractant), and semen are injected into the female's reproductive tract during mating. The siphon sac secretions also help lubricate the claspers and provide a medium to increase sperm viability.

Instead of siphon sacs, rays have smaller structures known as clasper glands, located at the base of each clasper. These solid structures are composed of glandular tissue and secrete a fluid that may serve to transport sperm, lubricate the clasper, seal the clasper groove, or plug the female's oviduct to prevent her from being fertilized by other males.

Although the behavior patterns of courtship vary somewhat between species, many similarities exist. The courtship of most sharks and rays begins with the male following close to the female, often with his nose near her cloaca. Male benthic elasmobranchs may approach resting females and place their snouts near the female's pelvic fins, possibly assessing the female's reproductive condition by sampling chemical signals.

Biting is another universal behavior in elasmo-

Bluespotted Ribbontail Ray showing claspers: these male external organs allow quick visual sexual identification of elasmobranchs.

Shark Mating Behaviors

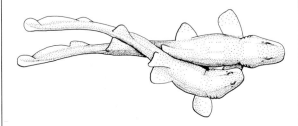

Classic pre-mating behavior in the elasmobranchs, in which the male bites and holds one of the female's pectoral fins in hopes that she will prove receptive to his advances.

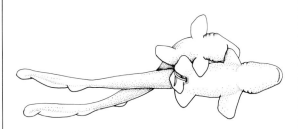

During mating, the male twists into position to insert one semen-transporting clasper into her cloaca.

branch premating rituals. In the majority of cases, the male bites the female prior to, and often during, copulation. In fact, many male sharks and rays have teeth with more elongate, slender cusps than the females, possibly an adaptation for grasping their mates. In some species, the male's teeth may actually change shape just prior to the breeding season. For example, in the Atlantic Stingray (*Dasyatis sabina*) the male's teeth are molariform, just like those of the female, at the time of the nonmating phase (July through September). However, from October through June (the mating season) the male's teeth have a sharp cusp curved toward the tail.

This type of tooth shape is much more effective for grasping and holding potential mates. Male elasmobranchs bite the females to induce their cooperation and to maintain contact to ensure successful fertilization.

Males of some shark species bite the female's back, flanks, or fins, to induce cooperation, while in rays, males are known to bite the back, pelvic, and pectoral fin margins. When holding a female before and during copulation, male sharks bite and grasp the female's pectoral fin or gill area, while male rays hold the female's pectoral fin margin or disc edge. Some male stingrays (e.g., Smooth Stingray [*Dasyatis brevicaudata*]) have been observed grasping the pectoral fin of a female for extended periods before copulation even occurs.

Sharks employ several different mating postures. Most lie or swim alongside each other with the male's posterior body region under that of the female (e.g., Whitetip Reef Sharks, Epaulette Sharks, Arabian Bamboo Sharks, Japanese Wobbegongs, and Lemon Sharks), while a few species, such as the Blacktip Reef Shark, mate with the ventral surfaces opposed. In the more supple-bodied catsharks (e.g., Cloudy Catsharks and Smallspotted Catsharks) the male coils around the female while they lie on the seafloor. Most ray species adopt a ventrum-to-ventrum (belly-to-belly) posture, but male Bat Rays (*Myliobatis californica*) swim under the female (so the male's back is in contact with the female's belly) and rotate a clasper up and to the side in order to insert it into the cloaca. Most rays lie on the seafloor (or aquarium bottom) during copulation. However, Smooth Stingrays swim as they mate. The smaller male flips underneath the female as he grasps her pectoral margin and inserts a clasper, but the female continues to swim with the male in this position.

After copulation the male's claspers are often splayed open and are usually red and swollen. This is

Different Routes, Same Destination

Elasmobranchs display several different forms of embryological development. Some sharks and skates are **oviparous**, laying eggs that are protected by a leathery egg case. In these species, the developing embryo relies solely on the egg yolk for nourishment.

Others are **ovoviviparous**; the eggs are retained in the oviducts of the female, where they hatch, usually from a thin, membranous egg case. There they remain until the young are fully developed. Some embryos of this type absorb the yolk from a yolk sac attached to their digestive system. In the electric rays, whiptail stingrays, and round stingrays, they absorb the yolk early in their development, then rely on nutrient-rich secretions from the uterine lining. This "uterine milk" enters the embryo's stomach via the spiracles and the mouth. In several species, fingerlike extensions from the uterus migrate into these openings and secrete the uterine milk directly into the digestive tract.

Finally, some sharks are **viviparous**; in these species, the embryo initially uses nutrients from the yolk sac and uterine milk. Meanwhile, the yolk sac begins to form an attachment to the oviduct wall. During the latter part of development, nutrients and waste products are exchanged through this placental structure.

Viviparous species produce relatively few, large young after a gestation period of 8 to 12 months.

one sign the aquarist can use to determine if mating has occurred in captivity.

Mating Systems

VERY LITTLE IS KNOWN about the mating systems of elasmobranch fishes. Up until the last few decades, we had to rely totally on fisheries catch data to make inferences about the social and reproductive organization of these fishes. Although scuba diving made it somewhat easier to study these animals in their natural environment, they are still difficult to observe because most move over a considerable area and live in a relatively concealing environment. Most of what we know

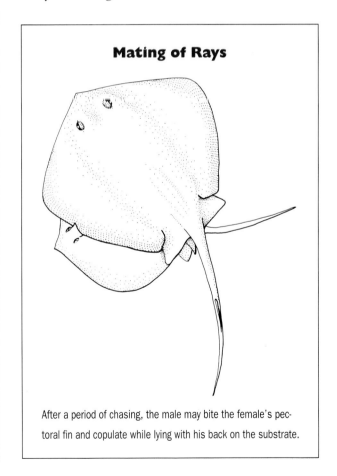

Mating of Rays

After a period of chasing, the male may bite the female's pectoral fin and copulate while lying with his back on the substrate.

TABLE 8-1.

Elasmobranch Species Known to Breed in Captivity

Horn Shark (*Heterodontus francisci*)

Japanese Bullhead Shark (*Heterodontus japonicus*)

Mexican Bullhead Shark (*Heterodontus mexicanus*)

Port Jackson Shark (*Heterodontus portusjacksoni*)

Crested Port Jackson Shark (*Heterodontus galeatus*)

Blind Shark (*Brachaelurus waddi*)

Japanese Wobbegong (*Orectolobus japonicus*)

Spotted Wobbegong (*Orectolobus. maculatus*)

Ornate Wobbegong (*Orectolobus ornatus*)

Arabian Bamboo Shark (*Chiloscyllium arabicum*)

Gray Bamboo Shark (*Chiloscyllium griseum*)

Indian Bamboo Shark (*Chiloscyllium indicum*)

Brownbanded Bamboo (*Chiloscyllium punctatum*)

Whitespotted Bamboo (*Chiloscyllium plagiosum*)

Epaulette Shark (*Hemiscyllium ocellatum*)

Zebra Shark (*Stegostoma varium*)

Nurse Shark (*Ginglymostoma cirratum*)

Sandtiger Shark (*Carcharias taurus*)

Coral Catshark (*Atelomycterus marmoratus*)

Pyjama Catshark (*Poroderma africanum*)

Leopard Catshark (*Poroderma pantherinum*)

Puffadder Shyshark (*Haploblepharus edwardsii*)

Dark Shyshark (*Haploblepharus pictus*)

Smallspotted Catshark (*Scyliorhinus canicula*)

Chain Catshark (*Scyliorhinus retifer*)

Nurse Hound Catshark (*Scyliorhinus stellaris*)

Izu Catshark(*Scyliorhinus tokubee*)

Cloudy Catshark (*Scyliorhinus torazame*)

Gray Smoothhound (*Mustelus californicus*)

Starspotted Smoothhound (*Mustelus manazo*)

Banded Houndshark (*Triakis scyllium*)

Leopard Shark (*Triakis semifasciata*)

Blotchy Swell Shark (*Cephaloscyllium umbratile*)

Swell Shark (*Cephaloscyllium ventriosum*)

Whitetip Reef Shark (*Triaenodon obesus*)

Blacktip Reef Shark (*Carcharhinus melanopterus*)

Sandbar Shark (*Carcharhinus plumbeus*)

Bonnethead Shark (*Sphyrna tiburo*)

Bowmouth Guitarfish (*Rhina anclyostoma*)

Atlantic Guitarfish (*Rhinobatos lentiginosus*)

Shovelnose Guitarfish (*Rhinobatos productus*)

Eastern Fiddler Ray (*Tygonorrhina* sp.)

Marbled Torpedo Ray (*Torpedo marmorata*)

Skates (*Raja* spp.)

Sepia Stingaree (*Urobatis aurantiacus*)

Round Stingray (*Urobatis halleri*)

Yellow Stingray (*Urobatis jamaicensis*)

Southern Stingray (*Dasyatis americana*)

Estuary Stingray (*Dasyatis fluviorum*)

Izu Stingray (*Dasyatis izuensis*)

Matubara's Whiptail Stingray (*Dasyatis matubarai*)

Spotted Eagle Ray (*Aetobatus narinari*)

Bat Ray (*Myliobatis californica*)

Cownose Ray (*Rhinoptera bonasus*)

Flapnose Ray (*Rhinoptera javanica*)

about shark and ray mating systems has been learned in the last decade. This is a result of our success in keeping these animals in large oceanariums and the discovery of several shallow-water sites where the mating behavior of some species can be readily observed.

It has long been known that many sharks and rays segregate by sex. This segregation is usually bathymetric in nature, with one sex inhabiting deeper water than the other. During specific times of the year, mature males and females move into common mating and parturition grounds. These breeding groups can best be described as explosive breeding assemblages. Males typically mate with as many females as possible and females, at least in some species, are thought to mate with more than one male. For example, in a captive colony of Smooth Stingrays (*Dasyatis brevicaudata*), females have been observed to mate at least three times in a reproductive period, while female Flapnose Rays (*Rhinoptera javanica*) in a large oceanarium have been observed to mate with several different males in a short time period. (Whether these observations are an artifact of captivity needs to be confirmed with more field observations.)

In many animal mating systems, males are promiscuous, while females are more selective about their breeding partners. Females have a larger parental investment in the offspring, producing protein-laden ova and having to carry the young to term (if they are vi-

Shallow-water mating behavior of Nurse Sharks in the Florida Keys: note male biting female's fin.

viparous). So do female elasmobranchs select their mates? Females of the majority of elasmobranchs studied to date are often resistant to the advances of amorous males. As mentioned earlier, males bite the females to induce cooperation and to hold them during the mating act. Females will often attempt to avoid males, or escape the male's grasp, and in the case of at least one species of stingray, the females will strike the male with their caudal spines (see sidebar, page 232).

In one study, Carrier et al. (1994) classified female Nurse Sharks (*Ginglymostoma cirratum*) as either "nonattracting," "attracting but uncooperative," or "attracting, cooperating." Those in the first group rested in the breeding area and were not courted by males. (They may not have been in a reproductively ready condition or may have already mated.) Females in the "attracting but uncooperative" group retreated into shallow water when approached and tried to resist copulation attempts. "Attracting, cooperating" females did not move into the shallows when followed and thus allowed copulation to occur. The researchers reported that females

Live birth of a Lemon Shark in the Bahamas, emerging tail-first and wrapped in chorionic membranes.

"relaxed" and allowed one larger, dominant male Nurse Shark to grasp their fin and attempt to mate, suggesting some selection does occur.

Accessory males often interfere with the activity of courting and mating pairs. It appears that interfering males may be attempting to mate with the female when her mobility is restricted or they may be trying to prevent a consexual competitor from fertilizing a female. However, in most cases the accessory male nudges or bites the female, but rarely acts aggressively toward the male that initiated the courtship. This type of interference competition is common in teleost fishes, but less well known in elasmobranchs.

Carrier et al. report that in 16 mating events observed, there were 10 in which multiple males were involved. Up to 10 males attempted to court a single female, and in several cases there was a male grasping each of the pectoral fins. Sometimes these male groups increase the chances of successful copulation. For example, smaller male Nurse Sharks cooperated to drag larger females into deeper water where at least one individual could succeed in mating with her.

Dodd (1983) observed a mating pair of Smallspotted Catsharks (*Scyliorhinus canicula*) being harassed by a group of accessory males. He reports, "They (the copulating pair) were being harried by a group of eight males which were swimming in tight circles around the copulating pair. One of these was seen to tug violently at the female's tail. It then moved round to face the female's head and carried out a similar assault whilst gripping her snout in its jaws. The female's only reaction was to close its eyes momentarily."

In a captive colony of Arabian Bamboo Sharks (*Chiloscyllium arabicum*) male competitors were observed biting the claspers of a courting male. Some stingrays have also been observed engaging in interference competition: the Round Stingray (see page 232) and the Yellow Stingray (*Urobatis jamaicensis*). In the case of the latter species, several males were observed swimming around and nudging a mating pair. In a captive colony of Smooth Stingrays, multiple males were observed grasping the disc margin of a single female and attempting to mate with her, while up to three male Flapnose Rays may simultaneously mount and nip the back of a female.

Once mating has occurred, sperm may be retained by the female and remain viable for a period of time, increasing the chances of fertilization. For example, the Chain Catshark (*Scyliorhinus retifer*) may retain viable sperm for up to at least 840 days after copulating, and perhaps longer

Parturition

BIRTHING HAS BEEN DESCRIBED in a handful of viviparous sharks and rays. From the relatively few accounts that do exist, it appears that females utilize sudden movements and/or sharp contact with the water's surface or inanimate objects to help them expel their young. In the islands of Micronesia, locals report having observed Blacktip Reef Sharks (*Carcharhinus melanopterus*) and Gray Reef Sharks (*Carcharhinus amblyrhynchos*) rubbing their abdomens against submerged logs and mangrove roots to facilitate parturition. Similarly, a gravid female Whitetip Reef Shark (*Triaenodon obesus*) was observed rubbing her belly against the seafloor, possibly to initiate the birthing process. In the Bonnethead Shark (*Sphyrna tiburo*) the pups protrude from the cloaca for few minutes to several hours before they are liberated. To facilitate parturition, the female shark drags the cloaca against the bottom and/or suddenly accelerates or turns. The Sandtiger Shark (*Carcharias taurus*) has been reported to swim with its ventrum toward the water surface as it banks and ac-

celerates during the birthing process. In the Smooth Stingray, males have been observed nudging the female's abdomen. It has been suggested that this may encourage the birth of the young rays. The female suddenly dashes forward, leaving the newborn ray at the spot the female just vacated. Some of the more active myliobatidiforms, including mantas and eagle rays, have been observed to leap from the water and give birth when they impact the water's surface.

In most species where birth has been observed, the pups are born tailfirst. Bonnethead Sharks are born tailfirst and inverted, with the fins and the lobes of the head folded back against the body. These unfold within a day of birth. The inverted pups immediately turn upright and swim in an uncoordinated anguilliform (eel-like) fashion. The only shark known to give birth to its young headfirst is the Sandtiger Shark. The Spotted Eagle Ray (*Aetobatus narinari*) has been seen giving birth to its young both headfirst and tailfirst.

Captive Breeding

BREEDING SOME OF THE SUITABLE aquarium species in captivity will not only reduce collecting pressure on wild stocks, but it can also ensure that there will be a captive pool that can be reintroduced to the wild if population numbers become depleted. Many more of these fishes are captured for food than for the aquarium trade, and because they mature relatively slowly and display low fecundity, they can easily be overexploited.

The four key ingredients to breeding sharks and rays in the home aquarium are a large enough tank, sexually mature animals, optimal temperature, and a good diet. For many of the smaller sharks, such as the hemiscylliids or some of the catsharks, a standard 684 or 912 L (180 or 240 gal.) aquarium will suffice. If the aquarium is large enough, you will increase your chances for suc-

Selecting & Hatching Shark Eggs

Bamboo shark egg cases are frequently offered for sale at aquarium stores. Many aquarists find the idea of watching these eggs develop and hatch in their own aquariums irresistible. Unfortunately, eggs harvested in the wild are more likely to perish in captivity than are young sharks of the same species. The collection of such eggs may thus put more pressure on wild bamboo and epaulette shark populations than the harvesting of viable young animals. However, captive-produced egg cases could be made available to aquarium hobbyists by those public aquariums with breeding colonies of these elasmobranchs. Public aquariums could trade the egg cases to marine fish wholesalers for more desirable livestock, and at the same time take some pressure off wild hemiscylliid stocks.

The egg case walls are composed of two layers. In some cases, sections of the fibrous, outer layer are worn away, which allows viewing of the case's contents without having to manipulate it. Usually, however, it is necessary to backlight the egg capsule in order to check the condition of the developing embryo (as in the inspection of chicken eggs, this is referred to as **"candling"**). This can be done by lifting the case off the aquarium bottom and kneeling down so that it is backlit by the aquarium light above, or moving a light source to the side of the tank and holding the submerged egg in front of it. The embryo within should wriggle about when the case is backlit. When purchasing an egg case, avoid those that contain an inactive embryo, smell bad, or have a white fungus on the outer surface.

Even if you select an egg case carefully, there is still a chance that it will never yield a healthy juvenile shark. In a study conducted on the fate of 160 eggs cases laid by captive Epaulette Sharks (*Hemiscyllium ocellatum*), only about 30% of them hatched. More than 30% of the original total developed fungal infections within the first few days after deposition, while 26% perished within 42 days after the cases were laid. In a study on the reproduction of captive Arabian Bamboo Sharks (*Chiloscyllium arabicum*), of 264 eggs laid over an 8-year period,

A green Swell Shark (*Cephaloscyllium ventriosum*) egg case rests on rocky substrate with several purple burrowing sea urchins.

Hatching begins with the baby Swell Shark poking its head from the case that has held it for 30 to 40 weeks.

18% of the embryos died before hatching and about 7% were infertile, or **"wind eggs"** (see information on bullhead shark egg cases, page 222). In 10% of the egg cases, the fully developed juvenile shark had difficulty breaking free. If this situation arises in the home aquarium, try enlarging the opening at the end of the case with a pair of scissors while it is still submerged in the tank. Unfortunately, most individuals too weak to work their way out of an egg case will die in days or weeks after hatching.

How long will it take for your shark egg case to hatch? This is a question without an easy answer, and it can be difficult to estimate when a particular egg was laid. Perhaps the best method is to candle the egg and attempt to see the stage of development of the embryo. Following is a rough guide to determine how old a hemiscylliid egg might be:

Stage 1 (about 2 to 21 days): Embryo 1.5 to 2.5 mm, moves constantly. External gill filaments begin to appear. By end of this stage, fins apparent along body contour. Embryo pinkish.

Stage 2 (about 28 to 35 days): Embryo 30 to 60 mm. External gill filaments apparent, about 15 mm in length. End of case has split open. Embryo pinkish, not as active.

Stage 3 (about 42 to 60 days): Embryo 85 to 118 mm. Gill filaments reabsorbed. Shaped like adult. Rich pink at beginning of this stage, color appearing at end.

Stage 4 (about 70 to 90 days+): Embryo 140 mm. Replica of adult.

The incubation period is also greatly affected by the ambient water temperature. For example, in one study, the incubation periods for the Epaulette Shark and the Brownbanded Bamboo Shark (*Chiloscyllium punctatum*) egg cases were reported to be 138 days and 160 days, respectively, at 24°C (75°F). However, a temperature increase of 3°C (7.2°F) was shown to decrease the incubation period by 14% in the Epaulette, and 27% in the Brownbanded Bamboo. To expedite the embryo's development (and the hatching), raise the water temperature to 28°C (82°F). (Note that it can be dangerous, because of the reduced carrying capacity of water at high temperatures, to exceed this maximum.)

The 14 cm (5.5 in.) long, perfectly formed Swell Shark shakes itself loose from the egg case.

On its own, the Swell Shark rests before seeking out a hiding place. It will begin to feed in about 1 month.

TABLE 8-2.

Suggested Tank Sizes and Population Density for Captive Breeding

Shark	Tank Size (L / gal.)	Number of Individuals
Bamboo sharks	684 / 180	2
(*Chiloscyllium* spp.)	912 / 240	3
	1,140 / 300	4
Epaulette Shark	684 / 180	2
(*Hemiscyllium ocellatum*)	912 / 240	3
	1,140 / 300	4
Coral Catshark	684 / 180	3
(*Atelomycterus marmoratus*)	912 / 240	4
	1,140 / 300	5

cess by keeping two or three females with a single male (see Table 8-2).

Sexual maturity is mandatory, of course. In most elasmobranch species, the size and rigidity of the claspers can determine the sexual maturity of males. Those of juvenile sharks and rays are shorter than the posterior tips of the pelvic fins and are very pliant. On an adolescent shark or ray, the claspers extend past the pelvic fin tips, and while the skeletal elements composing the tips, or glands, are developed, the claspers themselves are still flexible. At the onset of maturity, the claspers of many elasmobranchs undergo a growth spurt. In one study, for example, the claspers of an immature 31 cm (12.1 in.) Spadenose Shark (*Scoliodon laticaudus*) male measured 8.3% of its total body length, while those of a sexually mature, 34 cm (13.3 in.) male

of the same species measured 11.5% of its total body length. Not only do the claspers rapidly increase in length at this time, but the glands at their tips also become fully developed, and the claspers become stiff due to the hardening of their skeletal elements. The glands of an actively mating male shark will appear red and swollen and, in some species, may be spread open. Palpitation of the male's cloacal region will often cause sperm to flow from the clasper glands and groove.

Determining whether a female is sexually mature by examining her external anatomy is difficult, although actively mating females often display bite marks and the cloacal region may appear red and swollen. Males and females typically become sexually mature within a specific size range; these size ranges are included in the species accounts (Chapter 4) when available.

An aquarium collection of hemisyclliid sharks: pioneering breeders can find a ready market for healthy, captive-bred elasmobranchs.

Water temperature can also stimulate elasmobranchs to spawn. Many sharks and rays mate and give birth during the warmer seasons, and higher water temperatures probably stimulate mating behavior, at least in part. This is especially true for those species native to temperate waters. By increasing the temperature in your aquarium a few degrees, you may achieve the same result.

Obviously, most fishes will only reproduce when they are in optimal physical condition, which means that they must be well nourished. This is especially true for females, who must have enough energy reserves to produce nutrient-laden eggs. Therefore, increasing the feeding frequency may help elicit mating and ensure the successful development of eggs. The act of mating itself will also result in increased energy expenditure. Among some elasmobranch species, heavy exertion during courtship and copulation may even kill females. This is especially true in captivity, where females have a difficult time avoiding amorous males. For example, female Flapnose Rays (*Rhinoptera javanica*) died after being chased, bitten, and copulated with by numerous males, while female Sandtiger Sharks (*Carcharias taurus*) have been killed as a result of male courtship biting. In situations where a female is constantly being harried by males, especially when copulation has already taken place, it may be necessary to separate the sexes.

The following sections include captive-breeding observations and advice on several elasmobranch groups that may be of interest to amateur and professional breeders, as well as hobbyists attempting to rear a shark from an egg case.

Bullhead Sharks (Heterodontidae)

SEVERAL SPECIES OF BULLHEAD SHARKS have mated in captivity, but their large size at maturity makes them candidates for breeding programs only in very large home aquariums. Sexually receptive male Horn Sharks (*Heterodontus francisci*) have been observed to chase female tankmates and bite them. In one case, a male bit a female on the gill region and reportedly held her for a few minutes, during which time she remained motionless. After the female was released, she began spinning with her nose on the substrate. This unusual behavior ceased in about 30 minutes.

Two copulatory postures have been observed in bullhead sharks. In the Japanese Bullhead (*H. japonicus*) and Port Jackson Shark (*H. portusjacksoni*) the male shark grasps the female's pectoral fin in his mouth, wraps the posterior portion of its body under the female's, and inserts one clasper into her cloaca. In the Horn Shark, the female lies partially on her side and faces the male, who rests across her with a single clasper inserted; copulation lasts as long as 35 minutes. In the Japanese Bullhead, mating bouts of up to 15 minutes have been reported.

If you think your adult bullhead sharks have copulated, it is usually easy to determine by visual examina-

A Port Jackson Shark hatchling begins to break out of its egg case.

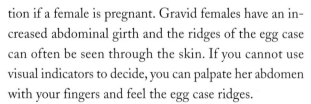

Algae-encrusted Crested Port Jackson Shark egg cases with sea squirts.

The hatchling Port Jackson Shark emerges onto the reef.

tion if a female is pregnant. Gravid females have an increased abdominal girth and the ridges of the egg case can often be seen through the skin. If you cannot use visual indicators to decide, you can palpate her abdomen with your fingers and feel the egg case ridges.

The egg case, which is soft and slimy at this time, rotates out of the cloaca during oviposition. In at least one species, this process takes several hours. If the egg case has tendrils, these structures will protrude from the cloaca first. The female will then swim around an anchoring site, like macroalgae or rock, wrapping the tendrils around it, which helps to pull the egg case out of her cloaca and provides an attachment site for the developing egg. Because the adults of two bullhead shark species have been observed to eat their eggs, it is best to remove the egg cases and place them in a separate aquarium as soon as they are laid.

Bullhead shark egg cases are occasionally sold in North American aquarium stores. It used to be that the most common egg cases were those of the Horn Shark. However, Port Jackson and Crested Port Jackson (*H. galeatus*) egg cases show up occasionally. The incubation period for bullhead shark eggs ranges from 7 to 12 months, depending upon the species and the water temperature. Aquarists who purchase these egg cases may have to wait as long as a year for them to hatch, and in some rare instances the embryo may never develop. Although it is impossible to know precisely how old an egg case is and how much longer until it hatches, you can get a general idea by looking at its condition. When first laid, the egg cases of some bullhead sharks are "bottle green" and they become a paler brown in time, while those of other species are reported to be light brown at oviposition, becoming darker brown with time. "Young" egg cases are typically shiny, clean, and in perfect shape. As the egg case spends time on the ocean floor, coralline algae and encrusting invertebrates grow on its surface, the case becomes "leathery," and the ridges begin to erode or break off. Gradually, the walls of the case become thinner, and a slit opens on the broader end, allowing oxygenated seawater to enter and providing an escape route for the young shark. The presence of this slit is a good indicator that the incubation process is almost complete. You can often inspect the developing shark by pulling the slit open slightly, but be careful not to rip it—this may result in a premature hatching. Do not lift the egg case out of the water.

When purchasing an egg case, inspect the surface closely for boreholes. Some predatory snails drill holes through egg case walls to extract their contents. Also beware of **"wind eggs,"** which are perfectly formed capsules that never contained an egg or developing embryo. Wind eggs are much lighter than those housing miniature sharks.

Hatching is more of a spontaneous event than a process, with the young shark popping out of its embryonic home very quickly. It is not uncommon for a newly hatched bullhead shark to fast for a month or more after hatching, relying on nutrients from the yolk that is still present in the alimentary tract. An occasional individual will continue to refuse food and perish several months after hatching. Juvenile bullhead sharks have extremely small mouths and often have difficulty chewing fibrous foods. They should be offered finely cut pieces of fish or marine worms, if you have access to them. Once it acclimates to captivity, a bullhead shark is long-lived, with some having survived in aquariums for over 25 years.

A freshly laid egg case of the Port Jackson Shark rests on a sandy substrate with an unusual reddish-colored sea anemone.

A typical egg case after many weeks resting in a bed of macroalgae. A high proportion of elasmobranch eggs may fail to hatch.

Wobbegongs (Orectolobidae)

ALTHOUGH MOST OF THE MEMBERS of this group are too large to breed in the home aquarium, three species are potential candidates. These are the Tasseled Wobbegong (*Eucrossorhinus dasypogon*), the Japanese Wobbegong (*Orectolobus japonicus*), and Ward's Wobbegong (*Orectolobus wardi*). All three of these attain a manageable size (less than 1.8 m [5.9 ft.]), and thus are sexually mature at lengths that can be housed in very large home aquariums. The only one of these species that has been observed to reproduce in captivity is the Japanese Wobbegong. (The other two species are rare in public aquariums, and when present are usually kept singly.)

Most of what is known about wobbegong reproduction is from observations made of *O. japonicus* in public aquariums. During copulation, the smaller male lies alongside the female while biting her gill region. (During the mating period, one or both sets of gill slits will have tooth marks and be bloodied.) The male then curls the posterior part of his body around so that he can insert a single clasper. Similar mating behavior has been reported for the Spotted Wobbegong (*Orectolobus maculatus*). Males have also been reported to bite the pectoral fins of females during courtship. Gestation lasts about 1 year in the Japanese Wobbegong and litter size ranges from 1 to 27. The size at birth of *O. japonicus* is 19.6 to 22.7 cm (7.6 to 8.9 in.) in total length, with a body weight of 49 to 89 grams. The larger Spotted Wobbegong can have as many as 37 pups in a litter.

There is a detailed report of copulation in a pair of Ornate Wobbegongs (*Orectolobus ornatus*) off Byron Bay, New South Wales (Hartley, 2000). Simon Hartley and Mark Baker happened upon a mating pair in 3.5 to 4 m (11 to 13 ft.) of water, lying on the sand near a shipwreck. The male was biting the female just above the pectoral fin. The posterior part of the male was po-

sitioned under the female's tail so that it was lifted off the bottom. This enabled the male to insert his right clasper. The pair was being washed back and forth by the surge. While the observers were not sure how long the pair of sharks had been copulating when they arrived on the scene, the portion of the copulatory bout they witnessed lasted 20 to 25 minutes (the event may have been abbreviated because of diver interaction with the pair).

Hartley noted that the male was 84 cm (32.8 in.) long, while the female was 86 cm (33.5 in.) in total length. Last and Stevens (1994) suggest that these sharks are not mature until they exceed 175 cm (68.3 in.) in length (although they do note a report of a 63 cm [24.5 in.] male from Queensland that was sexually mature).

Hartley's observations indicate that the more northern Ornate Wobbegong populations may represent a distinct species (or subspecies). In his study of the population dynamics of this species, 114 of 135 individuals measured were between 50 and 100 cm (19.5 to 39.0 in.) in length. In more southern climes, the majority of *O. ornatus* I have seen have been over 1.5 m (4.9 ft.) in length and ranged up to 3 m (9.8 ft.).

Mature male wobbegongs have been reported to fight among themselves during the breeding season, as well as behave aggressively toward scuba divers. For this reason, it is probably best to keep only one male per tank (at least in the more limited confines of the larger home aquarium). Even though it has been reported that female Japanese Wobbegongs are anorexic during the birthing period, newborn wobbegongs should be separated from their parents as soon as possible. If the near-term female is housed in a tank with other sharks, be sure there are plenty of tight cracks and crevices where the newborn wobbies can hide.

Bamboo and Epaulette Sharks (Hemiscylliidae)

MEMBERS OF THIS GROUP are best suited for captive breeding in reasonably sized home aquariums. Four members of the family have been observed to mate in captivity. These are the Arabian Bamboo (*Chiloscyllium arabicum*), Whitespotted Bamboo (*C. plagiosum*), Brown-banded Bamboo (*C. punctatum*), and Epaulette Sharks (*Hemiscyllium ocellatum*). Some of the smaller members of the genus *Hemiscyllium* that rarely reach home aquariums because of their limited distributions would be even better suited for aquarium breeding programs.

Courtship in the Whitespotted Bamboo Shark usually begins with the male chasing the female and grasping her pectoral fin in his mouth. With the male biting the female's pectoral fin, the pair will then swim about the tank and occasionally rest on the substrate for 30 minutes or more. The male will then twist his body into position so he can insert one clasper into the female's cloaca opening. Copulation lasts about 5 minutes. On one occasion, a male *C. plagiosum* was observed biting the tail of a hidden female and dragging her out of her refuge.

The male Arabian Bamboo Shark grasps the pectoral fin of the female and shakes it several times to induce her cooperation. She responds by spreading her pelvic fins apart. The male inserts a single clasper for 5 to 15 minutes. Dral (1981) reports that the male may rotate the clasper forward, in typical elasmobranch fashion, or cross the opposite clasper across the body and insert it. The male Brownbanded Bamboo Shark also bites the female's pectoral fin and may also bite her gill region.

During courtship, the male Epaulette Shark grasps the female's pectoral fin in his mouth. The male engulfs the fin up to the pectoral base. The female may attempt to resist the male's advances, dragging him through staghorn coral or over the seafloor. West and Carter (1990) report that a female resisted the male's attempt to get his claspers into "striking range" by arching her back and forcing her cloaca against the substrate. In a pair of *H. ocellatum* I observed mating in the wild, the female swam off the bottom with the male still attached to her pectoral fin. The male then twisted his body around and under the female's so that he could insert a single clasper. (In this pair, the male was considerably longer than the female.) West and Carter report that the male and female lie alongside each other during copulation and the clasper opposite the pectoral fin grasped is often crossed over the body and inserted in the cloaca (i.e., right pectoral fin grasped, left clasper inserted). They also report that the pair rolled over the aquarium bottom as they copulated. In the pair I observed, copulation lasted 2 minutes, while captive individuals are reported to mate for 1.5 minutes. When the pair break their union, the end of the clasper remains in the flared position.

In some species, there is interspecific competition, which can include aggression, for mates. In the Arabian Bamboo Shark, for example, interfering males may attempt to bite the female in a courting pair and will even nip the clasper of the competing male. Mature male Epaulette Sharks have been reported to attack males of their own and different shark species.

Both bamboo and epaulette sharks are oviparous; they lay a leathery egg case with a tuft of filaments on one side that anchors the egg to the ocean floor. Captive female Arabian Bamboo Sharks laid an average of four eggs at 9-day intervals for about a 6-month period. Although some of these eggs were infertile and a number of the embryos did not develop, the majority of them hatched in 70 to 80 days at a water temperature of 24°C (75°F). The eggs of the Epaulette Shark, which are similar in general appearance to those of bamboo sharks, are laid at night, two or three at a time, and hatch in about 130 days at 25°C (77°F). Eggs occasionally succumb to adult sharks in captivity, often eaten by the parents—especially the males.

Zebra Sharks (Stegostomatidae)

IN RECENT YEARS, the reproductive behavior of the Zebra Shark (*Stegostoma varium*) has been witnessed in large public aquariums. Some behaviors related to reproduction have also been observed in the field. For example, at certain times of the year Zebra Sharks form breeding assemblages off the coast of Queensland. In these groups, individuals spend much of their time swimming high in the water column rather than sitting on the seafloor (a behavior commonly seen during the non-reproductive season). A mating pair of Zebra Sharks in captivity also spent much of their time swimming about the aquarium. Although simply speculation, it may be that females swim about to avoid the unwanted attention of amorous males. Males in these breeding groups will occasionally roll on their sides, with their bodies and tails curled into U-shapes, and begin sinking toward the bottom. During one of these unusual episodes a male had the ends of one of its claspers splayed open. Before hitting the bottom, these sharks would upright themselves and begin swimming again.

In captive Zebra Sharks, courtship includes the male biting the female's pectoral fin. Unlike the Nurse Shark (*Ginglymostoma cirratum*), where the male "swallows" the entire fin, the male Zebra Shark only bites the tip or edge of the fin. In some cases, pectoral biting does not result in copulation. It is not uncommon for the female to try to get the male to release his grip. The male may hold the female's fin for over an hour. Usually the pair will lie on the bottom, in a side-by-side orientation, during pectoral biting. But in some cases, the female will flip over on her back while the male grasps the fin. They may remain like this for many minutes (in at least one case, over 15 minutes), before the female uprights herself.

Kay Kunze and Mitch Carl at Omaha's Henry Doorly Zoo report that pectoral grasping is commonly observed. The male has also been observed grasping the tail of the female on a number of occasions. In one case, the male bit the female's upper caudal lobe, which caused her to stop swimming and slowly sink to the bottom. In an apparent mating aggregation of Zebra Sharks, I saw males attempting to bite the tail fin of other individuals. I have also seen photographs taken off Thailand (of two different pairs of sharks) where a male Zebra Shark was grasping the caudal fin of the female. In one of these photographs, the female is lying on her side as the male grasps her tail in his mouth. It may be that the male uses this tactic to subduc swimming females, as has been described in a colony of Smallspotted Catsharks (*Scyliorhinus canicula*). According to the Henry Doorly aquarists, copulation takes place with the male and female in a venter-to-venter position while the male holds the pectoral fin of the female.

Zebra Sharks in the athletic throes of courtship: the male bites the female's pectoral fin and attempts to flip her over prior to mating.

The Zebra Sharks lay large, atendril adhesive egg cases with hair-like threads on its surface. As an egg case begins protruding from the cloaca, the female rapidly swims around a reef structure until the hairs adhere to it. The female continues to circle until the egg case is pulled from the female's cloaca. The eggs are amber brown to purple in color and hatch in approximately 170 days (K. Kunze, personal communication).

Nurse Sharks (Ginglymostomatidae)

RECENT STUDIES, CONDUCTED IN the Dry Tortugas, have greatly added to our knowledge on the reproductive behavior and mating system of the Nurse Shark (*Ginglymostoma cirratum*). This shark has also been observed mating in public aquariums.

Courtship begins when a male Nurse Shark follows a female (often for 15 minutes, and as long as 90 minutes) or the pair swim side by side. While next to, and slightly behind the female, the male engulfs the female's pectoral fin with his mouth. In response, the female will often pivot in front of the male so that the axis of her body is perpendicular to his. The male will attempt to roll the female onto her back by pushing underneath her, or by pulling the pectoral fin up toward the surface. Sometimes more than one male will attempt to turn a female over. Females often resist the male's efforts, bracing themselves against the substrate and arching their backs. When the female is successfully turned over, the male moves alongside her and rolls over in an attempt to move his claspers close to the female's cloaca. If a female is receptive, she may arch her back to bring her cloaca closer to the male's claspers. During this sequence, the caudal fins of the courting sharks often flail in the air and slap the water's surface.

Copulation usually occurs in a side-by-side orientation, but occasionally the pair will mate in a venter-to-venter posture. During the mating act, the male thrusts and undulates his body, possibly to facilitate insemination. Copulation lasts about 2 minutes. The duration of courtship and copulation seems to be a function of male exhaustion. In some cases, a male ended the mating act apparently because it had a hard time respiring with the female's pectoral fin stuffed in its mouth.

In many cases, more than one male will attempt to mate with the same female. Carrier et al. (1994) reported seeing smaller male Nurse Sharks "cooperating" to drag larger females into deeper water where at least one of these males would have a greater chance to mate with her successfully.

Catsharks (Scyliorhinidae)

SEVERAL SPECIES OF CATSHARKS have mated and laid eggs in captivity. The ideal candidate for captive-breeding programs is the Coral Catshark (*Atelomycterus marmoratus*) because of its small adult size (less than 60 cm [23.4 in.]). Some of the other catsharks that have reproduced in captivity and are small enough to be bred in the home aquarium include the Puffadder Shyshark (*Haploblepharus edwardsii*), adult size 60 cm (23.4 in.); Dark Shyshark (*H. pictus*), 56 cm (21.8 in.); Pyjama Catshark (*Poroderma africanum*), 101 cm (39.1 in.); Leopard Catshark (*P. pantherinum*), 84 cm (32.8 in.); Smallspotted Catshark (*Scyliorhinus canicula*), 100 cm (39.0 in.); Chain Catshark (*S. retifer*), 47 cm (18.3 in.); and the Cloudy Catshark (*S. torazame*) 48 cm (18.7 in.).

One of the earliest known observations of elasmobranch mating involved a pair of Smallspotted Catsharks. In 1881, Bolau published an illustration documenting copulation in this species. Since that time, much more has been learned about catshark mating behavior, primarily because of their small size and relative success in captivity.

TABLE 8-3.

Incubation Periods For Catshark Eggs

Species	Incubation Time	Sources
Swell Shark (*Cephaloscyllium ventriosum*)	7.5 to 10 months	Grover, 1974.
Smallspotted Catshark (*Scyliorhinus canicula*)	5 to 11 months	Compagno, 1984b.
Nurse Hound (*Scyliorhinus stellaris*)	about 9 months	Compagno, 1984b.
Cloudy Catshark (*Scyliorhinus torazame*)	13.5 to about 18 months	Uchida et al, 1990.

Courtship in scyliorhinids may include the male following the female and the pair swimming parallel to one another or in slow, tight circles. Biting is also an important part of the courting repertoire of at least some catsharks. The male will bite the female in the gill region, on the sides, and/or on the tail. Usually the male grasps the pectoral region or anterior flank just prior to intromission and may or may not retain his grasp during mating. Numerous catsharks are known to exhibit sexual differences in tooth shape, with males having longer teeth than females. It has been suggested that the longer cusps facilitate holding the females during courtship.

Copulation in most of the catsharks involves the male coiling his body around the female. The male will wrap tightly around the pelvic region of the rigid female, with his ventral surface facing her tail. The clasper is erected at about a 90° angle and inserted into the cloacal opening. This is not the case in all catsharks. The male Cloudy Catshark bites and holds the female, while curling the posterior portion of his body under hers in order to insert a clasper. However, the pair does not always copulate in this posture. The duration of copulation has been reported to range from 4 to 20 minutes.

Courtship and copulation in the Chain Catshark has also been observed in captivity. A male and female swam alongside each other near the bottom, sometimes in tight circles, or occasionally lay next to each other on the substrate. The male bit the female in the gill region, the flanks, and the tail, then released his grip. While the pair swam about the tank, the male bit the female's tail again, but this time did not let go. The female struggled initially, but then became more listless. The male moved up the female's body until he reached the axil of her left pectoral fin, which he promptly grasped in his jaws. The male wrapped his body around the female, erected the left clasper, and inserted it into the female's cloaca. The pair sank to the bottom and remained still for 30 seconds. The male released his grip on the female's fin but still lay, coiled around her. Moments later, the pair separated and both sharks swam off.

More information is available on the mating of the

Smallspotted Catshark than almost any other shark species. Houziaux and Voss (1997) reported on the mating activities of a captive colony of these sharks. One of the most common behaviors observed was **testing**, in which a male positioned its snout near a resting female, usually in the region of the pelvic fins. This behavior indicates that females may emit a pheromone that signals reproductive readiness. The males would also follow females and occasionally seize (bite) them. In an observation period of 1 hour and 10 minutes, males were observed following conspecifics 81 times and seizing them on 9 occasions. Although males usually bit females, they would also seize other males. Males bit other males more frequently when the seized male was resting on the substrate. In most cases, the males bit each other on the area posterior to the first dorsal fin, especially the caudal fin. When females were swimming, they were usually bitten on the caudal fin; when they were resting, the males would most often bite them on the pectoral fins and adjacent body region. The observed copulation events typically lasted over 20 minutes.

As mentioned above, males may compete with one another for females. There are reports of groups of male Smallspotted Catsharks harrying a mating pair of conspecifics (see account on page 216).

In those catshark species that have tendrils extending from the corners of the egg case, oviposition usually requires some structure that affords a place for the tendrils to attach. As egg-laying nears, the posterior tendrils of the case begin to extend from the female's cloaca, and she will search out a vertical structure appropriate to receive the eggs. She slowly swims around and nuzzles the laying site, eventually dragging the tendrils over the structure, then swimming rapidly once they have adhered. When there is no slack left in the tendrils, the egg case is jerked from the cloaca.

A tank that contains gravid catsharks should have an anchored, vertical structure for them to use as an oviposition site. This could be a piece of narrow diameter PVC pipe, an artificial or live gorgonian, or a branching faux or stony coral skeleton. (These will need to be secured to the aquarium bottom so they remain in place as the female deposits the egg cases.) Eggs are laid in pairs, with several minutes to over a week passing between the deposition of the first and second egg cases.

As in all other oviparous sharks, incubation rates are greatly affected by water temperature. Embryonic development in the Smallspotted Catshark takes 1.64 times as long at 13°C (55°F) than it does at 16°C (61°F). (For more information on the incubation periods of catshark eggs, see Table 8-3, facing page.) Catshark egg cases darken over time and are known to produce an anti-fouling agent that prevents algae and sessile invertebrates from growing on the surface. Eggs and young should be separated from the adults because they may be eaten.

Smoothhounds (Triakidae)

LITTLE INFORMATION IS AVAILABLE on the reproductive behavior of the smoothhounds. Because they are a larger, more active shark, they are not good candidates for home breeding programs. However, there have been some reports of courtship and mating in larger public aquariums. A paper published in 1921 (Leigh-Sharpe) suggested that male Dusky Smoothhounds (*Mustelus canis*) insert both claspers when mating. In the Leopard Shark (*Triakis semifasciata*), males are reported to bite the female during copulation. A male Banded Houndshark (*Triakis scyllium*) bit the pectoral fin of a female and while remaining in a parallel orientation, moved the posterior part of his body under hers so he could insert a single clasper.

Requiem Sharks (Carcharhinidae)

THERE ARE FEWER OBSERVATIONS of mating in requiem sharks, because relatively few can be kept successfully. They are also difficult to observe in the wild because they range over large home territories. However, public aquarists and shark enthusiasts may find the following information of interest.

Biting during courtship and copulation is well known in the carcharhinids. It probably serves as a pre-copulatory releaser (triggering ovulation and causing the female to cooperate) as well as a bond-maintenance mechanism (enabling the male to maintain contact with the female). Many species have been reported with mating wounds or scars on the flanks and gill region. In at least one species, the Blue Shark (*Prionace glauca*), the female has thicker skin than the male to protect the vital organs from male biting. Male Whitetip Reef Sharks (*Triaenodon obesus*) have been observed biting the pectoral fin of females during copulation. Clark (1975) reported the following account of mating behavior in the Gray Reef Shark (*Carcharhinus amblyrhynchos*): "Two days earlier we had seen 15 sharks of this genus, *Carcharhinus*, in a courtship frenzy. They were milling around in a loose group. Then a female broke away from the throng and swam upward with a male following and biting her repeatedly, tearing the edges of her fins, slashing the sides of her body, leaving a crescent of tooth marks on her flanks. It looked like vicious, aggressive behavior, but we knew well what size chunks he might have torn from her, and so could only conclude that these were love bites."

Males of other species, such as Bull Sharks (*Carcharhinus leucas*) and Sandbar Sharks (*C. plumbeus*), have been observed chasing and nipping females in captivity. It has been suggested that non-sexually receptive females may turn on amorous males and kill or injure

A female Whitetip Reef Shark drags a biting male prior to copulation.

them. This may explain the bitten or amputated claspers seen in some mature male sharks.

Copulation takes place with the male and female swimming alongside each other or the pair resting parallel on the bottom. In the case of the Whitetip Reef Shark, the male grasps the entire pectoral fin of the female in his mouth and curls the posterior part of his body under hers. He inserts a single clasper (the same clasper as the pectoral fin grasped—e.g., right fin, right clasper) as the pair assumes a side-by-side (or parallel) orientation. In one report of *T. obesus* mating, the pair rested with their heads on the seafloor and their bodies angled upward. The Whitetip pair would occasionally pivot on the female's snout. In a captive mating of this species, the male released his grip on the pectoral fin during copulation as the pair lay on the bottom (the male on his side and the female on her back) (Uchida et al., 1990). The end of the clasper is spread open when withdrawn from the cloaca, as has been observed in a number of shark species.

In the Lemon Shark (*Negaprion brevirostris*), the male swims alongside the female and bites her during courtship. Blacktip Reef Sharks (*Carcharhinus melanopterus*) are reported to lie side by side during copulation (biting was not reported). Johnson and Nelson (1978) related a secondhand account wherein a pair of these sharks were seen rolling on the bottom as they mated. The authors also observed a male following close behind and slightly under a female, with his nose near her cloaca (called "close-following behavior" by the authors).

In at least some of the carcharhinids, more than one male will try to mate with the same female. Off Cocos Island, Costa Rica, male competition for a mate was observed in Whitetip Reef Sharks. A group of sharks were seen circling a sand patch, when a female split from the group and "lodged herself in the rocks." *The Undersea Hunter Newsletter* (June, 1995) continues: "Two or three males dove in, locked their jaws around her pectoral fin and struggled to free her from the rocks. As they went up to midwater, one of the males won the contest. Locked in the male's jaws, she descended to the rocks where she braced herself again and the mating process was completed."

Mike DeGruy's film, *Shark Encounters*, also documents several female Whitetip Reef Sharks pursuing a female. In the Maldives, I saw four adult males following a large female that bore fresh bite marks on her gills.

The author of *The Undersea Hunter Newsletter* reports seeing courtship behavior in the Silky Shark (*Carcharhinus falciformis*) similar to that described for Whitetips, but copulation was not observed. Another more active carcharhinid, the Sandbar Shark (*Carcharhinus plumbeus*) was observed mating in Omaha's Henry Doorly Zoo. Courtship began with the male persistently following the female around the tank. Suddenly, the male dashed forward and bit the female's pectoral fin. He lunged forward again until the whole pectoral fin was engulfed. An aquarist in the tank said he could hear the crunching sound as the male bit the female's fin. The male then twisted the posterior portion of his body under the female's so that he could insert a single clasper. The pair careened through the tank, almost ramming the divers as well as the aquarium aquascaping. Copulation was brief, lasting about 2 or 3 minutes.

Skates (Rajidae)

THE MATING BEHAVIOR of the captive Clearnose Skate (*Raja eglanteria*) has been studied in great detail (Luer & Gilbert, 1985). Unlike mating in other elasmobranchs, courtship and copulation in the skates can be a long, drawn out affair. Another interesting difference between the skates and other sharks and rays (at least those species that have been observed mating) is that females often initiate courtship. They have been observed to position their pelvic regions near the rostrum of a male, then raise and lower their pectoral fins. The receptive female may also arch her back upward and raise her tail. Females may initiate courtship in other elasmobranchs, but it does not appear to be a trend of the entire subclass.

When the male skate is ready to copulate, he grasps the rear pectoral fin margin in his jaws. The enlarged, sharp scales on the pectoral fins and on the head of the male, known as alar spines, help anchor the male to the body and pelvic area of the female. After the male is firmly attached to his mate, he swings his tail beneath hers. In some cases, males have been known to rest in this precopulatory position for as long as 4 hours.

To initiate copulation, the male flexes his clasper medially and begins to insert it into the female's cloaca. If the male is griping the right pectoral fin, he flexes his right clasper. If he is biting the left pectoral fin, he uses his left clasper. (Fowler [1906] reported that skates sometimes use both claspers simultaneously—something that has not been confirmed by more recent ob-

Field Observations on the Mating Behavior of the Round Stingray

A number of years ago, I had the unprecedented opportunity to study the reproductive behavior of the Round Stingray (*Urobatis halleri*) in the Gulf of California. What follows is a brief description of my findings. The mating system of the Round Stingray has several behavioral components, or fixed action patterns.

Following, a behavior employed during courtship by many elasmobranchs, consisted of one or more males swimming behind a female. Often a male would follow closely, so that his rostrum was positioned near the female's pelvic region. (This suggests that the female may release a chemical signal, like a pheromone, that could communicate information on her reproductive condition.)

Inspection occurred when a male approached, usually from behind, a buried or exposed female. When the female was buried, the male would push his rostrum into the substrate, often provoking the female to flutter her pectoral fin margins. (Fluttering the disc margin made it more difficult for the male to grasp the female's disc margin in his mouth.)

One of the more dynamic behaviors that had not been reported in a ray before was **pelvic grasp**, wherein the male bit and held the female's pelvic fin in his mouth, and the pair began swimming in a circular or linear trajectory with intermittent periods of inactivity. During this behavior, the unreceptive female sometimes attempted to stab the male with her tail spine (I recorded this on 30 occasions). The male would respond to this violent response by curling his disc toward the midline of the body, in an apparent effort to cover his vulnerable eyes and spiracles. On one occasion, I observed a female sting a male 27 times before he released his grip and swam away. Sometimes during pelvic grasp, the exhausted female would lie on her back, with her pelvic fin twisted, while the male rested on his ventrum. (I observed 117 bouts of pelvic grasp, with the longest lasting 220 seconds.) This behavior results in extensive epidermal lacerations on the pelvic fins and occasional tearing or notching of the fin margins.

Rostral grasp, a less-common behavior, describes the male biting and holding the rostrum of a female. The pair would remain stationary, except for sporadic pivoting, until the male released his grip.

Pectoral grasp occurred when a male bit and held the disc margin of the female. Females may thrust their caudal spine at the grasping male or the pair may swim along together. If the latter occurs, the male may attempt to mate with the female. As the male held the female's fin margin in his mouth, he would lift her disc, pivot under her, and insert a single clasper. The pair then settled to the substrate, usually with the male underneath the female for most of the bout.

On a number of occasions, that male would begin rapidly beating his tail in the lateral plane, which caused the posterior portions of the mating rays to rise off the substrate and occasionally resulted in the pair being upended. Usually the female would undulate one side of her disc and return to her superior position. This behavior, called **lateral tail sweep**, might help increase clasper penetration or may assist sperm transfer.

In a rarely seen act, two male Round Stingrays grasp the pectoral fins of a female.

In this instance, the male has mounted the female in eelgrass to complete the mating.

Another pair of Round Stingrays copulates on a muddy bottom in the Gulf of California.

I observed 124 bouts of copulation. Thirteen bouts timed from the onset lasted from 184 to 410 seconds (an average of 304 seconds). Copulation ended when the female vigorously undulated her disc and broke free of the male's grip. Sometimes one or more other males would appear on the scene and try to dislodge the mating male. Female Round Stingrays would occasionally have one male grasping each pectoral fin and simultaneously trying to flip under her into a copulatory position.

During the mating period, females often formed groups, which were classified into two different types. **Buried groups** consisted of 3 to over 50 partially or completely buried individuals that would often lie side by side with their disc margins overlapping. **Piles** were defined as large groups of females (40 individuals or more) that would lie on the substrate and on top of one another. While males occasionally inspected, bit, or copulated with females in buried groups, they frequently engaged in these behaviors with females in piles. (Females in piles copulated five times more frequently with males than those in buried groups.) Numerous males were observed to swim around the periphery and over the piles. It appears that buried females are attempting to avoid amorous males, possibly because they have already mated or because they are not yet in reproductive condition. In contrast, the piles are comprised of sexually receptive females.

All reproductive behavior was observed in the morning, between 6:00 and 10:00 a.m. At the start, most females were either buried in the sand or mud, quiescent on the grass near the front of an eelgrass bed, or in piles. Males, in contrast, actively patrolled the sand and mud margin in front of a seagrass meadow. Between 11:00 and 12:00 noon, a fascinating behavioral shift occurred—many of the males began to bury, while females began to emerge from the substrate and forage in the eelgrass beds. As the day went on, more females came out of the sand and began to feed. Males were rarely observed feeding at any time during the reproductive period.

The cycle began again the next morning, with the whole reproductive phase probably lasting several weeks.

servations.) The clasper is slowly thrust forward into the cloaca, with complete insertion sometimes taking as long as an hour. When fully inserted, the end of the clasper is expanded. This firmly anchors the male's sex organ in position. The clasper gland secretions and the thrusting of the organ, which occurs intermittently throughout copulation, may aid in sperm transfer. The clasper gland secretions also serve to lubricate the clasper. Copulation has been observed to last from 1 to 4 hours. Why does copulation last so long in skates, compared to other elasmobranchs? It maybe because they lack the siphon sacs that sharks possess. Conception can occur quite some time after copulation, as the female is capable of storing viable sperm in the nidamental glands for at least 3 months after mating.

Competition has been observed between male skates during the reproductive period. Referring to the Clearnose Skate, Norman (1931) stated, "several males will pursue one female, fighting among themselves and buffeting each other with their fins."

When the female skate is ready to deposit her egg cases she will rest on the bottom, fold her pelvic fins ventrally, and then violently shake her pelvic region from side to side. She then swims off, leaving an egg case in her wake. In those species studied, the egg case in the right oviduct is deposited first, while the egg in the left oviduct is laid several minutes to 24 hours later (in most cases, the second egg is released within several hours of the first). Successive pairs of eggs are usually deposited from 2 to 6 days after the first pair is laid. Female Clearnose Skates lay from 23 to 35 pairs of eggs in a reproductive season. Incubation is temperature dependent, with the duration ranging from 64 to 96 days. Those eggs laid later in the reproductive period tend to have a shorter incubation period than those deposited early in the season.

Whiptail Stingrays (Dasyatidae)

A FEW SPECIES OF STINGRAYS have been observed mating in public aquariums, and in two species reproductive behavior has been witnessed in the wild. Dasyatid courtship usually begins with the male grasping the margin of the female's pectoral fin. Male Southern Stingrays (*Dasyatis americana*) and Smooth Stingrays (*D. brevicaudata*) have been observed grasping the female's pectoral fin in this way. In the Roughtail Stingray (*Dasyatis centroura*) a male closely followed a female with his snout near the posterior edge of her pectoral fins. The female stopped and remained stationary on the substrate. The male then moved over her back and began nipping the upper portion of her disc. No copulation was observed.

In most species, the male will attempt to swing underneath the female after grasping the edge of her pectoral fin. In this way, he can bring his claspers into contact with her cloaca. However, in a presumed copulation event involving the Southern Stingray, a male mounted the female dorsally and apparently curled its ventral fins and clasper under her while maintaining this position. This species has also been observed to mate in a venter-to-venter orientation. DeLoach (1999) reported that seven or eight smaller Southern Stingray males chased a female. One of the males was able to bite her disc margin and flip underneath her so they were venter-to-venter. He inserted a single clasper. DeLoach states, "During the 5-minute copulation period, the writhing female was partially restrained by the other males, who pressed down on her body as she swam over the sand." When the initial suitor was finished, a second male flipped under the female and copulated with her, after which the group members dispersed.

In one unidentified *Dasyatis* species, mating was reported to last 19 minutes, while in the Smooth

Stingray, observed matings lasted 3 to 5 minutes. In the Smooth Stingray, the male undulates its tail during copulation, possibly to assist in sperm transfer.

In the Marbled Ribbontail Ray (*Taeniura meyeni*) numerous males will also "mob" a single, larger female. Off Cocos Island, Costa Rica (where this species is quite common), large groups of males have been observed swimming around and resting on females lying on the substrate. The males also follow the females as they swim and attempt to grasp a pectoral fin.

Round Stingrays and Stingarees (Urolophidae)

THE ROUND STINGRAYS AND STINGAREES are the best batoid candidates for captive breeding. Their small size at maturity and diminutive maximum sizes make them well suited to the larger home aquarium.

More is known about the mating behavior and mating system of the Round Stingray (*Urobatis halleri*) than any other elasmobranch species. (For details on the reproductive behavior of this ray see page 232.) As in most of the urolophids, mating occurs with the male and female in a venter-to venter orientation; the male grasps the disc margin of the female, swings under her, and inserts a single clasper. In both the Round Stingray and Yellow Stingray (*Urobatis jamaicensis*), interfering males will swim around, nudge, and bite the courting female. Sometimes more than one male will attempt to pivot under the same female simultaneously.

Courtship can be hard on females. They may become exhausted trying to resist amorous males and may sustain scrapes, bite marks, ripped fins, and gouges as a result of male biting behavior. During the mating season, I have found a number of female rays washed up on the beach, possibly as a result of the energy expended and injuries inflicted during courtship. For this reason it is best to house only one male with several females if your aquarium is large enough. If the male continues to bite the female(s) after they have already mated, it may be a good idea to separate the sexes.

The Role of the Aquarist

WHILE MUCH REMAINS TO BE LEARNED about the reproduction of elasmobranchs, determined amateur aquarists have an exciting opportunity to help lead the way. Captive breeding of other marine fishes and invertebrates, once thought nearly impossible, is becoming more commonplace today. A number of smaller elasmobranch species are well suited to reproduction in home-scale systems, and the demand for captive-bred specimens should far exceed the supply for many years to come. I would urge anyone who has success with any of these animals to share their experiences with others via hobbyist periodicals, internet forums, and the Breeder's Registry (see Contacts, page 240).

References

Breder & Rosen (1966), Brockman (1975), Carrier et al. (1994), Castro et al. (1988), Clark (1963, 1975), Compagno (1984b), Deloach (1999), Dempster & Herald (1961), Dodd (1983), Dral (1980), Fowler (1906), Grover (1974), Hagiwara (1989), Hartley (1998), A. Henningsen (personal communication), Houziaux & Voss (1997), Johnson & Nelson (1978), Kajiura & Tricas (1996), Klimley (1980), K. Kunze (personal communication), Leigh-Sharpe (1921), Libby & Gilbert (1960), Luer & Gilbert (1985), McCourt & Kerstitch (1980), Norman (1931), Parsons (1991), Rouse (1985), C. Schreiber (personal communication), T. Schmid (personal communication), Teshima et al. (1978), Tricas & LeFeuvre (1985), Tyson (1998), Uchida et al. (1990), West & Carter (1990), R. Withrow (Aquarium of the Americas, personal communication).

Glossary

alimentary tract: the connected series of anatomical parts (including the stomach and intestines) leading from the mouth to the cloaca.

ampullae of Lorenzini: skin pores containing receptor cells that can detect even very faint electrical fields, including those emitted by living prey.

anguilliform: an eel-like body plan seen in some bottom-dwelling (benthic) sharks, in which the main portion of the body is very elongate, cylindrical, and flexible.

anterior: pertaining to the front, head, or leading end of the body.

barbel: a long tentacle-like protuberance, usually present near the nostrils, that serves a sensory function.

batoid: a ray; a fish in the Superorder Rajomorphii.

benthic: referring to bottom-dwelling flora and fauna (compare to **pelagic**).

bivalve: a class of mollusks that includes clams, oysters, and mussels.

bony fishes: members of the Class Actinopterygii. A diverse group that contains most of the living species of fishes.

branchial: pertaining to the gills (branchiae) of an aquatic animal.

buccal: pertaining to the mouth.

candling: visual inspection of the condition of the contents of an unbroken egg by holding it up to a bright light.

cartilage: firm, elastic, whitish connective tissue that forms the skeleton of elasmobranchs; gristle.

cartilaginous: pertaining to cartilage; in fishes, those having skeletons of cartilage, rather than bone.

caudal fin: the tail fin, which in sharks can be divided into the upper and lower caudal lobe.

caudal peduncle: the narrow portion of a fish's body, forward of the tail fin.

cephalopods: the class of mollusks that includes octopuses, squid, cuttlefishes, and nautiluses.

carcharhinid: member of the Family Carcharhinidae, large active sharks not suitable for most home-scale aquariums.

chimera: unusual elasmobranchs in the Subclass Holocephali, which includes the so-called ghost sharks, ratfishes, spookfishes, and elephantfishes.

claspers: rod-like modifications of the male elasmobranch's pelvic fins that are used to transfer sperm during mating.

cloaca: cavity into which the intestinal, urinary, and reproductive canals open in elasmobranchs; also seen in birds, amphibians, and reptiles.

congener: referring to a member of the same genus.

consexual: referring to a member of the same sex.

conspecific: referring to a member of the same species.

coralline algae: red, calcareous algae of the Family Corallinae; usually encrusting and pink in color.

countershading: color scheme in certain animals, in which the dorsal or upper body is dark and the underside light, making the animal less visible to prey or predators in sunlit conditions.

crepuscular: most active at dusk and dawn.

Crustacea: a subphylum of the Phylum Arthropoda that includes the barnacles, copepods, mantis shrimps, mysids, crabs, shrimps, and krill.

cryptic: difficult to see or camouflaged; usually in reference to color pattern or behavior (e.g., hiding in reef crevices).

cuticle: the heavy slime coat covering certain fishes, especially some scaleless batoids.

cycloid scales: scales with a smooth posterior margin, as in many bony fishes.

death curl: usually fatal condition in rays, in which the pectoral fin edges curl up or inward.

demersal: living on the sea bottom.

dermal denticles: minuscule, toothlike protective scales that make up the armored skin of many elasmobranchs; also called **placoid scales**.

depressiform: a dorsally flattened body plan seen in rays, skates, and some benthic sharks; pectoral fins are typically enlarged for propulsion.

diel: pertaining to the day-night cycle.

dimorphism: the existence of two distinctive forms, as in sexual dimorphism, in which the males and females have different external appearances.

disc: pertaining to the head, pectoral fins, and trunk of a ray.

disc width: refers to the widest portion of the disc.

disc length: refers to the longest portion of the disc (i.e., from the tip of the snout to the posterior edge of the pectoral fin).

diurnal: active during the day.

dorsum: (adj. **dorsal**) the back or upper part of the body.

dasyatid: referring to a member of the Family Dasyatidae, the whiptail stingrays.

Echinodermata: the phylum of echinoderms, which are comprised of sea stars, serpent stars, sea cucumbers, and sea urchins. They are radially symmetrical and some have sharp spines.

elasmobranch: a member of the Subclass Elasmobranchii of sharklike fishes with skeletons of cartilage, a skin covered in denticles, and multiple gill slits; the sharks, rays, and skates.

endolymphatic pore: one of a pair of openings on the top of the head of sharks and rays connected to the inner ears; transmits pressure waves via the endolymphatic duct.

euryhaline: pertaining to an aquatic organism that can withstand a broad salinity range (compare to **stenohaline**).

facultative: capable of living in varying conditions; e.g., facultative cleaners do not rely strictly on parasites for food (compare to **obligatory**).

hemiscylliid: a member of the Family Hemiscylliidae, the bamboo and epaulette sharks.

heterospecific: referring to a member of a different species.

heterocercal: a tail shape in which the upper caudal lobe is larger than the lower.

homocercal: a tail shape in which the upper and lower caudal lobes are equal in size; also called **lunate**.

hypersaline: referring to water with a salinity higher than that of natural seawater.

hyposaline: referring to water with a salinity lower than that of natural seawater.

falcate: long, narrow, and curved (sickle-shaped).

foam fractionator: device used to extract polluting fats, proteins, and other wastes from marine aquariums; also called a **protein skimmer**.

fusiform: a body plan seen in many fast-swimming sharks in which the main portion of the relatively stiff body tapers toward each end; the snout is conical.

gape: the width of the open mouth.

gills: the primary respiratory organs of fishes and certain invertebrates.

gill slits: external vertical openings on each side of the head of an elasmobranch through which water is expelled after it has passed over the gills; usually numbering five in sharks, but up to seven.

infaunal: living within the sediment of the seafloor.

inner margin: the inner edge of a fin.

intertidal: a part of the shore or reef that is exposed to the air at low tide and covered by water at high tide.

invertebrate: any animal lacking a backbone in its adult form.

krill: small shrimplike marine crustaceans that are an important food source for certain fishes in the wild and in the aquarium.

labial furrows: folds of skin around the edge of the mouth.

lateral: pertaining to the side.

lateral-line: an assemblage of pressure-sensitive organs attached to a perforated, water-filled canal running along the sides of fishes and allowing a sense of "distant touch."

live rock: biologically active coral rock usually collected from rubble areas near coral reefs or aquacultured; used to provide natural filtering functions and aquascaping for marine aquarium systems.

luciferin: organic compound that produces light when oxidized by the enzyme luciferase in the photophores of certain fishes.

lunate: shaped like a crescent; see **homocercal**.

marginal: just along the edge of the fin.

molariform: flat, broad, and round; molarlike in shape.

Mollusca: a diverse phylum of animals, many of which have an external shell; members include the chitons, snails, bivalves, octopuses, and squids.

monogenetic trematodes: flatworms that are primarily ectoparasites. Species in the genera *Dermophthirius*, *Dendromonocotyle*, and *Neodermophthirius* are some of those commonly encountered on captive elasmobranchs.

morphology: the form and structure of an organism, considered as a whole; also, the study of the form and structure of organisms.

motor patterns: a stereotypical group of actions or behaviors.

nasal barbel: one of a pair of elongated anterior nasal flaps in some shark species, used as sensory tool (like a thick whisker) to detect hidden prey.

nasal flap: a skin flap just in front of the nostril.

nasoral groove: a channel that connects the mouth to the nostrils, allowing the shark or ray to irrigate its nostrils with fresh seawater to detect the presence of scents.

neuromasts: clusters of sensory hairlike cells or cilia in the lateral-line system of fishes.

nictitating membrane: a movable lower eyelid present as a protective organ in certain sharks, particularly the carcharhinids.

nocturnal: active at night.

obligatory: obligate or required; e.g., an obligatory cleaner fish relies entirely on this feeding mode to obtain nutrients (compare to **facultative**).

oceanic: pertaining to the open ocean.

ocellus (plural: ocelli): a pigment pattern that resembles an eye; also known as an eyespot or false eye and thought to serve an antipredation function.

ontogenetic: referring to a change that occurs with age.

operculum pupillare: structure in the eyes of some rays used to screen light from entering the pupil.

oviparous: egg-laying; in sharks, the eggs are laid in egg cases.

oviposition: the process of depositing eggs.

ovoviviparous: having the ability to produce and hatch eggs within the body of the mother; young are born live.

papilla: a small fleshy projection (plural: **papillae**), such as a tastebud in the mouth or pharynx of an elasmobranch.

parturition: the process of giving birth.

pelagic: pertaining to organisms that live in the water column (compare to **benthic**).

pharynx: that part of the alimentary tract with the gill arches.

pH: a measure of the hydrogen ion content of water or its relative acidity; a pH of 7 is neutral; natural seawater is slightly basic, with a pH of about 8.3.

photophore: a light-emitting organ found in some sharks.

phytoplankton: tiny photosynthetic organisms that drift in the sea (compare to **zooplankton**).

piscivorous: fish-eating.

pit organs: external neuromasts or sensory cells on various parts of the body of a fish.

plankton: plant and animal organisms that drift about in the ocean and serve a vital function in marine food chains; mostly minute in size but also up 5 cm (2 in.) or larger in the case of macroplankton or megaloplankton. Permanent floaters are termed holoplankton; meroplankton includes larval organisms that drop out of the plankton as they mature.

placoid scales: toothlike, tiny exterior plates making up the skin of most elasmobranchs; also called **dermal denticles**.

polychaetes: a class of worms in the Phylum Annelida; includes about 800 species, including ragworms, lug worms, bristle-worms, and fanworms.

posterior: anatomical term pertaining to the area toward the tail or rear of the body.

ram-jet ventilation: in sharks, a system of forcing water over the gills and out through the gill slits to irrigate the gill chamber with fresh, oxygenated water.

ray: a dorsally flattened elasmobranch or cartilaginous fish in the Superorder Rajomorphii, which includes the stingrays, electric rays, skates, sawfishes, and guitarfishes; a **batoid**.

requiem shark: member of the Family Carcharhinidae, the large, active species most commonly associated in the public mind with sharks and shark attacks on humans.

remora: loose term for members of the Family Echeneidae; the discfishes, including *Remora remora*, that commonly associate with elasmobranchs.

rostrum: an elongate or extended snout.

sagittiform: a body plan seen in many sharks in which the main portion of the body is slightly compressed and cylindrical, with a long tail.

sea anemones: invertebrates belonging to the Class Anthozoa that have a central disc surrounded by stinging tentacles.

selachian: fish in the Superorder Squalomorphii; a shark.

sessile: permanently attached or stationary.

sexual dimorphism: structural or size differences between the sexes.

shark: an elasmobranch or cartilaginous fish in the Superorders Squalomorphii, Squatinomorphii, or Galeomorphii; a selachian.

siphon sacs: a pair of sacs located under the skin of the abdomen in male sharks and rays that secrete a fluid or seawater to help transport sperm into the clasper groove.

spawning: the laying and fertilizing of eggs.

species: the lowest taxonomic ranking, designating a population or series of populations which have common characteristics and which are able to breed freely among themselves.

spiracle: a respiratory opening located behind the eye on each side of the head.

spiral valve: a corkscrew-like fold of the intestine in elasmobranchs that increases surface area and enhances the absorption of nutrients.

stenohaline: pertaining to an aquatic organism that can only withstand a narrow salinity range (compare to euryhaline).

suborbital: below the eye.

substrate: any solid surface or substance (e.g., rock, sand bed) on the seafloor in a marine environment.

subtropical: in fishes, pertaining to those from areas bordering the Tropics and subject to greater variations of water temperature.

supraorbital crest: a bony ridge above the eye.

tapetum lucidum: internal eye structure that increases the sensitivity to light and causes the "eyeshine" observed in some animals, such as sharks and cats.

teleosts: bony fishes with a swim bladder and thin scales.

temperate: in fishes, refers to those found in climatic zones within the mid-latitudes, between the Arctic zones and the subtropics.

terminal: anatomical term pertaining to the end or extremity of a body part, such as the head, tail, or an appendage.

tropical: in fishes, refers to those found in the Tropics, a frost-free area with generally reliable warm temperatures year round; also defined as the zone between the Tropic of Cancer, 23.5°N, and the Tropic of Capricorn, 23.5°S.

tubercles: enlarged, thornlike denticles.

urolophid: member of the Family Urolophidae, the smallish rays known as stingarees.

ventrum: (adj. ventral) the stomach or lower part of the body.

vertebrate: a chordate animal with a segmented spinal column, usually of bone or cartilage, and a brain encased in a brain pan.

viviparous: giving birth to live young.

wind eggs: light, empty, infertile shark or ray egg cases.

worms: a general term used for the annelid, sipunculid (peanut), and echiuran (innkeeper) worms; most of these live on the seafloor, often within bottom sediments.

zooplankton: animal organisms, mostly tiny, that drift in the sea (compare to phytoplankton).

Contacts

Online Information

American Elasmobranch Society
www.elasmo.org
Website of the American Elasmobranch Society.

Argent Chemical Laboratories
www.argent-labs.com
Aquatic animal health care products, including MS222.

Breeder's Registry
www.breeders-registry.gen.ca.us
Nonprofit association of marine ornamental propagators.
Includes a databank on captive reproduction events.

Coral Realm Online Marine Life Resource
www.coralrealm.com
User-pay website with extensive information on the biology of
sharks and rays, including information on food habits,
reproductive behavior, and habitat preferences.

Florida Museum of Natural History
www.flmnh.ufl.edu/fish/sharks/sharks.htm
Information on the natural history of sharks and rays and
current research on shark-related topics. Includes a link to
Shark News, a newsletter specializing in shark conservation.

Mediterranean Shark Site
www.zoo.co.uk/~z9015043/index.html
Informative resource on Mediterranean shark species.

National Audubon Society
www.audubon.org/campaign/lo
Information on shark conservation.

The Pelagic Shark Research Foundation
www.pelagic.org
Information on pelagic sharks, with special emphasis on species
from the Eastern North Atlantic.

The Shark Trust
www.sharktrust.org
A website that promotes the study, management and
conservation of sharks, skates, and rays. Good information on
some shark species.

Large Aquariums

Most aquarium shops will be able to special-order larger tanks
and can provide invaluable help in planning the configuration
and plumbing of the system, as well as in installing heavy tanks
and stands. Some North American suppliers include:

Aquatic Eco-Systems, Inc.
1767 Benbow Court
Apopka, FL 32703
800-422-3939
www.aquaticeco.com
Components for building very large systems, including aquatic
pond liners, pumps, filters, sumps, controllers, and chillers.

Inter-American Pet Supply
1847 48th St. SE
Calgary, Alberta T2A 0T8 Canada
403-273-2843
Glass aquariums in standard sizes up to 6,080 L (1,600 gal.)
and larger custom tanks. Ships throughout North America.

Oceanic Systems, Inc.
11839 Shiloh Road
Dallas, TX 75228
214-320-6050
www.oceanicsystems.com
Heavy-duty glass aquariums, including bowfront models, up to
760 L (200 gal.) and custom tanks up to 2,052 L (540 gal.).

Tenecor
4300 East Magnolia Street
Phoenix, AZ 85034
602-437-4373
www.tenecor.com
Acrylic aquariums in standard sizes to 5,700 L (1,500 gal.);
custom tanks to 38,000 L (10,000 gal.).

U.S. Aquarium
2665 S. Santa Fe Drive
Denver, CO 80223
303-871-8682
www.usaquarium.com
Acrylic aquariums in standard sizes to 684 L (1,700 gal);
custom tanks on request.

Bibliography

Adamson, M.L., and J.N. Caira. 1991. *Lockenloia sanguinis* n. gen., n. sp. (Nematoda: Dracunculoidea) fron the heart of a nurse shark, *Ginglymostoma cirratum*, in Florida. *J. Parasitology*, 77:663-665.

Allee, W.C., and J.C. Dickinson, Jr. 1954. Dominance and subordination in the smooth dogfish, *Mustelus canis* (Mitchell). *Physiol. Zool.* 27:356-364.

Allen, G.R., and D.R. Robertson. 1994. *Fishes of the Tropical Eastern Pacific*. University of Hawaii Press, Honolulu, 332 pp.

Babel, J.S. 1967. Reproduction, life history, and ecology of the round stingray, *Urolophus halleri* Copper. *Dept. Fish Game, Fish Bull.* 137:104 pp.

Bass, A.J., J.D. D'Aubrey, and N. Kistnasamy. 1975a. Sharks of the east coast of southern Africa. 2. The families Scyliorhinidae and Pseudotriakidae. *Invest. Rep. Ocean. Res. Inst. Durban*, 37:63 pp.

Beebe, W., and J. Tee-Van. 1941a. Eastern Pacific expeditions of the New York Zoological Society. 25. Fishes from the tropical eastern Pacific. Part 2. Sharks. *Zool., N.Y.* 26:93-122.

Beebe, W., and J. Tee-Van. 1941b. Eastern Pacific expeditions of the New York Zoological Society. 26. Fishes from the tropical eastern Pacific. Part 3. Rays, Mantas and Chimeras. *Zool., N.Y.* 26:245-279.

Bennett, M.B., M.R. Heupel, S.M. Bennett, and A.R. Parker. 1997. *Sheina orri* (Myodocopa: Cypridinidae), an ostracod parasitic on the gills of the epaulette shark, *Hemiscyllium ocellatum* (Elasmobranchii: Hemiscylliidae). *Int. J. Parasitology*, 27: 275-281.

Belbenoit, P. 1986. Fine analysis of predatory and defensive motor events in *Torpedo marmorata* (Pisces) *J. Exp. Biol*. 121:197-226.

Benz, G.W. 1980. Tissue proliferations associated with *Nemesis lamna* Risso, 1826 (Copepoda: Eudactylinidae) infestations on the gill filaments of shortfin makos (*Isurus oxyrinchus* Rafinesque). *J. Fish Disease*, 1980(3):443-446.

Bigelow, H.B., and W.C. Schroeder. 1948. *Sharks*. Mem. Sears Found. Mar. Res. 1(pt 1):53-576.

Bigelow, H.B., and W.C. Schroeder. 1953. *Sawfishes, Guitarfishes, Skates and Rays*. Mem. Sears Found. Mar. Res. 1(pt 2):1-514.

Bird, P.M. 1981. The occurrence of *Cirolana borealis* (Isopoda) in the hearts of sharks from Atlantic coastal waters of Florida. *Fish. Bull. NOAA*, 79:376-383.

Bleckmann, H., and M.H. Hofmann. 1999. Special Senses. In: *Sharks, Skates, and Rays. The Biology of Elasmobranch Fishes*. (W.C. Hamlett, ed.). John Hopkins University Press, Baltimore, 300-328.

Bradley, J.L. 1996. www.hawaii.edu/fishlab/labstud.htm.

Branstetter, S. 1987. Age and growth validation of newborn sharks held in laboratory aquaria, with comments on the life history of the Atlantic sharpnose shark, *Rhizoprionodon terraenovae*. *Copeia*, 1987(2):291-300.

Bray, R.N., and M.A. Hixon. 1978. Night shocker: predatory behavior of the pacific electric ray (*Torpedo californica*). *Sci,*. 200:333-334.

Breder, C.M. Jr., and D.E. Rosen. 1966. *Modes of Reproduction in Fishes*. The Natural History Press, Garden City, N.J. 941 pp.

Bret, J.R., and T.D. Groves. 1976. Fish energetics. In: *Fish Physiology* (W.S. Hoar, D.J. Randall, eds.). Academic Press, New York, 8:79-31 pp.

Brockman, F.W. 1975. An observation on mating behavior of the southern stingray, *Dasyatis americana*. *Copeia*, 1975:784-785.

Capapé, C. 1979. La torpille marbrée, *Torpedo marmorata*, Risso, 1810 (Pisces, Fajiformes) des côtes tunisinennes; nouvelles données sur l'écologie et la biologie se la reproduction de l'espece, avec une comparaison entre les populations méditerranéennes et atlantiques (1). *Annales de Sciences Naturelles, Zoologie, Paris 1979*(1): 79-97.

Carlson, J.K., and G.R. Parsons. 1997. Age and growth of the bonnethead shark (*Sphyrna tiburo*) from northwest florida, with comments on clincal variation. *Env. Biol. Fish*. 50:331-341.

Carrier, J.C., and C.A. Luer. 1990. Growth rates in nurse sharks *Ginglymostoma cirratum*. *Copeia*, 1990:676-682.

Carrier, J.C., H.L. Pratt, and L.K. Martin. 1994. Group reproductive behavior in free-living nurse sharks, *Ginglymostoma cirratum*. *Copeia*, 1994:646-656.

Castro, J.I. 1983. *The Sharks of North American Waters*. Texas A&M Univ. Press, College Station, 180 pp.

Castro, J.I., P.M. Bubucis, and N.A. Overstrom. 1988. The reproductive biology of the chain dogfish, *Scyliorhinus retifer*. *Copeia*, 1988:740-746.

Cheung, P.J. 1992. Parasitic diseases of elasmobranchs. In: *Fish Medicine* (M.K. Stoskopf, ed.). W.B. Saunders and Co. Philadelphia, 782-807.

Cheung, P.J., R.F. Nigrelli, G.D. Ruggieri, and A. Cilia. 1982. Treatment of skin lesions in captive lemon sharks, *Negaprion brevirostris* (Poey), caused by monogeneans (*Dermophthirius* sp.). *J. Fish Disease*, 5:167-170.

Cisio, P.R., and J.N. Caira. 1993. The parasite assemblage in the spiral intestine of the shark, *Mustelus canis*. *J. Parasitol.*, 79:886-899.

Clark, E. 1963. The maintenance of sharks in captivity, with a report on their instrumental conditioning. In: *Sharks and Survival* (P.W. Gilbert, ed.). D.C. Heath and Co., Boston, 115-149.

Coleman, N. 1981. *Australian Sea Fishes North of 30°S*. Doubleday Australia, Sydney, 297 pp.

Coleman, N. 1992. *Australia's Sharks and Rays*. Weldon Publ., Sydney, NSW, 64 pp.

Compagno, L.J.V. 1973. Interrelationships of living elasmobranchs. In: *Interrelationships of Fishes* (P.H. Greenwood, R.S. Miles, and C. Patterson, eds.). *J. Linn. Soc. (Zool.) 53 Suppl.* 1:37 pp.

Compagno, L.J.V. 1984a. Sharks of the World. *FAO Species Catalogue*. FAO Fisheries Synopsis No. 125, vol. 4, part 1. Rome: United Nations Development Programme, Food and Agriculture Organization of the United Nations, 250 pp.

Compagno, L.J.V. 1984b. Sharks of the World. *FAO Species Catalogue*. FAO Fisheries Synopsis No. 125, vol. 4, part 2. Rome: United Nations Development Programme, Food and Agriculture Organization of the United Nations, 251-655.

Compagno, L.J.V. 1990. Alternative life-history styles of cartilaginous fishes in time and space. *Env. Biol. Fish*, 28:33-75.

Compagno, L.J.V. 1999a. Systematics and Body Form. In: *Sharks, Skates, and Rays. The Biology of Elasmobranch Fishes* (W. C. Hamlett, ed.). John Hopkins University Press, Baltimore, 1-42.

Compagno, L.J.V. 1999b. Checklist of Living Elasmobranchs. In: *Sharks, Skates, and Rays. The Biology of Elasmobranch Fishes* (W. C. Hamlett, ed.). John Hopkins University Press, Baltimore, 471-498.

Compagno, L.J.V., D.A. Ebert, and M.J. Smale. 1989. *Guide to the Sharks and Rays of South Africa*. New Holland Ltd. London 158 pp.

Copper, A.R., and S. Morris. 1998. Osmotic, ionic and haematological response of the Port Jackson shark *Heterodontus portusjacksoni* and the common stingaree *Trygonoptera testacea* upon exposure to diluted seawater. *Mar. Biol.*, 132:29-42.

Cortés, E., and S.H. Gruber. 1990. Diet, feeding habits and estimates of daily ration of young lemon sharks, *Negaprion brevirostris* (Poey). *Copeia*, 1990:204-218.

Cortés, E., and G.R. Parsons. 1996. Comparative demography of two populations of the bonnethead shark (*Sphyrna tiburo*). *Can. J. Fish. Aquat. Sci.*, 53:709-718.

Cortés, E., C.A Manire, and R.E. Hueter. 1996. Diet, feeding habits, and diel feeding chronology of the bonnethead shark, *Sphyrna tiburo*, in southwest Florida. *Bull. Mar. Sci.* 58(2):353-367.

Cressey, R.F., and E.A. Lachner. 1970. The parasitic copepod diet and life history of diskfishes (Echeneidae). *Copeia*, 1970:310-318.

Crow, G.L. 1990. A synoptic review of the monogenetic trematodes: I. Introduction. *J. Aquacul. and Aquat. Sci.* 5:74-78.

Crow, G.L., and J.A. Brock. 1993. The use of gentamycin sulfate therapy in a captive blacktip reef shark (*Carcharhinus melanopterus*) with intestinal biting syndrome. *Zoo Biology* 12:479-482.

Crow, G.L., and J. D. Hewitt, IV. 1988. Longevity records for captive tiger sharks, *Galeocerdo cuvieri*. *Int. Zoo. Ybk.* 27: 237-240.

Crow, G.L., J.C. Howe, S. Uchida, S. Kamolnick, M. Wisner, and J.N. Caira. 1991. Protrusion of the valvular intestine through the cloaca in sharks of the Family Carcharhinidae. *Copeia*, 1990:226-229.

Daiber, F.C., and R.A. Booth. 1960. Notes on the biology of the butterlfly rays, *Gymnura altavela* and *Gymnura micrura*. *Copeia*, 1960:137-139.

Davies, D.H. 1963. The story of Sally the sawfish. *Bull. S. Afr. Ass. Mar. Biol. Res.* 4:10-13.

Deloach, N. 1999. *Reef Fish Behavior*. New World Publications, Jacksonville, FL, 359 pp.

Dempster, R.P., and E.S. Herald. 1961. Notes on the hornshark, *Heterodontus francisci*, with observations on mating activities. *Occ. Pap. Calif. Acad. Sci.* 33:1-7.

Devadoss, P. 1978. On the food of rays, *Dasyatis uarnak* (Forskal), *D. alcockii* (Annandale), and *D. sephen* (Forskal). *Indian J. Fish.* 25:9-13.

Dingerkus, G., and T.C. DeFino. 1983. A revision of the Orectolobiform shark Family Hemiscylliidae (Chondrichthyes, Selachii). *Bull. Am. Mus. Nat. Hist.* 176:1-93.

Dodd, J.M. 1983. Reproduction in cartilaginous fishes (Chondrichthyes). In: *Fish Physiology* (W.S. Hoar, D.J. Randall, and E.M. Donaldson, eds.). Vol. 9A, Academic Press, New York, 31-95.

Dral, A.J. 1981. Reproduction en aquarium du requin de fond tropical *Chiloscyllium griseum* MÜll. et Henle (Orectolobidés). *Rev. Fr. Aquariol.* 7:99-104.

Dunn, R.F. 1990. Anesthetics in elasmobranchs: A review with emphasis on halothane-oxygen-nitrous oxide. *J. Aquacul. and Aquat. Sci.* 5:44-52.

Euzen, O. 1987. Food habits and diet composition of some fishes of Kuwait. *Kuwait Bull. Mar. Sci.* 1987:65-85.

Feder, H.M., C.H. Turner, and C. Limbaugh. 1974. Observations on fishes associated with kelp beds in Southern California. *Fish Bull. Calif. Dept. Fish and Game* 160:144 pp.

Francis, M.P. 1981. Von Bertalanffy growth rates in species of *Mustelus* (Elasmobranchii: Triakidae). *Copeia*, 1981:189-192.

Francis, M.P. 1992. Growth estimates for New Zealand Rig (*Mustelus lenticulatus*). *Aust. J. Mar. and Freshw. Res.* 43:1157-1176.

Francis, M.P., and J.T. Mace. 1980. Reproductive biology of *Mustelus lenticulatus* from Kaikoura and Nelson, *N.Z. J. Mar. Freshw. Res.* 14:303-311.

Fouts, W.R., and D.R. Nelson. 1999. Prey Capture by the Pacific Angel Shark, *Squatina californica*: Visually Mediated Strikes and Ambush-Site Characteristics. *Copeia*, 1999:304-312.

Fowler, H.W. 1906. The fishes of New Jersey. *Ann. Rep. Mus.* 1905 (pt 2):35-477.

Garman, S. 1913. The Plagiostomia (Sharks, skates and rays). *Mem. Mus. Comp. Zool., Harvard Coll.* 36:515 pp.

Gilbert, P.W., and F.G. Wood, Jr. 1957. Method of anesthetizing large sharks and rays safely and rapidly. *Science* 126:211-213.

Gilliam, D., and K.M. Sullivan. 1993. Diet and feeding habits of the Southern Stingray *Dasyatis americana* in the central Bahamas. *Bull. Mar. Sci.* 52:1007-1013.

Gordon, I. 1993. Pre-copulatory behavior of captive sand tiger sharks, *Carcharias taurus*. *Env. Biol. Fishes* 38:159-164.

Grieg, R.A., and R.H. Gnaedinger. 1971. Occurrence of thiaminase in some common aquatic animals of the United States and Canada. *Spec. Sci. Rpt. Fish. No. 631, U.S. Nat. Mar. Fish. Serv.* 7 pp.

Grover, C.A. 1972. Predation on egg-cases of the swell shark, *Cephaloscyllium ventriosum. Copeia,* 1972:871-872.

Grover, C.A. 1974. Juvenile denticles of the swell shark *Cephaloscyllium ventriosum*: function in hatching. *Can. Jour. Zool.* 52:358-362.

Gruber, S.H. 1977. The visual system of sharks: adaptations and capability. *Amer. Zool.* 17:453-470.

Gruber, S.H. 1980. Keeping sharks in captivity. *J. Aquariculture* 1:6-14.

Gruber, S.H. 1981. Lemon sharks: supply-side economists of the sea. *Oceanus* 24:56-64.

Gruber, S. H. 1982. Role of the lemon shark, *Negaprion brevirostris* (Poey) as a predator in the tropical marine environment: A multidisciplinary study. *Fla. Sci.* 45:46-75.

Gruber, S.H. (ed.) 1990. Discovering Sharks. *Amer. Littor. Soc. Spec. Publ.* 14, 122 pp.

Gruber, S.H., and R. Keyes. 1981. Keeping sharks for research. In: *Aquarium Systems* (A.D. Hawkins, ed.). Academic Press, New York, 373-402.

Gruber, S.H., and R.G. Stout. 1983. Biological material for the study of age and growth in a tropical marine elasmobranch, the lemon shark, *Negaprion brevirostris* (Poey). In: *Proceedings of the International workshop on age determination of oceanic pelagic fishes.* (E.D. Prince and L.M. Pulos, eds.). NOAA Tech. Rep. NMFS 8:193-205.

Gruber, S.H., D.R. Nelson, and J.F. Morrissey. 1988. Patterns of activity and space utilization of lemon sharks, *Negaprion brevirostris*, in shallow Bahamian lagoons. *Bull. Mar. Sci.* 43:61-76.

Hagiwara, S. 1989. Reproduction of Chondrichthyans in captivity at Shimoda Floating Aquarium. American. Elasmobranch Society Meetings, San Francisco (abstract).

Halver, J.E. 1989. The vitamins. In: *Fish Nutrition, 2nd edition* (J.E. Halver, ed.). Academic Press, San Diego, California, 32-109.

Hamlett, W.C. 1999. Male Reproductive System. In: *Sharks, Skates and Rays. The Biology of Elasmobranch Fishes* (W.C. Hamlett, ed.). John Hopkins University Press, Baltimore, 444-470.

Harker, R. 1999. The case for the counter-current skimmer. *Marine Fish and Reef USA Annual,* 1(1): 56-66.

Hartley, S.L. 1998. www.sc.edu.au/staff_pages/shartley/projects/wobbies.

Henningsen, A.D. 1994. Tonic immobility in 12 elasmobranchs: use as an aid in captive husbandry. *Zoo Biol.* 13:325-332.

Henningsen, A.D. 1996. Captive husbandry and bioenergetics of the spiny butterfly ray, *Gymnura altavela* (Linnaeus). *Zoo Biol.* 15:135-142.

Henningsen, A.D. 2000. Notes on reproduction in the southern stingray, *Dasyatis americana* (Chondrichthyes: Dasyatidae), in a captive environment. *Copeia,* 2000:826-828.

Heupel, M.R., and M.B. Bennett. 1998. Observations on the diet and feeding habits of the epaulette shark, *Hemiscyllium ocellatum* (Bonnaterre), on Heron Island Reef, Great Barrier Reef, Australia. *Mar. and Freshw. Res.* 49:753-756.

Heupel, M.R., and M.B. Bennett. 1999. The occurrence, distribution and pathology associated with gnathiid isopod larvae infecting the epaulette shark, *Hemiscyllium ocellatum. Int. Jour. Parasitology* 29:321-330.

Holmgren, S., and S. Nilsson. 1999. Digestive System. In: *Sharks, Skates, and Rays. The Biology of Elasmobranch Fishes* (W.C. Hamlett, ed.). John Hopkins University Press, Baltimore, 144-173.

Houziaux, J-S., and J. Voss. 1997. Premiere observation filmee des comportements associes a l'accouplement chez la petite rousette, *Scyliorhinus canicula* (Linne, 1758). *Rev. Fr. Aquariol.* 24:15-26.

Iwamasa, H. 1981. Fisheries biology of the wobbegong, *Orectolobus japonicus* Regan. *Rpt. Jap. Grp. Elasmobranch Stud.* 12:93-97.

Jensen, C.F., and F.J. Schwartz. 1994. Extreme habitat occurrences for two species of hammerhead sharks (Family Sphyrnidae) in North Carolina and the western Atlantic Ocean waters. *J. Elisha Mitch. Sci. Soc.* 110:46-48.

Johnson, R. H. and D. R. Nelson. 1978. Copulation and possible olfaction-mediated pair formation in two species of carcharhinid sharks. *Copeia,* 1978:539-542.

Johnson, M.R., and F.F. Snelson, Jr. 1996. Reproductive life history of the Atlantic Stingray, *Dasyatis sabina* (Pisces, Dasyatidae), in the freshwater St. Johns River, Florida. *Bull. Mar. Sci.* 59: 74-88.

Johnson, R.H. 1978. *Sharks of Polynesia.* Papeete, Tahiti, Les Editions du Pacifique, 170 pp.

Johnson, R.H. 1978. Copulation and possible olfaction-mediated pair formation in two species of carcharhinid sharks. *Copeia,* 1978:539-542.

Jones, B.C., and G.H. Green. 1977. Food and feeding of spiny dogfish (*Squalus acanthias*) in British Columbia waters. *J. Fish. Res. Board Can.* 34:2067-2078.

Kajiura, S.M., and T.C. Tricas. 1996. Seasonal dynamics of dental sexual dimorphism in the Atlantic Stingray *Dasyatis sabina. J. Exp. Biol.* 199: 2297-2306.

Kalmijn, A.J. 1978. Electric and magnetic sensory world of sharks, skates, and rays. In: *Sensory Biology of Sharks, Skates, and Rays* (E.S. Hodgson and R.F. Mathewson, eds.). Arlington, Virginia. Office of Naval Research, 507-528.

Kemp. N.E. 1999. Integument System and Teeth. In: *Sharks, Skates, and Rays. The Biology of Elasmobranch Fishes,* (W. C. Hamlett, ed.). John Hopkins University Press, Baltimore, 43-68.

Keyes, R.S. 1982. An unusual example of cleaning symbiosis. *Copeia,* 1982:225-227.

Klimley, A.P. 1980. Observations of courtship and copulation in the nurse shark, *Ginglymostoma cirratum. Copeia,* 1980:878-882.

Kuiter, R. H. 1993. *Coastal Fishes of South-Eastern Australia.* University of Hawaii Press, Honolulu, Hawaii, 437 pp.

Laird, M. 1951. Studies on the trypanosomes of New Zealand fish. *Proc. Zool. Soc. Lond.* 121:285-309.

LaVerane, A., and F. Mesnil. 1901. Deux hemogregarines nouvelles des poissons. *C. R. Acad. Sci. Paris* 133:572-577.

Last, P.R., and J.D. Stevens. 1994. *Sharks and Rays of Australia.* CSIRO Division of Fisheries, Australia 513 pp.

Leibovitz, L., and S.S. Leibovitz. 1985. Skin diseases of sharks. In: *A captive symposium on the captive maintenance of elasmobranchs.* An international meeting, Baltimore (abstract).

Leigh-Sharpe, W.H. 1921. The Comparative Morphology of the Secondary Sexual Characteristics of Elasmobranch Fishes, Vol. II. The claspers, clasper siphons, and clasper glands. *Journal of Morphology*, Philadelphia, 35:359-380.

Libby, E.L., and P.W. Gilbert. 1960. Reproduction in the clearnosed shark, *Raja eglanteria. Anat. Rec.* 138:365.

Limbaugh, C. 1961. Cleaning symbiosis. *Sci. Amer.* 205:42-49.

Limbaugh, C. 1963. Field notes on sharks, In: *Sharks and Survival* (P.W. Gilbert, ed.). Heath and Co., Boston, 63-94.

Lloyd, N. 1995. Treatment of goiter in Atlantic nurse sharks *Ginglymostoma cirratum* in the Blackpool Sea Life Centre. *Int. Zoo Ybk.* 34:95-98.

Longval, M.J., R.M. Werner, and S.H. Gruber. 1982. Cyclical patterns of food intake in the lemon shark *Negaprion brevirostris* under controlled conditions. *Fla. Sci.* 45:25-33

Luer, C.A., and P.W. Gilbert. 1985. Mating behavior, egg deposition, incubation period and hatching in the clearnose skate, *Raja eglanteria. Env. Biol. of Fish* 13:161-171.

Luer, C.A., P.C. Blum, and P.W. Gilbert. 1990. Rate of tooth replacement in the nurse shark, *Ginglymostoma cirratum. Copeia,* 1990:182-191.

Lyle, J.M. 1983. Food and feeding habits of the lesser spotted dogfish, *Scyliorhinus canicula* (L.), in Isle of Man waters. *J. Fish Biol.* 23:725-737.

Lyle, J.M. 1987. Observations on the biology of *Carcharhinus cautus* (Whitley), *C. melanopterus* (Quoy and Gaimard) and *C. fitzroyensis* (Whitley) from Northern Australia. *Aust. J. Mar. Freshw. Res.* 38:701-710.

Martin, L.K., and G.M. Cailliet. 1988a. Aspects of the reproduction of the bat ray, *Myliobatis californica*, in Central California. *Copeia,* 1988:754-762.

Martin, L.K., and G.M. Cailliet. 1988b. Age and growth determination of the bat ray, *Myliobatis californica* Gill, in Central California. *Copeia,* 1988:762-773.

Martini, F.H. 1978. The effects of fasting confinement on *Squalus acanthias.* In: *Sensory Biology of Sharks and Rays* (E.S. Hodgson and R.F. Mathewson, eds.). Arlington, Virgina. Office of Naval Research, pp. 609-646.

Masuda, H., K. Amaoka, C. Araga, T. Uyeno, and T. Yoshino, eds. 1984. *The Fishes of the Japanese Archipelago.* Tokai Univ. Press, Tokyo, 437 pp., 370 pls.

McConnell, R. 1978. Mating yellow spotted stingrays. *Skin Diver,* 27:33.

McCourt, R.M., and A.N. Kerstitch. 1980. Mating behavior and sexual dimorphism in dentition in the stingray *Urolophus concentricus* from the Gulf of California. *Copeia,* 1980:900-901.

McKay, R.J. 1966. Studies on western Australian sharks and rays of the Families Scyliorhinidae, Urolophidae, and Torpedinidae. *J. R. Soc. West. Aust.* 49:65-82.

McLaughlin, R.H., and A.K. O'Gower. 1971. Life history and underwater studies of a heterodont shark. *Ecol. Monogr.* 41:271-289.

Medved, R.J., C.E. Stillwell, and J.G. Casey. 1988. The rate of food consumption of young sandbar sharks (*Carcharhinus plumbeus*) in Chincoteague Bay, Virginia. *Copeia,* 1988:956-963.

Michael S.W. 1993. *Reef Sharks and Rays of the World; A Guide to their Identification, Behavior and Ecology.* Sea Challengers, Monterey, California, 107 pp.

Moe, M.A. 1982. *The Marine Aquarium Handbook, Beginner to Breeder.* Norns Pub. Co. Marathon, Florida, 170 pp.

Moe, M.A. 1989. *The Marine Aquarium Reference: Systems and Invertebrates.* Green Turtle Publ., Plantation, Florida, 512 pp.

Moss, S.A. 1984. *Sharks—An Introduction for the Amateur Naturalist.* Englewood Cliffs, New Jersey: Prentice-Hall, Inc. 246 pp.

Murru, F.L. 1989. The care and maintenance of elasmobranchs in controlled environments. *NOAA Technical Report* 90, NMFS, 209-215.

Murru., F.L. 1990. The care and maintenance of elasmobranchs in controlled environments. *NOAA Tech. Rpt. NMFS* 90:203-209.

Nelson, D.R. 1980. Behavior of the reef sharks of Rangiroa, French Polynesia. *Nat. Geo. Soc. Res. Rpt.* 12:479-499.

Myrberg, A. 1987. Shark behavior. In: *Sharks* (J. Stevens, ed.). Facts on File Publ., New York, 84-93.

Myrberg, A., and S.H. Gruber. 1974. The behavior of the bonnethead shark, *Sphyrna tiburo. Copeia,* 1974:358-74.

Nelson, D.R., and R.H. Johnson. 1970. Diel activity rhythms in the nocturnal, bottom-dwelling sharks, *Heterodontus francisci* and *Cephaloscyllium ventriosum. Copeia,* 1970:732-739.

Nishida, K., and K. Nakaya. 1990. Taxonomy of the genus *Dasyatis* (Elasmobranchii, Dasyatidae) from the North Pacific. *NOAA Technical Report* 90, NMFS, 327-346.

Norman, J.R. 1926. A synopsis of the rays of the family Rhinobatidae, with a revision of the genus *Rhinobatus. Proc. Zool. Soc.* 62:941-982.

Northcutt, R. G. 1977. Elasmobranch central nervous system organization and its possible evolutionary significance. *Amer. Zool.* 17:411-430.

Parsons, G.R. 1991. Notes on the behavior of the bonnethead shark, *Sphyrna tiburo* (Linnaeus). *J. Aquacul. and Aquat. Sci.* 6:6-8.

Parsons, G.R., and K.A. Killam. 1991. Activity patterns of the bonnethead shark, *Sphyrna tiburo* (Linnaeus). *J. Aquacul. and Aquat. Sci.* 6:8-13.

Penrith, M.L., S.S. Bastianello, and M.J. Penrith. 1994. Hepatic lipidosis and fatty infiltration of organs in a captive African stonefish, *Synanceia verrucosa* Bloch and Schneider. *J. Fish Dis.* 17:171-176.

Pike, C.S. III, C.A. Manire, and S.H. Gruber. 1993. Nutrition and nutritional diseases in sharks. In: *Fish Medicine* (M.K. Stoskopf, ed.). W.B. Saunders and Co., Philadelphia, Pennsylvania 763-769.

Pratt, H.L., and J.C. Carrier. 1995. Wild mating of the nurse sharks. *Nat. Geogr.* May:44-53.

Randall, J.E. 1967. Food habits of reef fishes of the West Indies. *Stud. Trop. Oceanogr.* 5:665-847.

Randall, J.E. 1977. Contribution to the biology of the whitetip reef shark. *Pac. Sci.* 31:143-164.

Randall, J.E. 1986. *Sharks of Arabia.* London: Immel Pub. 148 pp.

Rudloe, J. 1989a. Captive maintenance of the lesser electric ray, *Narcine brasiliensis*, with observation of feeding behavior. *Prog. Fish Cult.* 51:37-41.

Rudloe, J. 1989b. Habitat preferences, movement, size frequency patterns, and reproductive seasonality of the lesser electric ray, *Narcine brasiliensis. Northeast Gulf Sci.* 10:103-112.

Ross, R. 1999. *Freshwater Stingrays.* Barron's Educational Series Inc. Hauppauge, NY, 95 pp.

Russo, R.A. 1975a. Observations on the food habits of leopard sharks (*Triakis semifasciata*) and brown smooth-hounds (*Mustelus henlei*). *Calif. Fish Game* 61:95-103.

Russo, R.A. 1975b. Notes on the external parasites of California inshore sharks. *Calif. Fish Game* 61:228-232.

Rouse, N. 1985. Nurse sharks mating ballet. *Sea Front.* 31 (1):54-57.

Sabalones, J. 1995. Considerations on the husbandry of sharks for display purposes. *Int. Zoo Ybk.* 34:77-87.

Salini, J.P., S.J.M. Blaber, and D.T. Brewer. 1990. Diets of piscivorous fishes in a tropical Australian estuary, with special reference to predation on penaeid shrimp. *Mar. Biol.* 105:363-374.

Sazima, I., and R.L. Moura. 2000. Shark (*Carcharhinus perezi*), cleaned by the goby (*Elacatinus randalli*), at Fernando de Noronha Archipelago, Western South Atlantic. *Copeia*, 2000:297-299.

Schmahl, G., and H. Mehlhorn. 1985. Treatment of fish parasites. 1. Praziquantel effective against monogenea (*Dactylogyrus vastator*, *Dactylogyrus extensus, Diplozoon paradoxum*). *Z. Parasitenkunde* 71:727-737.

Schmid, T.H., F.L. Murru, and F. McDonald. 1990. Feeding habits and growth rates of bull (*Carcharhinus leucas* [Valenciennes]), sandbar (*Carcharhinus plumbeus* [Nardo]), sandtiger (*Eugomphodus taurus* [Rafinesque]) and nurse (*Ginglymostoma cirratum* [Bonnaterre]) sharks maintained in captivity. *J. Aquacul. and Aquat. Sci.* 5:100-105.

Schreiber, C.M. 1997. Captive husbandry of smooth butterfly rays (*Gymnura micrura*). *American Zoo and Aqua. Assoc. Region. Conf. Proc.* 1997:122-126.

Schurdak, M.E., and S.H. Gruber. 1989. Gastric evacuation of the lemon shark, *Negaprion brevirostris* (Poey), under controlled conditions. *Exp. Biol.* 48:77-82.

Schwartz, F.J., and M.D. Dahlberg. 1978. Biology and ecology of the Atlantic Stingray, *Dasyatis sabina* (Pisces: Dasyatidae), in North Carolina and Georgia. *Northeast Gulf Sci.* 2:1-23.

Sims, D.W., S.J. Davies, and Q. Bone. 1996. Gastric emptying rate and return of appetite in lesser spotted dogfish, *Scyliorhinus canicula* (Chondrichthyes: Elasmobranchii). *J. Mar. Biol. Ass. U.K.* 76:479-491.

Smith, B.G. 1942. The Heterodontid sharks: their natural history and the external development of *Heterodontus japonicus* based on notes and drawings by Bashford Dean. In: *Bashford Dean Memorial Volume; Archaic Fishes.* New York, Amer. Mus. Nat. Hist. 649-770.

Smith, J.W., and J.V. Merriner. 1982. Association of cobia *Rachycentron canadum*, with cownose ray, *Rhinoptera bonasus. Estuaries* 5:240-242.

Snelson, Jr., F.F., S.H. Gruber, F.L. Murru, and T.H. Schmid. 1990. Southern stingray, *Dasyatis americana*: host for asymbiotic cleaner wrasse. *Copeia*, 1990:961-965.

Snelson, Jr., F.F., S.E. Williams-Hooper, and T.H. Schmid. 1988. Reproduction and ecology of the Atlantic Stingray, *Dasyatis sabina*, in Florida coastal lagoons. *Copeia*, 1988(3): 729-739.

Snelson, Jr., F.F., S.E. Williams-Hooper, and T.H. Schmid. 1989. Biology of the Bluntnose Stingray, *Dasyatis sayi*, in Florida coastal lagoons. *Bull. Mar. Sci.* 45: 15-25.

Soderstrom, V., G.M.C. Renshaw, and G.E. Nilsson. 1999. Brain blood flow and blood pressure during hypoxia in the epaulette shark *Hemiscyllium ocellatum*, a hypoxia-tolerant elasmobranch. *J. Exp. Biol.* 202:829-835.

Spotte, S. 1992. *Captive Seawater Fishes.* Johm Wiley and Sons, Inc., New York, 942 pp.

Springer, V.G., and J.P. Gold. 1989. *Sharks In Question.* Smithsonian Institution Press, Washington D.C., 187 pp.

Standora, E.A., and D.R. Nelson. 1977. A telemetric study of the behavior of the angel shark, *Squatina californica. Bull. S. Calif. Acad. Sci.* 76:193-201.

Stead D.G. 1963. *Sharks and Rays of Australian Seas.* Angus and Robertson, London, 211 pp.

Stevens, J.D. 1984a. Biological observations on sharks caught by sport fishermen off New South Wales. *Aust. J. Mar. Freshw. Res.* 5:573-590.

Stevens, J.D. 1984b. Life-history and ecology of sharks at Aldabra Atoll, Indian Ocean. *Proc. R. Soc. Lond. B.* 222:79-106.

Stevens, J.D. (ed.). 1987. *Sharks.* Facts on File Publ., New York, 240 pp.

Stillwell, C.E. 1993. Food habits of the sandbar shark *Carcharhinus plumbeus* off the U.S. northeast coast with estimated daily ration. *Fishery Bull.* 91:138-150.

Stillwell, C.E., and N.E. Kohler. 1982. Food, feeding habits, and estimates of daily ration of the shortfin mako (*Isurus oxyrinchus*) in the Northwest Atlantic. *Can. J. Fish. and Aquat. Sci.* 39:407-414.

Stillwell, C.E., and N.E. Kohler. 1993. Food habits of the sandbar shark *Carcharhinus plumbeus* off the U.S. north coast, with estimates of daily ration. *Fish. Bull.* 91:138-150.

Stratsburg, D.W. 1958. Distribution, abundance, and habits of pelagic sharks in the central Pacific Ocean. *Fish. Bull. U.S. Fish. Wildl. Serv.* 58:335-361.

Stoskopf, M.K. 1990. Shark diagnostics and therapeutics: A short review. *J. Aquacul. and Aquat. Sci.* 5:33-43.

Stoskopf, M.K. 1993. Clinical pathology of sharks skates and rays. In: *Fish Medicine*, M.K. Stoskopf (ed.) W.B. Saunders and Co., Philadelphia, 754-757.

Stoskopf, M.K. 1993. Environmental requirements and diseases of sharks. In: *Fish Medicine*, M.K. Stoskopf (ed.) W.B. Saunders and Co., Philadelphia, 758-763.

Stoskopf, M.K. 1993. Shark pharmacology and toxicology. In: *Fish Medicine* M.K. Stoskopf (ed.) W.B. Saunders and Co., Philadelphia, 809-816.

Strong, W.R. 1989. Behavioral ecology of the horn shark, *Heterodontus francisci*, at Santa Catalina Island, California, with emphasis on patterns of space utilization. Masters Thesis, C.S.U., Long Beach, 255 pp.

Strong, W.R. 1990. Instruments of natural selection: How important are sharks. *Amer. Littor. Soc. Spec. Publ.* 14:70-73.

Sweatman, H.P. 1984. A field study of the predatory behavior and feeding rate of the piscivorous coral reef fish, the lizardfish *Synodus englemani*. *Copeia*, 1984:187-194.

Talent, L.G. 1976. Food habits of the leopard shark, *Triakis semifasciata*, in Elkhorn Slough, Monterey Bay, California. *Calif. Fish Game* 62:286-298.

Talent, L.G. 1982. Food habits of the gray smooth-hound, *Mustelus californicus*, the brown smooth-hound, *Mustelus henlei*, the shovelnose guitarfish, *Rhinobatus productus*, and the bat ray, *Myliobatis californica*, in Elkhorn Slough, California. *Calif. Fish Game* 68:224-34.

Taniuchi, T. 1988. Aspects of reproduction and food habits of the Japanese swellshark (*Cephaloscyllium umbratile*) from Choshi, Japan. *Nippon Suisan Gakkaishi* 54:627-633.

Tasaka, S. 1986. Mating behavior of rays in captivity. Alley in the sea. *Shimoda Floating Aquarium*, 2:6.

Taylor, L. (ed.) 1997. *Sharks and Rays. Nature Company Guides.* US Weldon Owen Pty Inc. San Francisco, California, 288 pp.

Teaf, C.M. 1987. Seasonal occurrence of multiple caudal spines in the Atlantic Stingray, *Dasyatis sabina* (Pisces: Dasyatidae). *Copeia*, 1987:224-227.

Teshima, K., M. Ahmad, and K. Mizue. 1978. Studies on sharks—XIV. Reproduction in the Telok Anson shark collected from Perak River, Malaysia. *Jap. Jour. Ich.* 25:181-189.

Thoney, D.A. 1989. The effects of various chemicals on monogeneans parasitizing the skin of elasmobranchs. In: *AAZPA 1989 Annual Conference Proceedings. American Association of Zoological Parks and Aquariums*, Wheeling, 217-222.

Thorson, T.B., J.K. Langhammer, and M.I. Oetinger. 1988. Periodic shedding and replacement of venomous caudal spines, with special reference to South American freshwater stingrays, *Potomotrygon* spp. *Env. Biol. Fish.* 23:299-314.

Timmons, M., and R.N. Bray. 1997. Age, growth and sexual maturity of the shovelnose guitarfish, *Rhinobatos productus* (Ayres). *Fishery Bull.* 95:349-359.

Tricas, T.C. 1980. Courtship and mating-related behaviors in myliobatid rays. *Copeia*, 1980:553-556.

Tricas, T.C., and E.M. LeFeuvre. 1985. Mating in the reef whitetip shark *Triaenodon obesus. Mar. Biol.* 84:233-237.

Tricas, T.C., S.W. Michael, and J.A. Sisneros. 1995. Electrosensory optimization to conspecific phasic signals for mating. *Neuroscience Letters*, 202:129-132.

Tyson, P. 1998. Courtship of the marbled ray. PBS website, (www.pbs.org): 3 pp.

Uchida, S. 1982. Elasmobranch fishes around Ryukyus Islands and their cultural status in the big water tank of aquarium. *Rept. Japanese Grp. Elasmobranch Stud.* 14:1-7.

Uchida, H., and Y. Abe. 1987. The prevention of goiter in captive sharks. *Int. Zoo Ybk.* 26:59-61.

Uchida, S., and Y. Abe. 1987. The prevention of goiter in captive sharks. *Int. Zoo Ybk.* 26:59-61.

Uchida, S., M. Toda, and Y. Kamei. 1990. Reproduction of elasmobranchs in captivity. *NOAA Technical Report 90 NMFS* 211-237.

Uyeno, T., and T. Tsutsumi. 1991. Stomach contents of *Latimeria chalumnae* and further notes on its feeding habits. *Env. Biol. Fish.* 32:275-279.

Van Dykhuizen, G., and H.F. Mollet. 1992. Growth, age estimation and feeding of captive sevengill sharks, *Notorhynchus cepedianus*, at the Monterey Bay Aquarium. *Aust. J. Mar. Freshw. Res.* 43:297-318.

Villavicencio-Garayzar, C.J. 1995. Biologia reproductiva de la guitarra pinta, *Zapterix exasperata* (Pisces, Rhinobatidae), en Bahia Almejas, Baja California, Sur Mexico. *Ciencias Marinas* 21:141-153.

West, J.C., and S. Carter. 1990. Observations on the development and growth of the epaulette shark *Hemiscyllium ocellatum* (Bonnaterre) in captivity. *J. Aquaric. Aquat. Sci.* 5:111-117.

Wetherbee, B.M., S.H. Gruber, and E. Cortés. 1990. Diet, feeding habits, digestion, and consumption in sharks, with special reference to the lemon shark, *Negaprion brevirostris. NOAA Technical Report 90 NMFS* 29-47.

Whitley, G.P. 1940. *Fishes of Australia.* Part 1. The Sharks, Rays and Devilfish, and other Primitive Fishes of Australia and New Zealand. Royal Zool. Soc. of N.S.W. 280 pp.

Whitley, G.P. 1951. Studies in ichthyology No.15. *Rec. Aust. Mus.* 26:389-408.

Whitley, G.P. 1967. Sharks of the Australasian region. *Aust. Zool.* Vol. 14:173-188.

Whitman, P.A., J.A. Marshal, and E.C. Keller, Jr. 1986. Tonic immobility in the smooth dogfish shark, *Mustelus canis* (Pisces, Carcharhinidae). *Copeia*, (3)1986:829-832.

Windell, J.T. 1978. Digestion and the daily ration of fishes. In: *The Ecology of Freshwater Fish Production* (S.D. Gerking, ed.). John-Wiley and Sons, New York, 159-183.

Yudin, K.G., and G.M. Calliet. 1990. Age and growth of the gray smoothhound, *Mustelus californicus*, and the brown smoothhound, *Mustelus henlei*, sharks from central California. *Copeia*, 1990:191-204.

Photograph & Illustration Credits

Photographs

Scott W. Michael: Front cover, 14, 15, 17, 20, 21(T), 24(BL, BR), 26, 32(R), 33, 35, 38, 39(B), 40(C, B), 46, 52, 54, 62(R), 63, 66, 68, 74, 83(L), 88(R), 89, 91, 93, 95, 96, 97, 101(R), 102, 105(R), 110, 112, 115(L), 117(BL, BR), 122, 125(R), 127, 128, 131, 133, 137, 138(R), 140(L), 143, 145, 147, 148(TL), 151, 152, 153, 154, 156, 157, 166, 167(R), 168(TL, TC, BL, BC), 169, 175, 177, 180, 181(T, B), 182, 188, 192, 197, 200, 201, 204, 210, 211, 221, 223(R), 226, 233, Back cover(T, C)

Kelvin Aitken: 18, 21(B), 31, 32(L), 36, 42, 53, 70, 72, 79(BR), 81, 83(R), 88(L), 107, 121, 138(L), 148(TR, CL, BL, BR), 170, 178, 222

Fred Bavendam: 24(T), 27, 77, 78, 90, 164, 174, 184, Back cover(B)

Mark Conlin: 40(T), 79(CL, CR), 118, 142(T, C)

Robert Fenner: 55, 58, 64, 124, 125(L), 202

Roger Steene: 16, 39(C), 114, 150, 173

Mark Sasahara: 47, 51, 185

Gerald Allen: 62(L), 104(L), 106(L), 181(C)

Janine Cairns-Michael: 28(L), 39(T), 171

Bob Halstead: 86, 104(R), 109

Audubon Aquarium of the Americas/New Orleans, LA: 49, 56

Deborah Fugitt: 85, 106(R)

Keisuke Imai: 71, 79(TR)

John E. Randall: 100, 168(TR)

Foster Bam: 65

K.H. Choo: 79(BL)

Lynn Funkhouser: 115(R)

Paul Humann: 75, 159

John Hoover: 168(BR)

Ken Kates: 223(L)

Dennis Kemp: 167(L)

Rudie Kuiter: 148(CR)

Aaron Norman: 101(L)

Gregory Schiemer: 44

Christian M. Schreiber: 190

Norbert Wu/www.norbertwu.com: 105(L)

Innerspace Visions:
Mark Conlin: 73, 208, 218, 219
Don DeMaria: 117(TL, TR, CL, CR)
Doug Perrine: 29, 60, 155, 216
Mike Bacon: 136
Jeffrey C. Carrier: 215
Phillip Colla: 162
Bob Cranston: 21(C)
Helmut Debelius: 119
David B. Fleetham: 28(R)
Dan Gotshall: 161
Florian Granger: 41
Richard Herrmann: 140(R)
Michel Jozen: 230
Jim Knowlton: 130
Mike Nolan: 142(B)

Illustrations

Joshua Highter: 38

Laura Williams: 22, 23, 25, 27, 30, 194, 212, 213

Index

Numbers in **boldface** indicate photographs or illustrations; numbers in **boldface with an asterisk** (*) indicate main entry for that group.

About the Author

Author Scott W. Michael in Bonaire.

SCOTT W. MICHAEL IS AN internationally recognized writer, underwater photographer, and marine biology researcher specializing in elasmobranchs and other reef fishes. He is a regular contributor to *Aquarium Fish Magazine* and *SeaScope* and is the author of *Reef Sharks & Rays of the World* (Sea Challengers), the *Reef Fishes* series, and *PocketExpert Guide: Marine Fishes* (Microcosm/ T.F.H. Professional Series).

Having studied marine biology at the University of Nebraska, he has been involved in research projects on sharks, rays, frogfishes, and the behavior of reef fishes. He has also served as a scientific consultant for National Geographic Explorer and the Discovery Channel.

His research and photographic endeavors have led him from Cocos Island in the Eastern Pacific to various points in the Indo-Pacific, including the Maldive Islands, Sulawesi, the Fiji Islands, Papua New Guinea, Australia's Great Barrier Reef, as well as the Red Sea, the Gulf of Mexico, and many reefs in the Caribbean.

A marine aquarist since boyhood, he has kept aquarium sharks and rays for more than 25 years, with many years of extensive involvement, including a period of retail store ownership, in the aquarium trade. He lives with his wife, underwater photographer Janine Cairns-Michael, and their Golden Retriever, Ruby, in Lincoln, Nebraska.

Future Editions

THE AUTHOR AND EDITOR are committed to making all future reprints of this title as complete, accurate, and up-to-date as possible. Readers with suggestions, information, or photographs for possible publication are encouraged to contact one of the following in writing:

Reef Impressions
Attn: Scott W. Michael
4310 Garfield Street
Lincoln, NE 68506

Microcosm Ltd.
P.O. Box 550
Charlotte, VT 05445
e-mail: jml@microcosm-books.com

The Aquarium Suitability Index

THIS RATING SYSTEM, RANGING FROM A LOW of 1 to a top mark of 5, gives an indication of the durability, hardiness, and/or adaptability of each shark or ray to captive conditions and foods. Factors such as readiness to feed, dietary breadth, competitiveness, tolerance of sudden changes, and ability to withstand less-than-ideal water conditions have been taken into account when applying a suitability index. The following is a summary of the rating system:

1 = These species are very difficult to keep and best left in the wild. In most cases, these species are difficult to feed and even if they accept food their condition will slowly deteriorate or they will die suddenly for no obvious reason.

2 = While it is possible to keep this shark or ray in your aquarium, most individuals will have difficulty acclimating to aquarium life. They may refuse to accept standard aquarium fare (or any food at all), be susceptible to disease and/or parasites, or both. However, the occasional individual may adapt if special care is given.

3 = These sharks and rays are moderately hardy, with many of the individuals collected for the aquarium trade acclimating to aquarium life if special care is administered. This may include offering live food and meeting their special habitat and temperature requirements (e.g., providing a cave to hide in, fine sand to bury under, or cooler water temperatures).

4 = These sharks or rays are generally durable and hardy with most individuals acclimating to captivity. Even so, they should not be exposed to dramatic changes in environment or to poor water conditions. Live food may be needed to induce feeding, but in most cases they can be switched to fresh or frozen seafood. Maintaining lower water temperature may also be an important consideration for some of these species.

5 = These individuals are almost bulletproof! They are the most easily kept species, with almost all individuals readily acclimating to aquarium confines.

(X-large tank required) = If this appears after the rating, an aquarium larger than 2,280 L (600 gal.) will be needed to house the animal for its entire life (which should be the aquarist's intention). Take note of the optimal aquarium size listed for each species and plan accordingly.

REMEMBER, THERE ARE ALWAYS EXCEPTIONS to the rule. An occasional aquarist may have success keeping a Bluespotted Ribbontail Ray (*Taeniura lymma*), a species that I give a rating of 1-2. In the vast majority of cases, this stingray has difficulty adapting to captivity, but one in ten individuals may live a long, healthy life in a large, well-maintained aquarium. These rare exceptions help determine what is necessary to keep the more fragile species. If you have success with some of these difficult species, keep good notes on the water parameters, aquarium environment, feeding, tankmates, and any special behavior displayed by the shark or ray. I am always interested in hearing about these cases (author address, page 255).